LONGMAN

*h*OMEWORK *h*ANDBOOKS

GCSE

SCIENCE

Di Barton

LONGMAN

HOMEWORK HANDBOOKS

Series editors:

Geoff Black and Stuart Wall

Other titles in this series:
BIOLOGY
CHEMISTRY
GEOGRAPHY
MATHEMATICS
PHYSICS

Addison Wesley Longman Limited
Edinburgh Gate, Harlow
Essex CM20 2JE, England
and Associated Companies throughout the world

© Addison Wesley Longman Ltd 1999

First published 1999

British Library Cataloguing in Publication Data
A catalogue record for this title is available from the British Library

ISBN 0-582-36918-5

Set by 30 in Stone $9\frac{1}{2}/11\frac{1}{2}$
Produced by Addison Wesley Longman Singapore (Pte) Ltd
Printed in Singapore

CONTENTS

ACKNOWLEDGEMENTS

I would like to acknowledge the contribution made by Mike Evans and Stuart Farmer to some of the entries in this book. I would also like to thank Geoff Black and Stuart Wall for their help and guidance during my preparation of the text.

Di Barton

WHAT IS A HOMEWORK HANDBOOK?

This Homework Handbook is a resource. It is for you, the student, to decide exactly how you use the book. The main purpose of this book is to help you when you are working by yourself – when you are researching or revising. It is designed to be extremely flexible, both in content and organization.

What's in this book?

The Homework Handbook consists of hundreds of important scientific terms, listed alphabetically.

- **Definitions, explanations and examples:** These terms all relate to key ideas in the most recent GCSE syllabuses. Each idea or topic is defined and concisely explained, and often incorporates appropriate examples.

- **Remember bubbles:** Many topics include extra hints, tips and comments, which may reinforce learning, highlight how different topics relate or let you know of common pitfalls.

- **Checkpoint questions:** Many of the topics include 'Checkpoints' – these are questions based on recent GCSE examination questions.

- **Checkpoint answers:** Once you have had a go at answering a Checkpoint, you can turn to the answers at the back of the book to see how you got on.

- **Cross-references:** Most topics are cross-referenced to other topics. This allows you to broaden and deepen your understanding of related themes. The cross-references also give you a chance to go back over the basic principles of themes with which you are having difficulty. Cross-references are easily identifiable:

  - Either as words in bold italic type within the text:

    ...an electric **current** flows through a wire...

  - Or as words following the 'compass' symbol at the end of an entry:

    ✦ *Alternating current, Direct current*

Using this book?

- **Researching:** You can look up a particular term or topic just by finding it in the alphabetical list. Once you have the information you need, you can stop there; or your can follow up the related topics by using the cross-references; or you can try a Checkpoint question, to see if you have fully understood the topic.

- **Revising:** For revision, you can really test your understanding of GCSE Science by dipping into the Homework Handbook to check out terms and topics you are revising or have already revised.

GOOD LUCK!

MAKING THE MOST OF HOMEWORK

This topic is divided into seven subtopics:

- What you need to do homework
- Where to do homework
- Friends
- How to do homework
- Helpful hints
- When to do homework
- Libraries

What you need to do homework

- You will find homework easier if you sit at a table and have a good light, such as a table lamp. Drawing graphs while sitting in an armchair is not recommended!

- Basic equipment such as paper, a pencil, a pen, ruler, etc., are also needed.

- Coloured pens and highlighters, yellow stickers, correcting fluid, etc., can be useful.

- A dictionary and one or two books, such as this *Homework Handbook*, as well as your school textbooks, should be on hand.

> Remember: You can save time if you have all you need before you start work.

Where to do homework

- You need a fairly quiet environment to increase your concentration and make the most of your valuable time.

- You may have your own study–bedroom that you can use as a work-place. If so you have an ideal situation.

- You may have to share a room with a younger brother or sister and only be able to work in a room where the TV is on all the time. It is worth talking to your family and discussing the best ways of making a fairly quiet place where you can work, or having a couple of hours when the TV is switched off (or at least the volume is turned down).

- You need to look at all the rooms in the house and see if there is one room that could be used as a work-place by adding a table, chair and lamp.

> Remember: A large carton can be useful to move all your things about if you have to move from one work-place to another at home.

Friends

It can be a good idea to do homework with a friend provided you agree on exactly what you intend to achieve. This means you need to set a clear target for each hour and check that you have achieved that target in the time.

> Remember: Coursework assignments usually have to be your own unaided work.

How to do homework

At the start of each week

- Draw an outline chart showing the days of the week.

- Write in the times that you may have available for doing homework, for example, an hour when you get home from school before a meal, two hours before going to bed, maybe an hour before school. Don't forget to fill in times for eating!

- Fill in any regular activities that you do, such as sports or social activities. You can see that you

Time	Monday	Tuesday	Wednesday	Thursday	Friday	Saturday	Sunday
before school?							
after school (p.m.)							
5–6							
6–7							
7–8							
8–9							

may not have much time for homework on those nights.

> Remember: Discuss with your teacher at school if a room can be set aside for homework for a short time before or after school.

- Write in any homework you know you have to do on a regular basis; for example, after your science lesson you may have to write up practical work.

- Add to the chart any coursework or assignments that you are given during the week that may have a deadline. Give yourself enough time to complete this type of work and mark in the date the work has to be handed in. Assignments can usually be broken down into smaller tasks that can fit more easily into one hour time slots.

> Remember: Assignments and coursework may need to be carried over into more than one week. It is always possible to ask your teacher to extend a deadline if you have not been well or there has been a family crisis.

Every day

- Each day when you come home from school, make a list of your homework to see what you have to achieve in the time.

- Put this list in order of priority by writing a 1, 2, 3, etc. next to each item.

- Work out approximately how much time you can allocate to each item on your list so that you can cover the work in the time you have available.

- Start with the item listed priority one and make a note of your start time so that you can give each item the time you have allocated to it.

- Try to look at the whole task and see if you can divide it into smaller units of work, for example, writing an outline plan in rough, drawing a diagram, plotting a graph.

- Concentrate on one or two units of work for about half an hour or so, then have a few minutes break. When you come back to your work, scan it through quickly to see how much you have achieved and to check you are still on the right track.

- At the end of your homework session, look back at what you have done and how you could improve on your use of your time. Did a piece of work take more time than you had allocated to it? Perhaps you took a long time copying something

out neatly. Next time you could try making a rough draft, and then writing out a final copy.

Helpful hints

- For each piece of homework, there should be a clear heading or title. For scientific investigations there should be a short introduction that shows you understand what the investigation is about.

- Each piece of work should have a date, and headings should be clearly underlined.

- Any diagrams, tables or graphs should each have a clear heading and labels.

- List any references you may have used, especially where you may have copied out information from a book so that it is clear it is someone else's work.

> Remember: If you do not understand something or feel under too much pressure, arrange a time when you can speak to your teacher or tutor about the work.

When to do homework

- The chart you have made of your week should help you to decide when is the best time for you to do homework.

- It may be possible to find a time slot early in the morning before school starts, or immediately you get home from school. You have to take control of your time and make your own decisions about what is best for you.

> Remember: Try out different times of the day to do homework and see which works best for you.

Libraries

- You probably have a library at school and there may be one near your home, but they may not be open when you need to find a book!

- Find out when your school library and local library are open.

> Remember: You may be able to use lunchtime at school to go to the library.

- Have a good look round to work out the general layout of the library and where to find the science section. In most libraries, books are numbered according to the main category they are in. For example, the science books are grouped together under the number 500. These sections are subdivided into smaller sections, so that physics, for example, is 530 and so on.

- Get a general impression of what books there are in the science section. Ask the librarian to show you the cataloguing system, which lists each book; this system may be on a computer or on card indexes.

- When you start a new topic in science, go and have a look in the library to see if there are any books about the same topic that you may find useful. It's always worth taking a book out for reference, just in case you need it.

- Get into the habit of checking a contents list at the front of the book to see what topics are covered. Use the index at the end of the book to see how many detailed references there are to a particular topic.

Remember: This Homework Handbook highlights cross references throughout book to help you.

- You may be able to photocopy a particular article from a reference book, or make brief notes about a topic.

- Most libraries stock a wide range of reference books, and there are many other sources of information, such as newspapers, magazines and journals.

- Some libraries have information stored on CD-ROM (compact disc – read only memory). These discs, which store large amounts of information, are read by computer.

Remember: Librarians are often able to order a particular book for you, but you need to give plenty of notice.

ABIOTIC FACTORS

Abiotic factors are the non-living or physical factors that affect the organisms in an **ecosystem**, such as:

- Temperature
- Rainfall
- Light intensity
- Wind
- The type of soil
- The **nutrient cycles** of **nitrogen**, **carbon** and **water**

If you have studied ecology at school you will know that the abiotic factors can affect where plants and animals live: e.g. the amount of light and the type of soil can affect the *growth* of plants. The amount of exposure on rocky shores can affect the *distribution* of different animals and plants.

✦ **Biosphere, Biotic factors, Limiting factors, Sampling populations**

ABSOLUTE ZERO

✦ **Kelvin, Gas laws**

ABSORPTION

Absorption of food

Absorption of food takes place in the small intestine (ileum). The small molecules of **glucose** and **amino acids** diffuse through the wall of the small intestine into the blood stream. The surface of the small intestine has been increased in two ways:

- It is very long
- It is covered with tiny finger-like villi

Both of these features *increase* the surface area so that more molecules can be absorbed through the thin wall of the intestine and into the blood stream.

✦ **Digestion**

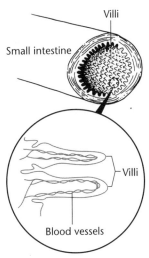

The villi in the small intestine increase the area for absorption

Absorption of water

✦ **Transport in plants, Transport of water**

ACCELERATION

Acceleration is the change in **velocity** per unit time.

$$\text{Acceleration (m/s}^2) = \frac{\text{Change in velocity (m/s)}}{\text{Time taken for change (s)}}$$

$$a = \frac{v - u}{t}$$

To find acceleration divide the change in velocity by the time taken to change it: e.g. if a car changes its velocity from 20 to 40 m/s in 10 s, then its

acceleration is $\frac{(40 - 20)}{10} = 2$ m/s^2.

If the answer to your calculation is a negative number it means that the vehicle is slowing down (decelerating). Acceleration is a vector because it takes place in a particular direction. The units of acceleration are metres per second per second (m/s^2).

✦ **Force and acceleration, Vehicle stopping distance**

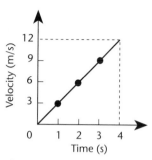

A graph showing constant acceleration

CHECKPOINT

1. The graph below represents the journey of a car. During what part of the journey is the car braking? (a) R–S, (b) S–T, (c) T–U, (d) U–V?

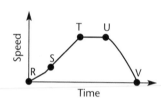

2. A bus is moving at 20 m/s. The bus driver brakes for 20 s until the velocity is 10 m/s. What is the deceleration?

ACCOMMODATION

 Eye

ACID

An acid is a substance that:

● Has a sour taste

● Will change the colour of plant dyes (**indicators**)

● Will neutralize **bases**

● Will react with metals to form **salts**

● Contains hydrogen **ions** when dissolved in water

We can recognize the sharp or sour taste in fruits or in vinegar. Acids can also be corrosive, they can dissolve many substances such as **metals** and some rocks. This can be very useful but can also be a nuisance, as with the **corrosion** of iron and buildings by acids in the atmosphere, e.g. **acid rain**.

Acids and water

Acids in water contain hydrogen ions

Acids only behave as acids when they are dissolved in water. So we only really meet them as **solutions** in water. The reason for this is that, in water, the acid produces hydrogen **ions** (H^+). All acids contain hydrogen ions in water. The importance of water can be demonstrated by dissolving some citric acid crystals (the acid from fruits such as oranges and lemons) in water and some citric acid crystals in another solvent such as propanone (nail varnish remover). When the citric acid crystals are dissolved in propanone the solution will *not* affect the colour of indicators nor will it react with bases or metals. However, in water the citric acid behaves as an acid, changing the colour of the indicator.

In fact the acid reacts with the water to produce a hydroxonium ion (H_3O^+):

$$H^+ + H_2O \rightarrow H_3O^+$$

It is really this ion that is responsible for acidity; however, in order to keep things simple we can think of acids as just providing hydrogen ions in water. The following ions can be regarded as being equivalent: H^+, $H^+(aq)$, $H_3O^+(aq)$, (aq means **aqueous**).

Strong acids and weak acids

Those acids that provide a lot of hydrogen ions in water are called *strong* acids, whereas those that only provide a few are called *weak* acids.

Examples of strong acids and weak acids	
Strong acids	*Weak acids*
Sulphuric acid	Citric acid (citrus fruits)
Nitric acid	Ethanoic acid (acetic) (vinegar)
Hydrochloric acid	Malic acid (apples)

Ethanoic acid (acetic acid) is a *weak* acid because only a proportion of its molecules in solution split up to provide hydrogen ions.

Some common acids

Some common acids			
Acid	*Formula*	*Ions present*	
Hydrochloric acid	HCl	H^+ Cl^-	(chloride)
Sulphuric acid	H_2SO_4	$2H^+$ SO_4^{2-}	(sulphate)
Nitric acid	HNO_3	H^+ NO_3^-	(nitrate)
Ethanoic acid	CH_3COOH	H^+ CH_3COO^-	(ethanoate)

Notice that the names of acids are taken from the **anion** present. This ion is referred to as the *acid radical*.

Concentration of acid solutions

Acid solutions can be *concentrated* or *dilute* depending upon how much water is present. The concentration of a solution can be measured in molarity (mol/dm^3 or g/dm^3). For example, a 1 M (1 **molar**) solution of sulphuric acid contains 98 g H_2SO_4 per dm^3.

This is calculated from the formula mass of H_2SO_4 = $(2 \times 1) + 32 + (4 \times 16) = 98$. Do not confuse *strong* acids with *concentrated* acids. There are concentrated solutions of strong and weak acids, as well as dilute solutions of strong and weak acids. The acids that are used in a laboratory are dilute acids of concentrations 2, 1, 0.1 M, etc.

-¦- *Molar solutions*

Acids and indicators

Acids change the colour of some dyes we call **indicators**. Acids will turn **litmus** indicator red and **universal indicator** red, orange or yellow:

● Strong acids have a low **pH** number and will turn universal indicator red

● Weak acids turn universal indicator yellow

-¦- *pH scale*

Patterns of acid reactions

Acids are very useful substances because they react with a large number of other substances in fairly predictable ways. They are used extensively in industry in the manufacture of a large variety of materials.

Reactions with metals

General pattern of reaction:

$$\text{acid} + \text{metal} \rightarrow \text{salt} + \text{hydrogen}$$

Examples

$$\text{zinc} + \text{hydrochloric acid} \rightarrow \text{zinc chloride} + \text{hydrogen}$$

$$\text{Zn} + 2\text{HCl} \rightarrow \text{ZnCl}_2 + \text{H}_2$$

$$\text{magnesium} + \text{sulphuric acid} \rightarrow \text{magnesium sulphate} + \text{hydrogen}$$

$$\text{Mg} + \text{H}_2\text{SO}_4 \rightarrow \text{MgSO}_4 + \text{H}_2$$

The solution that is produced is neutral and the salt produced depends on the acids. Some **metals** react with acids faster than others. The metal's reactivity depends on its position in the **reactivity series**:

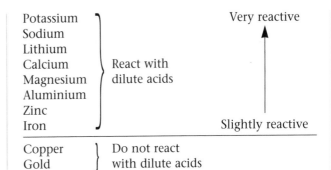

Potassium		Very reactive
Sodium		
Lithium		
Calcium	React with	
Magnesium	dilute acids	
Aluminium		
Zinc		
Iron		Slightly reactive
Copper	Do not react	
Gold	with dilute acids	

Note: The gas hydrogen can be tested for; if it is present in a test-tube, a lighted splint will produce a 'pop'.

Reactions with metal oxides

Metal oxides are **bases** and react with acids to produce salt and water. All metal oxides will react with dilute acids.

General pattern of reaction:

$$\text{metal oxide} + \text{acid} \rightarrow \text{salt} + \text{water}$$

Examples

$$\text{copper (II) oxide} + \text{nitric acid} \rightarrow \text{copper nitrate} + \text{water}$$

$$\text{CuO} + 2\text{HNO}_3 \rightarrow \text{Cu(NO}_3)_2 + \text{H}_2\text{O}$$

$$\text{magnesium oxide} + \text{sulphuric acid} \rightarrow \text{magnesium sulphate} + \text{water}$$

$$\text{MgO} + \text{H}_2\text{SO}_4 \rightarrow \text{MgSO}_4 + \text{H}_2\text{O}$$

Reactions with metal hydroxides

Metal hydroxides are bases that will react with acids to produce salt and water. Metal hydroxides that are soluble are called **alkalis**. All metal hydroxides react with acids.

General pattern of reaction:

$$\text{metal hydroxide} + \text{acid} \rightarrow \text{salt} + \text{water}$$
$$\text{OH}^-(aq) + \text{H}^+(aq) \rightarrow \text{H}_2\text{O}(l)$$

Examples

$$\text{calcium hydroxide} + \text{hydrochloric acid} \rightarrow \text{calcium chloride} + \text{water}$$

$$\text{Ca(OH)}_2 + 2\text{HCl} \rightarrow \text{CaCl}_2 + \text{H}_2\text{O}$$

$$\text{potassium hydroxide} + \text{sulphuric acid} \rightarrow \text{potassium sulphate} + \text{water}$$

$$2\text{KOH} + \text{H}_2\text{SO}_4 \rightarrow \text{K}_2\text{SO}_4 + 2\text{H}_2\text{O}$$

Reaction with carbonates

Metal **carbonates** can be thought of as bases. They too will react with acids to produce salt and water, but they also produce **carbon dioxide**.

General pattern of reaction:

$$\text{acid} + \text{carbonate} \rightarrow \text{salt} + \text{water} + \text{carbon dioxide}$$

Examples

sodium + nitric → sodium + water + carbon
carbonate   acid   nitrate   dioxide
Na_2CO_3 + $2HNO_3$ → $2NaNO_3$ + H_2O + CO_2

calcium + hydrochloric → calcium + water + carbon
carbonate   acid   chloride   dioxide
$CaCO_3$ + 2HCl → $CaCl_2$ + H_2O + CO_2

This is a general pattern for all carbonates. Since many rocks are carbonates, it can be used as a test to help identify rocks: e.g. *limestone*, marble and chalk are all mainly calcium carbonate and will therefore react with hydrochloric acid. When a small amount of acid is placed on the surface, the rocks 'fizz' and give off carbon dioxide. Carbon dioxide can be tested for. When the gas is bubbled through limewater, the limewater turns cloudy.

Note: There is an exception; sulphuric acid will *not* react well with calcium carbonate rock since, during the reaction, a layer of calcium sulphate builds up on the surface, which being insoluble in sulphuric acid, prevents any further reaction.

CHECKPOINT

Fill in the missing words in these sentences.

When a metal reacts with hydrochloric acid, ... gas is released.

When metal hydroxides react with acids, a .... and water are formed.

When metal carbonates react with acids, a salt and water are formed and .... gas is released.

Acids in action

Acids are **corrosive** and can be a nuisance; however, they can also be beneficial: e.g. acids are used in preserving food (in pickling and chutneys), and are present in the digestive system to assist with the breakdown of food.

Acids and food preservation

The 'pickling' of foods, e.g. onions and eggs, and the making of chutneys helps to preserve the food. The acid that is used is found in vinegar. This acid is called ethanoic acid or acetic acid (acetic acid is the common name). The reason it works is that any bacteria that enter the food are killed by dehydration due to **osmosis**. It also means that the **pH** is too low for **enzymes** (biological catalysts) to work, thereby preventing the natural deterioration of food. Also, adding lemon juice to sliced apples prevents them from going brown, since the acidity of the lemon juice stops the enzymes in the apple from working.

Acids and digestion

The stomach lining produces gastric juice. This contains hydrochloric acid (about pH 2) that kills most of the micro-organisms in the food. Gastric juice also contains the enzyme **pepsin**, which starts to break down large **protein** molecules. Pepsin obviously works best at a much lower pH than *salivary amylase*.

Indigestion is often caused by too much acid in the stomach and can be relieved by taking 'antacid' tablets. These contain bases that **neutralize** the excess acid in the stomach. Examples are 'Settlers' and 'Rennies', which contain calcium carbonate and magnesium carbonate.

Acidity and the soil

Most plants prefer to grow in a soil which is slightly acidic, about pH 6–7. There are even some plants that prefer more acidic soils (pH 4.5–6) such as azaleas, rhododendrons and heathers. No plants will grow in strongly alkaline soils, however, although some plants will grow in weakly alkaline soils (up to pH 8).

When changing from growing one type of plant to another, sometimes the acidity of the soil has to be changed to get the best results. In addition, the soil acidity itself may well change over a period of time due to the plants themselves. Needing to reduce the acidity of the soil is a common problem to farmers. They overcome this by adding 'lime' to the soil. Lime is calcium oxide, though calcium hydroxide (slaked lime) or calcium carbonate (*limestone* or chalk) is often used. The reactions involved are as follows:

Lime or quicklime

CaO + $2H^+$ → Ca^{2+} + H_2O

Slaked lime

$Ca(OH)_2$ + $2H^+$ → Ca^{2+} + $2H_2O$

Limestone

$CaCO_3$ + $2H^+$ → Ca^{2+} + H_2O + CO_2

✢ *Acid rain, Digestion, pH scale*

A**CID RAIN**

Normally, rain is very slightly acidic (**pH** 5), due to a small amount of **carbon dioxide** from the **atmosphere** that dissolves in the rain-water to produce a weakly acidic solution:

$$H_2O + CO_2 \rightleftharpoons H_2CO_3$$

Acid rain, however, has a pH of between 5 and about 2.2. The strongest acid rain has an acidity comparable to that of lemon juice. The causes of acid rain are not fully understood, but enough is known to realize that the burning of **fossil fuels** (**hydrocarbons**) and the exhaust emissions from cars contribute greatly to acid rain. Fossil fuels, like coal and oil, contain impurities of sulphur, so that when they burn they produce **sulphur dioxide** in addition to the normal products of combustion (carbon dioxide and water). Sulphur dioxide is an acidic gas.

The exhausts of cars also emit gases other than the normal products of combustion. In the car engine where the petrol (hydrocarbon fuel) is burned, the temperature is so high that nitrogen from the air reacts with oxygen to form *oxides of nitrogen* that escape through the exhaust, together with unburned hydrocarbons and carbon monoxide. This mixture of gases (particularly sulphur dioxide and the oxides of nitrogen) may react in the atmosphere with **ozone** to produce rain that contains sulphuric and nitric acids. It is these substances that give the rain its acidity.

Acid rain is a greater problem in parts of the world that are industrialized and therefore burn fossil fuels in power stations and factories and have large numbers of cars, e.g. Europe, USA, Canada and the former USSR.

Effects of acid raid

Acid rain will corrode metals and will react with some building materials (**limestone** and marble), gradually eating them away. Perhaps the largest worry, however, is the effect it has either directly, or indirectly, on living things. When acid rain falls onto the soil it dissolves away many of the **minerals** (salts) in the soil. These minerals contain **metal ions**, which are 'leached' (dissolved) out of the soil and washed into rivers and lakes. The rivers and lakes become increasingly acidic due to the rising concentration of metal ions. The first metal ions to be removed from the soil are those that dissolve more easily, magnesium and calcium. These ions are needed by plants to ensure healthy growth, so are no longer available to the plants.

Metal ions such as aluminium, lead and copper are the next to be leached out of the soil. These ions are particularly troublesome since they are poisonous. Aluminium, when dissolved in the water, prevents the gills of fish working, as well as being poisonous to other organisms. (*Note*: It is not the acid water that kills the fish but the dissolved metal ions).

The areas that are affected more than others are those that lie on thin soil and granite rock, e.g. Scotland, Dartmoor, the Black Forest in Germany and Scandinavia. Areas that have deep soil covering limestone rock are not so badly affected, since the limestone rock and its soil can **neutralize** the effects of the acid rain. How an area is affected depends on its position, since the acidic gases are carried on prevailing winds.

Combatting acid rain

- Some lakes that are very acidic have large amounts of lime (calcium hydroxide) added to them to neutralize the acidity. This is only a temporary measure, however, since it has to be repeated frequently and costs a large amount of money.

- Power stations that burn coal and oil can be fitted with equipment that will *remove* the sulphur dioxide from the gases before they are released into the atmosphere.

- Car exhausts can be fitted with 'catalytic converters' that can convert the *harmful* gases into *harmless* ones. These can only be fitted to cars that run on unleaded petrol. The lead in the petrol will prevent the **catalyst** from working.

✦ *Pollution*

ACTIVATION ENERGY

Almost all chemical reactions need a 'push', in other words an amount of **energy** to get them going. This initial amount of energy can be quite small or quite large, and is called the activation energy. It is the energy required initially to break the chemical bonds in order to allow a reaction to proceed. Fuels such as gas and coal need to be supplied with a source of heat (from a match) to start the **combustion**.

✦ *Covalent bonding, Endothermic, Exothermic, Ionic bonding*

ACTIVE TRANSPORT

Active transport is the movement of **molecules** into and out of cells, across a membrane, to a region where they are in *low* concentration to one where they are in *high* concentration. This process requires **energy**. It occurs where **diffusion** is too slow to meet the demands of the cells.

For example, **mineral ions** move from the soil into the root hairs by active transport This allows the plant to accumulate minerals above the concentration found in the soil.

✦ *Diffusion, Minerals required by plants, Osmosis*

ADAPTATION

Adaptation means an animal or plant having special features that enable it to survive in a particular environment.

For example, animals in desert and arctic regions need to adapt to extremes of climate in the following ways:

- Their body size and surface area

- The thickness of hair (fur)

- Amount of body fat

- Camouflage

A good example of adaptation is the polar bear, which is adapted to live in a very cold climate in the arctic. The bear:

- Is large and has a relatively small surface area to mass ratio

- Has a thick layer of fur that traps air and gives *insulation*

- Has large deposits of body fat for *insulation* and energy

- Has white fur to camouflage it against the snow and ice

In desert regions animals such as camels are adapted to withstand extremes of temperature and shortage of available water.
The camel has:

- A long, thin body shape that increases its surface area to mass ratio to allow heat to escape

- The ability to drink large amounts of water when available and to store water in fat deposits in its hump

- Large feet that spread out to prevent it sinking in the sand

Predators such as lions and cheetahs are adapted for hunting prey by having powerful muscles to enable them to chase their prey, eyes at the front of their heads to give good distance vision, and good camouflage to help them blend in with their surroundings and not be visible to their prey. The **prey** such as zebra and springbok have eyes at the side of their heads to give good all-round vision when they are feeding. They are also camouflaged and able to run very fast for long periods.

Plant adaptations

Plants adapt to survive arid conditions. One example is the thorn tree, which has very small leaves to reduce water loss by **transpiration**. The thorns prevent herbivores from eating the leaves and the seed pods have a very thick coat to withstand long periods of drought.

⊹ *Competition, Natural selection, Populations, Predator–prey*

ADDITION POLYMERS

Unsaturated **hydrocarbons**, which have a double carbon bond ($C=C$), can, under high pressure and in the presence of a **catalyst**, join to form addition polymers. For example, propene polymerizes to form poly(propene), ethene polymerizes to form a polymer, poly(ethene).

Uses of addition polymers	
Polymer	*Uses*
Polythene	Bags, food wrapping, film for packaging toys, household goods, insulation, pipes
Polypropene	Furniture, toilet seats
Polyvinyl chloride (PVC)	Waterproof clothing, water pipes, packaging
Polytetrafluoroethene (PFTE)	Non-stick pans, fabrics for stain-resistant clothing

Remember: A polymer is a long-chain molecule formed by the joining of many small molecules called monomers in a process known as polymerization. In plastics, the polymer molecules have very long chains and are able to be moulded into various shapes.

⊹ **Cracking, Hydrocarbons**

CHECKPOINT

1. What is an addition polymer?
2. Give **one** example of a polymer and state the monomer from which it is made.
3. State **two** uses of the addition polymer you have named in 2.

ADRENALIN

Adrenalin is a **hormone** that is secreted by the adrenal glands in response to demands made on your body. Adrenalin has several effects on the body. These include:

- Rapid pulse

- Deep, rapid **breathing**

- **Blood** being diverted from the skin to the muscles

- Stores of **carbohydrates** in the liver being converted from glycogen to **glucose** to prepare the body for action, such as running away from a frightening situation

⊹ **Insulin, Pituitary**

AEROBIC RESPIRATION

Aerobic respiration is the breakdown of **carbohydrates** and fats to release **energy**, using *oxygen*. The word equation below summarizes this process:

food + oxygen → carbon + water + energy
dioxide

The chemical equation for this process, with glucose as food, is:

$$C_6H_{12}O_6 + 6O_2 \rightarrow 6CO_2 + 6H_2O + 2830 \text{ kJ}$$

Aerobic respiration takes place in the cells in your body, for example, the muscle cells. Your *blood* carries food and oxygen *to* the cells, and transports the waste products, *carbon dioxide* and water, *from* the cells. These waste products are removed by your *lungs* when you breathe out.

One way of investigating aerobic respiration in living organisms is to identify the carbon dioxide produced. For example, the gas produced by a mouse can be bubbled through limewater. If the limewater turns cloudy, then the gas is carbon dioxide.

✛ *Anaerobic respiration, Breathing*

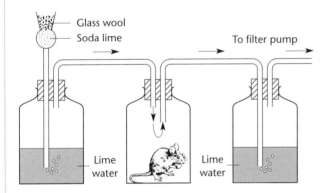

Testing for aerobic respiration

CHECKPOINT

Complete the equation for aerobic respiration:

food + ... → .... + water + energy

AEROSOL

A can of aerosol contains a product (deodorant, etc.) and a liquefied propellant *gas* under pressure. When the nozzle is pressed, the pressure in the can forces out a fine spray of the propellant mixed with the product. The propellant, no longer under pressure, very quickly *evaporates*, leaving the product (deodorant, polish, glue, etc.). There are two main types of propellant, *hydrocarbons* and *chlorofluorocarbons*.

● *Hydrocarbons* (usually propane or butane) are often used in furniture polish and air fresheners

● *Chlorofluorocarbons* (CFCs) are more often found in personal care products (deodorants, hairspray,

etc.). These are at present being phased out because they damage the **ozone layer**.

Aerosol safety

The aerosol contents are under pressure so there is a risk of an explosion if the can is overheated or punctured. In addition, hydrocarbons are very flammable; this is an important reason why CFCs started to be used as propellants because they were not flammable, but CFCs of course have other problems.

An aerosol can

✛ *Diffusion, Greenhouse effect, Ozone layer*

AIDS (ACQUIRED IMMUNE DEFICIENCY SYNDROME)

✛ *HIV*

AIR

Air is a *mixture* of *gases*, the proportions of which remain more or less constant. The air also contains varying amounts of water vapour, dust, soot particles and chemical pollutants such as *sulphur dioxide*.

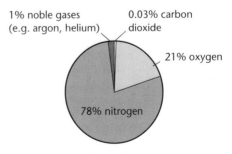

The proportions of gases in air

● Animals and plants are continually *respiring*, i.e. taking in *oxygen* and using it to convert food into energy; the waste product, **carbon dioxide**, is released into the atmosphere.

● During the process of **photosynthesis** green plants take in carbon dioxide and combine it with water using the sun's energy to produce simple sugars. The waste product is oxygen.

While these processes are in balance, the proportion of gases will remain the same; however, Man's burning of **fossil fuels** (in power stations, cars, etc.) releases more carbon dioxide into the **atmosphere** as well as other gases. In addition Man is cutting down large areas of tropical rain forest and hence reducing the global potential for **photosynthesis**.

⟐ *Greenhouse effect, Nitrogen, Noble gases, Ozone layer*

AIR PRESSURE

The Earth's gravitational pull holds the layer of gases around the surface of the planet, and the **weight** of **air** above any part of the Earth is described as air pressure. For example, the weight of air pressing down on 1 cm^2 is 10 **newtons** (N). Atmospheric pressure is therefore about 10 N/cm^2. This unit is also described as 1 bar or 1,000 millibar.

Pressure is usually measured with a barometer, but in an aeroplane a pilot uses a sensitive barometer, called an altimeter, which measures atmospheric pressure and height. Atmospheric pressure decreases with altitude: e.g. as you go higher up a mountain there is less air above you pressing down on you. If you were to go about 6 km high, the pressure drops to about half that at sea-level as the air molecules thin out.

⟐ *Atmosphere, Gas laws, Kinetic theory*

ALCOHOL

Alcohol is a chemical found in beers, wines and spirits. It is produced by the **fermentation** of sugars using **yeast**. Alcohol is a drug and excessive intake of alcohol on a regular basis can lead to addiction.

Alcohol has a number of effects on the body. It:

● Affects the **nervous system**

● Slows down a person's reaction time, causing a lack of co-ordination of the muscles

● Can lead to a lack of self-control, unconsciousness and even a coma.

When motorists drink alcohol they are more likely to have accidents. The legal limit for driving is three units of aclohol. One unit of alcohol is:

● Half a pint of beer or lager

● A glass of wine or sherry

● One measure of spirits

½ pint of beer = 1 glass of table wine = 1 glass of sherry = 1 single whisky = 1 unit of alcohol

Remember: One in three drivers killed in road accidents in the UK were found to have drunk alcohol just before the accident.

If a person drinks excessive amounts of alcohol over a number of years, he/she is described as an alcoholic and he/she becomes addicted to alcohol. This can have serious effects on the body:

● A diseased liver, leading to cirrhosis

● Damage to the stomach, pancreas, kidneys and heart

● High blood pressure

● Depression

⟐ *Anaerobic respiration, Drugs, Enzymes, Reflex arc*

ALKALI

An alkali is a substance that:

● Is a soluble **base**

● Will change the colour of **indicators**

● Will neutralize **acids**

● Contains **hydroxide ions**

Examples of common alkalis		
Alkali	*Formula*	*Ions present*
Potassium hydroxide	KOH	K^+ (potassium) OH^-
Sodium hydroxide	NaOH	Na^+ (sodium) OH^-
Ammonium hydroxide	NH_4OH	NH_4^+ (ammonium) OH^-
Calcium hydroxide	$Ca(OH)_2$	Ca^{2+} (calcium) $2OH^-$

In the same way that there are *strong* and *weak* **acids** so there are *strong* and *weak* **alkalis**. Strong alkalis provide a lot of free hydroxide ions in solution. Sodium and potassium hydroxides are *strong alkalis*, whereas an **aqueous** solution of ammonia (ammonium hydroxide) and calcium hydroxide are *weak alkalis*.

Alkalis turn *litmus indicator* blue, and will turn *universal indicator* blue or violet depending on their strength; violet indicates strong alkalis with a high pH number.

⟐ *Alkali metals, pH scale*

Alkalis will also neutralize acids:

$$H^+ + OH^- \rightarrow H_2O$$

Example

hydrochloric + sodium → sodium + water
acid hydroxide chloride

$$HCl + NaOH \rightarrow NaCl + H_2O$$

Hydroxide ion

The hydroxide ion, OH^-, is a negative ion, which is the cause of alkalinity. All *alkalis* contain OH^- ions.

Hydroxide ions react with hydrogen ions from acids to form the neutral substance water:

$$H^+(aq) + OH^-(aq) \rightarrow H_2O(l)$$

Most hydroxides are insoluble, but those of sodium, potassium, lithium and ammonium are soluble.

ALKALI METALS

Properties and reactions of the alkali metals (Group 1)

The *alkali metals*, Group 1, have one *electron* in their outer shell. Their *reactivity* increases down the group as the number of shells increases. The further away the outer shell is from the positive nucleus, the more easily the electron is lost. When one electron is removed from the outer shell the atoms form ions with a charge of +1.

Reaction with air

Lithium, sodium and potassium react with air to form oxides. When the metal is cut with a knife its surface quickly tarnishes. The speed of reaction *increases* as you move *down* the group. If any of the alkali metals are represented by M, the general reaction is:

$$4M + O_2 \rightarrow 2M_2O$$

Formulae of oxides formed: Li_2O, Na_2O, K_2O. These oxides dissolve in water to produce alkaline solutions.

> *Remember: Reactivity increases down the group.*

Reaction with water

Lithium, sodium and potassium react quickly with water. Lithium when placed on water 'fizzes' and quickly reacts. Sodium will buzz around on the surface of the water, giving the odd spark. Potassium reacts more violently, producing a lilac flame. Reactivity *increases* as you move *down* the group.

Each produces a strong alkaline solution with water. The general reaction is:

$$2M + 2H_2O \rightarrow 2MOH + H_2$$

Formulae of hydroxides produced: LiOH, NaOH, KOH.

Reactions with halogens

Each will react with halogens to form compounds called halides. The reactivity will *increase* as one moves *down* the group. For example, the reaction with chlorine:

$$2M + Cl_2 \rightarrow 2MCl$$

Formulae of the halides formed: LiCl, NaCl, KCl.

Reactivity trends

The atoms react to form ions that have a charge of 1+. In forming these ions, e.g. Na^+, an electron has to be removed from the outer shell. Those atoms that have outer shells further away from the positive nucleus (the bigger atoms) will require less energy to remove that electron, and so will tend to be more reactive: hence reactivity *increases* as you move *down* the group: $Cs \rightarrow Rb \rightarrow K \rightarrow Na \rightarrow Li$.

> *Remember: The Group 1 elements, the alkali metals:*
> ● *Are metals*
> ● *React with non-metals to form ionic compounds in which the metal ion carries a +1 charge*
> ● *React with water releasing hydrogen*
> ● *Form hydroxides that dissolve in water to give alkaline solutions*

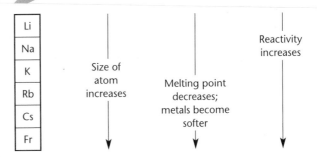

The alkali metals. Group 1

CHECKPOINT

1. What is formed when one electron is removed from the outer shell of an alkali metal?

2. Why does the reactivity of the alkali metals increase down the group?

3. What gas is released when the alkali metals react with water?

⟐ *Reactions of metals, Valency*

ALKANES AND ALKENES

-*- *Hydrocarbons*

ALLOTROPE

Some **elements** can exist in different forms or allotropes, e.g. giving rise to different shape crystals, depending on how their atoms can pack together. Sulphur has two allotropic forms:

● *Rhombic* sulphur is a crystalline form that is stable at room temperature

● *Monoclinic* sulphur is stable at 96 °C (and above, before melting)

Carbon can exist as the two allotropic forms *graphite* and *diamond*.

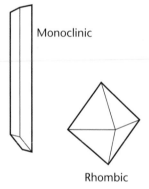

Monoclinic

Rhombic

Allotropes of sulphur

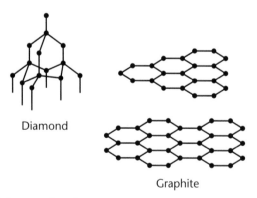

Diamond

Graphite

Allotropes of carbon

Allotropes can be converted from one form into the other, e.g. graphite could be converted to diamond (one of the hardest substances known) by heating under extreme pressure (about 15,000 atmospheres at 300 °C).

-*- *Giant structures*

ALPHA RADIATION (OR ALPHA PARTICLES)

-*- *Radioactivity*

ALTERNATING CURRENT (a.c.)

> *Remember: Alternating current changes direction 50 times per second. Direct current is a one-way flow.*

Alternating current describes an electric **current** that changes direction and is produced by a **generator**. The current increases to a certain value in one direction; it then decreases and reaches the same value in the opposite direction. The **frequency** of the current is the number of complete changes made in one second.

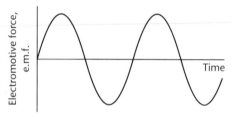

Alternating current

> *Remember: Mains electricity is generated at a frequency of 50 cycles a second, or 50 Hz.*

-*- *Alternator, Direct current, Generation of electricity*

ALTERNATIVE ENERGY

This term is used to describe any source of energy that does not involve using **fossil fuels** such as coal, oil or gas. For example:

● **Solar energy** is obtained from the Sun

● **Hydro-electric power** is obtained from fast-flowing rivers

● **Tidal energy** and **wave energy** are obtained from the movement of water

● **Wind energy** is obtained from the wind

● **Geothermal energy** comes from the heat deep inside the Earth

The table summarizes the main alternative sources of energy, and their advantages and disadvantages.

Alternative energy		
Energy source	Advantages	Disadvantages
Wind	Will not run out No fuel costs No pollution Useful for isolated communities	Windmills can spoil the environment Wind speeds may vary, so the generation of electricity is varied
Solar	Will not run out No fuel costs No pollution	Cloud cover blocks the Sun Difficult to store energy produced Huge solar panels needed
Tidal	No fuel costs No pollution	Expensive to build power stations May cause silting up of rivers
Geothermal	Long-term supplies can provide hot water	Not easily available Costly to obtain
Wave	Will not run out No pollution	Many technological problems Hazard to shipping
Hydro-electric power	No pollution Cost of energy source is free	High costs of building power station and maintenance Possible environmental damage if a valley is flooded to create a reservoir

There are *three* main reasons why alternative energy sources are being developed:

1. Fossil fuels are 'finite', which means that they will run out and cannot be replaced. It has been predicted that the coal supplies that are known about will have been used up in about 600 years.

2. Fossil fuels cause **pollution** as they produce **sulphur dioxide**, nitrogen oxides and **carbon dioxide** when they burn. Sulphur dioxide is one of the main causes of '**acid rain**'. Carbon dioxide is one of the main factors in the '**greenhouse effect**'.

3. There is an increasing demand, both from industry and from consumers, for **electricity**. This demand may exceed the amount of electricity that can be supplied by existing power stations that burn fossil fuels.

-+- **Greenhouse effect, Nuclear power, Solar cells**

ALTERNATOR

An alternator is a **generator** that produces **alternating current**. The alternating current is **induced** as a coil rotates between the permanent magnets. The coil is linked to the outside circuit by two carbon brushes that press against two carbon slip rings that are fixed to the end of the coil. The current can be increased by *four* factors:

1. Having more turns on the coil.

2. Using stronger **magnets**.

3. Winding the coil on a soft iron armature.

4. Rotating the coil at a higher speed.

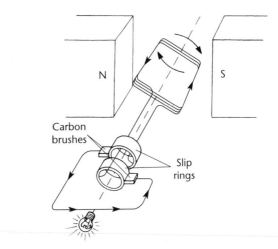

Carbon brushes

Slip rings

Alternator

-+- **Electromagnetism, Generation of electricity**

AMINO ACID

Amino acids are small **molecules** which are the building blocks of **proteins**. Proteins are made of long chains of amino acids. All amino acids contain the amino group – NH_2.

There are 22 different amino acids that can be combined to make thousands of different proteins. When protein is digested, the large molecules are broken down into amino acids that are then used by the body to form many different proteins, such as muscle, **blood** cells and **hormones**. Excess amino acids are broken down by the liver in a process known as **deamination**. The waste product, known as urea, is removed from the blood by the **kidneys**.

-+- **Balanced diet, Urea, Urine**

AMMETER

An ammeter is a device for measuring electric **current** in **amperes** (amps). It is always placed in series with a **resistance** or a circuit component through which the current flowing is to be measured. Ammeters should have a low **resistance** so that they do not reduce the flow of current.

> **Current electricity, Series circuit, Voltmeter**

AMMONIA

> **Reversible reactions**

AMPERE

The ampere (amp) is the SI unit of electric current. The symbol used is A.

> **Ammeter, Current electricity, Volt**

AMPLITUDE

The distance between the middle of a wave and the top or bottom of a wave is the amplitude. It is the amount by which a particle is displaced up and down.

The distance marked A on the diagram is the amplitude.

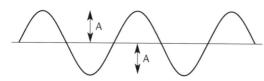

Amplitude

> **Frequency, Wavelength**

AMYLASE

Amylase is a digestive enzyme produced by the salivary glands in the mouth and by the pancreas. Its function is to speed up the rate at which **starch** is broken down to *maltose* in the gut. Amylase works in an **alkaline pH**, so it doesn't work in the **acid** pH of the stomach.

> **Carbohydrates, Digestion, Hydrolysis**

ANAEROBIC RESPIRATION

Anaerobic respiration is the breakdown of **carbohydrates** and fats to release **energy**, *without* using oxygen. The food is broken down to substances such as lactic acid and **alcohol.** Less energy is released compared to **aerobic respiration**, which uses oxygen.

An example of anaerobic respiration occurs in your **muscles** when you are doing vigorous **exercise**:

- There is not enough oxygen supplied to your muscles to break down the food quickly enough and release energy needed by the body

- Some energy is released from the food anaerobically and lactic acid is produced as a waste product

- This is known as the 'oxygen debt'

- When you stop the exercise, your rapid breathing provides extra oxygen to remove the lactic acid, 'repaying' the oxygen debt

You can try producing lactic acid in your muscle by putting your arm up and quickly clenching and releasing the muscles of your hand. After a few 'fists' you may begin to feel pain in the muscles of your arm. This pain is caused by lactic acid.

> *Remember: Athletes in sprint races usually use only anaerobic respiration to release energy quickly when they run, say, 100 m.*

Some **bacteria** and **fungi** use anaerobic respiration and produce alcohol and carbon dioxide as waste products. This process is known as **fermentation**.

CHECKPOINT

Complete the missing words.

During vigorous exercise, there may not be enough .... to break down food quickly and release energy and an oxygen .... builds up. Some energy is released. .... and .... is produced as a waste product.

> **Aerobic respiration, Yeast**

ANION

A negatively charged **ion**. Non-metals tend to form anions. During **electrolysis** anions are attracted to the **anode**, the positive electrode. Examples of some anions are shown opposite:

Some anions		
Name of ion	Symbol	Charge on ion
Oxide	O^{2-}	2–
Chloride	Cl^-	1–
Sulphide	S^{2-}	2–
Sulphate	SO_4^{2-}	2–
Carbonate	CO_3^{2-}	2–
Nitrate	NO_3^-	1–
Hydrogen carbonate	HCO_3^-	1–
Phosphate	PO_4^{3-}	3–

⟡ **Cathode, Cations, Ionic bonding, Solubility**

ANODE

Anode is the name given to a positive **electrode** either in an **electrolysis** cell, or in an electrical cell **(battery)**.

The anode in electrolysis

The anode and the **cathode** (the negative electrode) are attached to an electrical source (e.g. battery or power pack) and dipped into an electrolyte (liquid or solution containing **ions**). A current flows through the electrolyte when *negative* ions (**anions**) are attracted to the anode. At the anode these ions are converted to atoms:

$$X^- - e^- \rightarrow X$$

The anode must be able to conduct electricity and is usually carbon (graphite) or a metal. The anode that is chosen depends on the job the electrolysis cell has to do and the nature of the electrolyte; e.g. often the anode must not react with the electrolyte. Sometimes, however, an anode is chosen that *will* 'react': e.g. impure copper can be purified if it is used as an anode in an electrolysis cell with copper sulphate as the electrolyte.

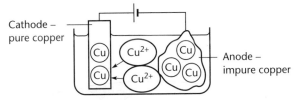

Cathode – pure copper

Anode – impure copper

Purification of copper

> Remember: The anode is the positive electrode and attracts negative anions.

The copper atoms at the *anode* lose electrons to form ions:

$$Cu - 2e^- \rightarrow Cu^{2+}$$

These ions are then transported through the electrolyte to the cathode. The cathode becomes coated with pure copper. The reaction occurring at the cathode is:

$$Cu^{2+} + 2e^- \rightarrow Cu$$

The anode in an electrical cell

When two different metals (which act as electrodes) are placed in an electrolyte and are connected together externally, for example with a wire, they produce an electric current (a flow of electrons). The anode – the *positive* electrode – will be the metal that has the least tendency to lose electrons (it is lower in the reactivity series). In the dry cells (batteries) that we buy, the anode is not always a metal:

● In zinc-carbon batteries the anode is **carbon** (carbon is lower in the activity series than zinc)

● In 'alkali batteries' the anode is *manganese (IV) oxide*

● In 'calculator batteries' the anode is *mercury oxide*

⟡ **Current electricity**

ANODIZING

This is the process of coating objects made of aluminium with a very thin layer of aluminium oxide. This layer protects the metal from **corrosion** but dulls the shiny surface of the aluminium. Anodizing is carried out by **electrolysis** using sulphuric acid as the electrolyte that releases **oxygen** at the **anode**. The oxygen reacts with the surface of the aluminium, covering it with the oxide layer, which can be dyed to produce different coloured finishes.

ANTIBODY

These are chemical substances produced by **white blood cells**. Their function is to attack disease-causing **bacteria** in the body and to make the bacteria harmless. Once antibodies have been made to attack a particular type of bacteria they can quickly be made again. This gives us protection against a disease-causing organism. This process is called immunity. They are transported around the body by **blood** and lymph.

⟡ **HIV, Lymphatic system, Vaccine**

AORTA

The aorta is the main **artery** in your body and carries oxygenated blood away from the **heart** to the rest of your body.

-+- **Blood system, Vein**

AQUEOUS

An aqueous **solution** means one in which the **solvent** is **water**; e.g. an aqueous solution of ammonia is produced by dissolving ammonia gas in water. In chemical equations, symbols of state can show whether a substance is dissolved in water. The **state symbol** for *aqueous* is aq e.g.:

$$Mg(s) + 2HCl(aq) \rightarrow MgCl_2(aq) + H_2(g)$$

The hydrochloric acid (HCl) is dissolved in water (diluted). The magnesium chloride ($MgCl_2$) that is formed in the reaction is also dissolved in the water. This information is shown by the symbol (aq).

-+- **Acid, Solubility, State symbols**

ARTERY

Arteries are blood vessels that carry blood *away* from the **heart**. The blood in the arteries is under pressure so the arteries have very thick elastic muscular walls. The arteries divide into smaller blood vessels called arterioles, which then divide up to form tiny blood vessels called **capillaries**.

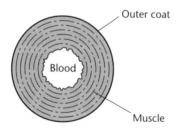

Artery

-+- **Blood system, Coronary artery disease, Vasoconstriction, Vasodilation, Vein**

ARTIFICIAL SELECTION

-+- **Selective breeding**

ASEXUAL REPRODUCTION

● Involves cell division by **mitosis** to produce identical copies of the parent; if the parent plant is successful in coping with its **environment**, then it is important that the parent's

characteristics are passed on exactly; plants that are genetically identical are called **clones**

● Involves only one parent and means that an isolated individual can reproduce on its own

● Is used by some plants to form bulbs, stem tubers and runners

● Is used by gardeners to grow new plants (propagate) and to make sure that the new plants are exactly like the parent. This has important commercial implications; e.g. growing exact copies (clones) of disease-resistant plants.

> Remember: In asexual reproduction, all the offspring are identical to the parent and are described as clones.

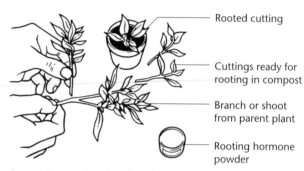

Rooted cutting

Cuttings ready for rooting in compost

Branch or shoot from parent plant

Rooting hormone powder

Asexual reproduction in plants

-+- **Food preparation, Sexual reproduction, Yeast**

ATMOSPHERE

The atmosphere is a layer of gases, a few hundred kilometres thick, which surrounds the **Earth** and acts as a 'blanket' keeping the Earth warm. The **Moon**, which is the same distance from the Sun as the Earth, has no atmosphere. In the sunlight the Moon's surface temperatures are as high as 100 °C, but at night fall to –150 °C. Our atmosphere is therefore very important to us in helping to keep the Earth's surface temperature more or less constant.

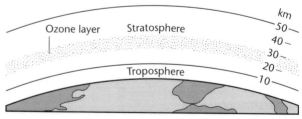

The layers in the atmosphere

The atmosphere is a mixture of gases, and provides oxygen which is essential for **respiration**. It also absorbs harmful **ultraviolet radiation** from the **Sun**:

● Sunlight passes through the atmosphere to the Earth's surface, which it warms.

- The warm surface of the Earth then re-radiates some of its heat into the lowest layer of the atmosphere, the troposphere (the layer where the weather occurs).

- The higher up you go, the cooler it becomes.

- At approximately 11 km temperature is about –60 °C.

- However, as you travel further up through the next layer, the stratosphere, the temperature starts to increase.

- This is because incoming sunlight is being absorbed in the **ozone layer** (within the stratosphere).

CHECKPOINT

1. State two ways in which carbon dioxide is added to the atmosphere.

2. How is carbon dioxide removed from the atmosphere?

✧ *Biosphere, Greenhouse effect, Radioactivity, Water cycle*

Evolution of the atmosphere

It is thought that volcanic activity during the evolution of the Earth released gases that formed the original atmosphere. This atmosphere probably consisted mainly of **carbon dioxide** some water vapour, methane and **ammonia**. Changes due to the following processes are thought to have occurred that have resulted in the present atmosphere:

- The carbon from carbon dioxide became trapped in **sedimentary rocks** as carbonates and **fossil fuels**

- The amount of **oxygen** increased due to colonization by plants

- The **ozone** layer developed to filter out harmful ultraviolet **radiation** from the Sun and allowed development of new organisms

- Methane and **ammonia** reacted with oxygen

- Nitrogen gas was released into the air from the reactions of denitrifying bacteria

Remember: The earth is the only planet in the solar system to have an atmosphere.

✧ *Earth, Solar system*

ATOM

All matter is made of three types of particles, atoms, **molecules** and **ions**. The atom is the most basic particle: there are just over 100 different atoms. We can imagine atoms to be small spheres which are packed closely together in a metal (e.g. zinc).

Remember: The periodic table provides a complete list of all the atoms.

Each atom is represented by its own name and symbol:

Some atoms	
Name	*Symbol*
Hydrogen	H
Oxygen	O
Carbon	C
Copper	Cu
Chlorine	Cl
Sodium	Na

Notice that each **chemical symbol** is either a single *capital* letter (for example, H) or else a *capital* letter followed by a *small* letter (e.g. Cl).

Substances that consist of just one type of atom are called **elements**. The element has the same name as the atom. Atoms of the *same* element are usually identical and have the same mass; e.g. the copper atoms in a piece of copper are all the same. However, those atoms from *different* elements have different masses; for example, hydrogen is a very light atom, whereas gold is a very heavy atom.

It is from these atoms, and combinations of these atoms, that the other two types of particles, ions and molecules, can be made. When atoms react they can do so to form substances containing ions or molecules. These particles are held together by strong forces of attraction called chemical bonds. Each atom has a **valency** associated with it (usually a number between one and four) which indicates how many bonds each atom can form.

✧ *Atomic mass, Atomic number, Atomic structure, Bonding*

ATOMIC MASS

Atoms are so very small that a special unit has to be used for measuring their masses. This unit is called the atomic mass unit and has the symbol u.

The lightest atom is hydrogen with an atomic mass of 1u, whereas nitrogen atoms have an atomic mass of 14u. Obviously there is no balance sensitive enough to measure the masses of atoms. However, atomic mass *can* be measured in a device called a mass spectrometer. This allows the atoms to be ionized before being passed through strong magnetic and electric fields. These fields deflect the ions as they pass through; the heavier the ion, the less it is deflected. Detecting by how much an ion has been deflected will give a measure of the atom's mass.

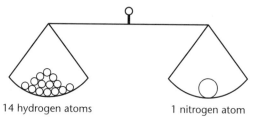

14 hydrogen atoms   1 nitrogen atom

An imaginary balance on which one nitrogen atom is balanced by 14 hydrogen atoms

The mass spectrometer can give very precise measurements, which are quoted in tables. In general, however, we use approximate atomic masses that are often rounded up to the nearest whole number. The following table gives a few examples:

Atomic masses		
Atom	Symbol	Atomic mass (u)*
Hydrogen	H	1
Magnesium	Mg	24
Oxygen	O	16
Copper	Cu	63.5
Silver	Ag	108

*6×10^{23} u = 1g

✛ *Atomic number, atomic structure*

ATOMIC NUMBER

Atoms differ from each other in the number of **protons**, **neutrons** and **electrons** from which they are made. The atomic number is the number of protons in the **nucleus**.

> Remember: The number of protons in the nucleus equals the number of electrons in the atom.

The atomic number can be added to the **chemical symbol**:

mass number → A
$$X$$
atomic mumber → Z ← chemical symbol

The atomic number identifies the type of atom (the name and the way in which it behaves chemically), e.g. the **carbon** atom has an atomic number of six (six protons); all carbon atoms have an atomic number of six, and they all behave in the same way in chemical reactions. Using the system described above, the carbon atom can be written as $^{12}_{6}$ C.

Carbon atoms can have different masses, but will *always* have six protons and six electrons.

CHECKPOINT

Complete this sentence.

The atomic number is the number of .... in the nucleus.

✛ *Atomic mass, Atomic structure, Isotopes*

ATOMIC STRUCTURE

The sub-atomic particles that **atoms** are made of are:

protons ⎫
neutrons ⎬ found in the nucleus
electrons – found orbiting the nucleus

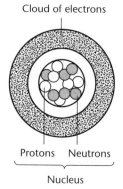

Cloud of electrons

Protons   Neutrons

Nucleus

The arrangement of the atomic particles that make up the atom

The differences in these particles are shown in the table.

Differences among sub-atomic particles		
Sub-atomic particle	Mass (u)*	Charge
Proton	1	+1
Neutron	1	0
Electron	Very small (1/2000)	–1

*u = atomic mass unit

PATTERNS FOR ATOMS

If we look closely at the atomic structure of materials, we see that there are several patterns:

- The number of protons in an atom is called the **atomic number**. Atoms have atomic numbers of 1–107

- There are *always* the same number of electrons and protons, so every atom is electrically neutral. Charges on the electrons and protons cancel out

- Electrons are arranged in a series of 'shells' around the nucleus. Each shell can only contain a limited number of electrons. The numbers for the first three shells are shown below, but after this the arrangement becomes more complex

first shell	maximum two electrons
second shell	maximum eight electrons
third shell	maximum eighteen electrons

For example, in the sodium atom, which has 11 electrons, the arrangement is two in the first shell; eight in the second shell and one in the third shell.

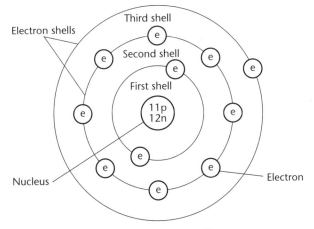

The electron arrangement of the sodium atom, Na: 2, 8, 1

- The total number of protons and neutrons in the nucleus is called the **mass number** (each proton and neutron has a mass of lu). There are usually about the same number of protons and neutrons in a nucleus.

> *Remember: You can work out the structure of an atom from two numbers:*
> **atomic number** = *number of* **protons**
> (= *number of* **electrons**)
> **mass number** = *number of* **protons** + *number of* **neutrons**

For sodium:

- The atomic number is 11; there are 11 protons and 11 electrons in the sodium atom.

- The mass number is 23, which is equal to the number of protons plus the number of neutrons.

- Therefore the number of neutrons is equal to the mass number minus the atomic number, i.e. (23 – 11 = 12).

- Therefore the sodium atom has 11 protons, 12 neutrons and 11 electrons. The sodium atom can be written as $^{23}_{11}$ Na.

The **periodic table** provides us with a complete list of all the atoms that exist in order of **atomic number** (i.e. increasing mass). Each period corresponds to filling an electron shell. Sometimes atoms of the same type (same atomic number) have different masses; these are called **isotopes**.

> *Remember: If you draw the arrangement of electrons, they are arranged in shells around the nucleus: the first shell has a maximum of two electrons; the second shells has a maximum of eight electrons.*

✦ **Covalent bonding, Ionic bonding, Radioactivity**

The atomic structure of some common elements						
Element	Number of protons in the nucleus	Number of protons and neutrons in the nucleus	Number of electrons in each shell			
	(atomic number)	(mass number)	Shell 1	Shell 2	Shell 3	Shell 4
Hydrogen	1	1	1			
Helium	2	4	2			
Lithium	3	7	2	1		
Beryllium	4	9	2	2		
Boron	5	11	2	3		
Carbon	6	12	2	4		
Nitrogen	7	14	2	5		
Oxygen	8	16	2	6		
Fluorine	9	19	2	7		
Neon	10	20	2	8		
Sodium	11	23	2	8	1	
Magnesium	12	24	2	8	2	
Aluminium	13	27	2	8	3	
Silicon	14	28	2	8	4	
Phosphorus	15	31	2	8	5	
Sulphur	16	32	2	8	6	
Chlorine	17	35.5	2	8	7	
Argon	18	40	2	8	8	
Potassium	19	39	2	8	8	1
Calcium	20	40	2	8	8	2

AUXIN

Plant hormones

BACKGROUND RADIATION

We are constantly exposed to **radioactivity**, largely from natural sources. This is referred to as background radiation. It arises from small amounts of radioactive **atoms** present in the air, soil, rocks (particularly granite in the UK) and building materials. Background radiation also occurs from the food we eat, mainly due to a radioactive **isotope** of potassium. Cosmic rays penetrating the **atmosphere** also give rise to background radiation. In addition, we receive small doses of radiation arising from artificial sources, such as:

- Medical treatment (chest and dental X-rays)
- Nuclear weapons testing (the dose attributed to this is very small and is dropping as a result of a test ban treaty in the 1960s)
- Nuclear power (estimated as being very small)

⟶ *Nuclear fission, Nuclear power, Radioactivity*

CHECKPOINT

State **one** natural cause and **one** man-made cause of background radiation.

BACTERIA

Bacteria are very small single-celled organisms that reproduce very rapidly (about every 20 min) by dividing into two. Bacteria respire either **aerobically** or **anaerobically**, and most are killed at temperatures above 50 °C. Bacteria live in the soil, in water and in any dead plants and animals. They are important because.

- They **decompose** dead plants and animals and release important nutrients for use by plants in the **nitrogen cycle**
- They break down sewage into harmless substances that can be released into rivers
- They live in your gut where they help to make vitamin B
- In cows, and other ruminants, bacteria produce **enzymes** to digest the cellulose in plants.

Some bacteria are harmful and cause disease by releasing poisonous substances called toxins into the body. These toxins cause diseases such as tetanus and diphtheria. However, a weakened form of the bacteria injected into the body will cause the production of **antibodies** that will destroy any more bacteria.

One important effect of bacteria is that they make food go bad and a great deal of money has to be spent on preserving food, such as heating food to kill bacteria.

Bacteria are now used in **genetic engineering** to make products useful to humans, e.g. **insulin** to treat **diabetics**.

⟶ *Acids, Acids and food preparation, Vaccine, White blood cells*

BALANCED DIET

A balanced diet contains **carbohydrates** (sugars and starches), **protein**, fats, **minerals**, **vitamins**, **fibre** (roughage) and **water**.

Your daily dietary requirements will vary according to age, pregnancy, illness, and how active you are; e.g.:

- If you do a lot of exercise you will use up a lot of energy and will need more **carbohydrate** and fats, which can be broken down to supply energy to your muscle cells.

Type of food	Reason	Source
	The main sources and uses of each component of a balanced diet	
Carbohydrate	Glucose, sucrose, starch – for energy	Jams, sweets, bread, potato, rice, pasta
Protein	Amino acids – for growth and repair of cells	Meat, cheese, eggs, nuts, fish, beans
Fats	Fatty acids – storage and energy	Butter, oils, margarine, cheese
Vitamins	A, B, C, D – good health	Fresh vegetables and fruit
Minerals	E.g. iron, calcium – good health	Fruit, green vegetables
Fibre	To help bowel movement	Vegetables, wholemeal bread, brown rice
Water	For all the reactions in the body	Fruit and vegetables

- A young person who is still growing will need to eat more foods rich in protein to supply **amino acids** for the growth of extra body cells to make more tissues and muscles.

- A labourer on a building site may need more carbohydrate than someone who works in an office.

- A person who has lost a lot of blood will need to increase his/her iron intake to form **haemoglobin**, an essential part of the **red blood cells**.

Children in less well-developed countries often lack one or more essential component of a balanced diet. Children lacking in **protein** suffer from kwashiorkor, and are unable to develop proper muscles. Children suffering from a lack of vitamin A may suffer from blindness.

-+- *Minerals, vitamins*

BASE

Bases are substances that can neutralize acids, they react with acids to produce salts. Bases include **metal oxides**, e.g. magnesium oxide; metal hydroxides, e.g. calcium hydroxide; and metal carbonates, e.g. zinc carbonate. Most bases do not dissolve (i.e. they are insoluble) in water; those that do dissolve are called **alkalis**.

> *Remember: Almost all compounds that contain **ions** can be classified as either **acid**, base or **salt**.*

-+- *Acid, Acid – patterns of acid reactions, Carbonates*

BATTERY

-+- *Anode, Cathode, Cell – electrical*

BAUXITE

Bauxite is the main ore of aluminium, the most common metal in the Earth's crust. Bauxite is a rocky material often reddish in colour that has a very high proportion of aluminium oxide (Al_2O_3).
  Aluminium is obtained from bauxite in two stages:

- In the first stage the bauxite is crushed and treated with *sodium hydroxide* to separate the aluminium oxide (a white powder) from its impurities

- In the second stage the metal is extracted from aluminium oxide by **electrolysis**

-+- *Extraction of metal*

BETA RADIATION

-+- *Radioactivity*

BIODEGRADABLE

Biodegradable means capable of being broken down by bacteria, e.g. leaves, vegetable peelings, paper, faeces, dead animals. However, substances such as **plastics**, which are widely used in packaging, are non-biodegradable. Research is being carried out to make biodegradable plastics by including short chains of sugar into the plastic molecule. Bacteria will then break down the sugar and leave very short chains that will degrade in the environment.

-+- *Pollution, Recycling*

BIOLOGICAL CONTROL

Biological control is when animals are introduced into the **food chain** to control another animal or plant that has become a pest. Sometimes a natural **predator** of the pest is introduced to feed on the pest; for example, the red spider mite is a very common insect pest that damages plants in greenhouses. Instead of spraying with insecticide, a gardener can introduce another insect that is a predator of the red spider and that eats about 20 red spiders a day!
  Disadvantages of biological control are:

- It is a much slower process than using chemical **pesticides**.

- The predator can itself become a pest, and may select a different source of food to the intended one.

Advantages of biological control are:

- There is no **pollution**

- There is no danger to the rest of the food chain in terms of accumulation of pesticide in the **carnivores**

- Dangerous chemicals are not used and therefore insects that are resistant to the pesticides do not develop.

> *Remember: Biological control methods are safer than using insecticides, but much slower.*

-+- *Competition, Population*

BIOMASS

The term biomass refers to the amount (mass) of living material in a **food web** or **ecosystem**. It can be determined by weighing all the living things at each **trophic level**; **producers**, **herbivores**, **carnivores**, etc. However, the biomass should be weighed over a period of time, for example, a year, as the amount of material will vary according to the season.

✛ **Food chain, Pyramid of biomass**

BIOSPHERE

This describes the part of the **Earth** and the **atmosphere** in which all living organisms live. On Earth the biosphere consists of land and water environments. Organisms are usually adapted to a particular **environment** and live in a specialized **habitat**.

✛ **Abiotic factors, Biotic factors, Ecosystem**

BIOTIC FACTORS

Biotic factors are the living community of animals and plants in an **ecosystem**. In other words, the green plants or **producers** that make food by **photosynthesis**, the **consumers** that obtain food from the plants or other animals, and the **decomposers** that break down and decompose the dead animals and plants.

✛ **Abiotic factors, Food chains and food webs**

BLAST FURNACE

There are two basic techniques for extracting a metal from its ore:

- **reduction**, using heat energy and carbon as the reducing agent
- **electrolysis**, using electrical energy

In either case the problem is the same, namely to reduce the metal **ion** to a metal **atom**. The technique that is chosen depends on cost and the reactivity of the metal. Reduction is carried out in a blast furnace.

Iron extraction

One metal to be extracted from its ore by reduction is iron. Iron ore, or **hematite**, contains iron oxide, and is 'smelted' in a blast furnace. Once the furnace is started it operates as a continuous process; the raw materials being added at the top and the molten iron and molten waste materials being run off at the bottom.

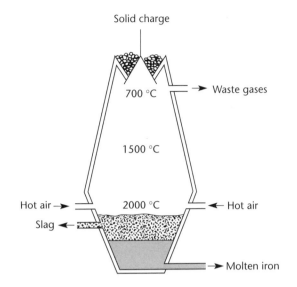

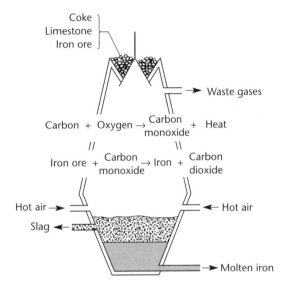

The blast furnace used to extract iron from iron ore

The raw materials

These are added at the top of the furnace. They consist of:

- Iron oxide ore, which will be reduced to iron
- **Coke**, which provides the **reducing agent**
- **Limestone**, which is added to remove the waste rock in the iron ore. Iron ore contains a lot of other impurities (mainly silica), which would soon clog the furnace and have to be removed, needing the furnace to be shut down and allowed to cool – a costly procedure. The limestone (calcium **carbonate**) reacts with the silica to produce a glassy material (calcium silicate) that is molten at the furnace temperature and runs to the bottom to be tapped off

At the bottom of the furnace, a blast of hot air is forced into the molten mass. This air provides oxygen that reacts with the carbon to produce carbon monoxide:

$$2C(s) + O_2(g) \rightarrow 2CO(g)$$

The reaction

Carbon monoxide is a powerful **reducing agent** and reduces the iron oxide to iron, which is molten at the temperature of the furnace:

$$\text{carbon monoxide} + \text{iron oxide} \rightarrow \text{iron} + \text{carbon dioxide}$$
$$3CO(g) + Fe_2O_3(s) \rightarrow 2Fe(l) + 3CO_2(g)$$

At the same time the high temperature of the furnace causes the calcium carbonate to be converted into calcium oxide, which then reacts with the silica to produce *molten calcium silicate* (slag).

> Remember: This is an example of how a less reactive metal can be extracted by reduction with carbon or carbon monoxide.

The products

- *Iron*: molten iron is very dense so travels down through the furnace and is tapped off at the bottom hole into large moulds called 'pigs'. The iron that is produced is called pig iron.

- *Slag*: this is the molten calcium silicate: it is less dense than the iron so it floats on the molten iron. It is tapped off from the higher hole and is a waste product.

- *Gases*: hot waste gases escape from the top of the furnace; these include carbon monoxide and carbon dioxide.

Other metals such as lead, **zinc** and copper can also be extracted by **reduction** Sulphide ores (e.g. galena; PbS) first have to be roasted in air to convert the compound to a metal oxide:

$$\text{lead sulphide} + \text{oxygen} \rightarrow \text{lead oxide} + \text{sulphur dioxide}$$
$$2PbS(s) + 3O_2(g) \rightarrow 2PbO(s) + 2SO_2(g)$$

-⊹- **Extraction of metals**

BLOOD

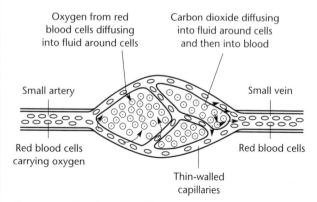

Oxygen from red blood cells diffusing into fluid around cells

Carbon dioxide diffusing into fluid around cells and then into blood

Small artery

Small vein

Red blood cells carrying oxygen

Red blood cells

Thin-walled capillaries

Oxygen and carbon dioxide transport

Blood is a watery liquid (**plasma**) that contains **red** and **white blood cells** and tiny particles called **platelets**. Adults have about 5–6 l of blood in their body. There are two main functions of blood.

- To maintain a constant internal environment for all the cells in the body by providing oxygen and food and removing waste products.

- To *transport* many different substances around the body in the circulatory system.

> *CHECKPOINT*
>
> What is the function of red blood cells:
>
> (a) to remove waste products from the cells,
> (b) to help form blood clots,
> (c) to destroy bacteria in the body,
> (d) to transport oxygen to the cells?

-⊹- **Artery, Blood System, Breathing, Homeostasis, Vein**

BLOOD SYSTEM

The blood system is a continuous series of tubes inside your body which carry **blood** to all the different parts of you. The main tubes are:

- **arteries**, carrying blood away from the **heart**

- **veins** carrying blood towards the heart

Blood constantly flows around in one direction pumped by the heart, a powerful muscle. The blood vessels divide up into smaller and smaller tubes and eventually form tiny thin-walled **capillaries**.

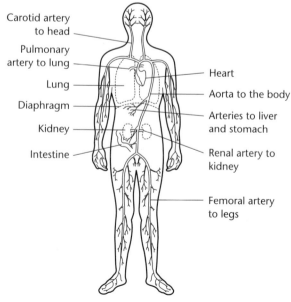

Carotid artery to head

Pulmonary artery to lung

Lung

Diaphragm

Kidney

Intestine

Heart

Aorta to the body

Arteries to liver and stomach

Renal artery to kidney

Femoral artery to legs

The blood system: the main arteries in your body

✦ **Coronary artery disease, Organ Systems**

BODY TEMPERATURE

In adult humans, body temperature is about 37 °C, but this can vary during the day for an individual person. Young children have slightly higher body temperatures than adults. The hypothalamus is part of the **brain** that responds to temperature changes both inside and outside the body. The temperature of the **blood** flowing through the brain is monitored by the hypothalamus and information about the external temperature is detected by special thermoreceptors in the skin, which are connected by nerves to the hypothalamus. The brain initiates responses that are appropriate to the information received. You are able to control your body temperature to keep it constant by various methods.

If you are too hot you *lose* heat by:

- The **evaporation** of sweat, which has a cooling effect on the body

- By losing heat from the blood in tiny vessels just under your skin, which widen (**vasodilation**) to allow heat loss by radiation.

If you are too cold you can *retain* heat by:

- Increasing the amount of clothing that traps air, a poor conductor of heat, around your skin. In other mammals and birds this function is carried out by fur and feathers

- The blood vessels under the skin becoming narrow and constricting (**vasoconstriction**) to reduce the amount of heat lost by radiation

✦ **Evaporation, Homeostasis, Insulation**

BONDING

Chemical bonds are strong forces that hold **atoms** together in substances. They are formed as a result of the interactions of **electrons** that orbit the nucleus of atoms. There are different types of chemical bonds:

> Remember: New substances are formed when atoms combine.

- **Covalent bonds:** These are formed when atoms share their electrons and are found in **molecules** (mostly between non-metal atoms)

- **Ionic bonds:** These are formed when one atom loses an electron to another atom resulting in **ions** of opposite charges being formed. This happens mostly between a **metal** atom (which gives an electron) and a non-metal atom (which accepts an electron)

- **Metallic bonds:** In metals the atoms 'float' in a sea of electrons

Comparing ionic compounds with covalent compounds		
Property	Ionic compounds	Covalent compounds
Relation to periodic table	Formed between atoms and non-metal atoms	Formed between non-metal atoms
Melting point	High > 250 °C	Low < 250 °C
Boiling point	High > 500 °C	Low < 500 °C
Electrical conductivity	Good conductor when molten or in solution	Non-conductor
Solubility in water	Usually soluble	Usually insoluble

> Remember: Chemical bonds are strong and have to be broken before one substance will react with another. This is the reason we often have to heat substances to make them react.

✦ *Activation energy, Atom, Endothermic, Exothermic, Giant structures*

BRAIN

The brain is a very large part of the **nervous system**. Its function is to co-ordinate many of the body's activities. It *receives* input from the sensory organs and *sends* motor impulses to the **muscles** and glands in the body. The brain is an important store of information so that animals can learn from past experiences.

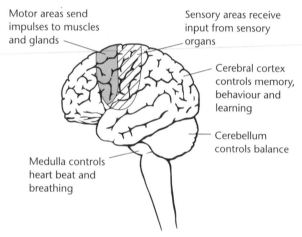

Motor areas send impulses to muscles and glands

Sensory areas receive input from sensory organs

Cerebral cortex controls memory, behaviour and learning

Cerebellum controls balance

Medulla controls heart beat and breathing

Main regions of the brain and their functions

✦ *Organ, Reflex arc*

BREATHING

Breathing describes the process by which air is inhaled and exhaled, to and from your lungs. At rest, you are breathing about 15 times a minute.

Try putting your hands over your ribs and taking a deep breath. You should be able to feel your chest cavity getting larger as you breathe in.

When you breathe in:

● The intercostal **muscles** between your ribs contract to pull your ribs up and out

● At the same time the diaphragm muscle at the base of your chest flattens so that your chest cavity is made larger

● Air outside your chest cavity is at greater pressure than air inside your chest

● This difference in pressure causes air to rush into your lungs

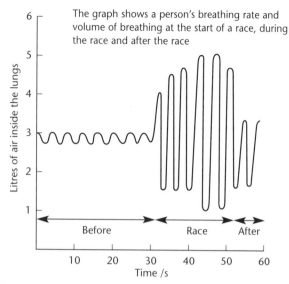

The graph shows a person's breathing rate and volume of breathing at the start of a race, during the race and after the race

Litres of air inside the lungs

Before · Race · After

Time /s

Breathing rates and lung volume

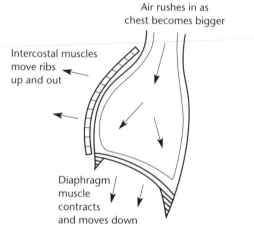

Air rushes in as chest becomes bigger

Intercostal muscles move ribs up and out

Diaphragm muscle contracts and moves down

Breathing in

When you breathe out:

● The intercostal muscles move the ribs down; the diaphragm muscle relaxes and the diaphragm pushes up, making your chest cavity smaller

● The pressure in the lungs is increased. As a result, the air is pushed out

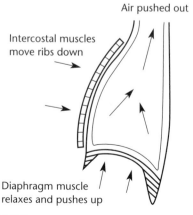

Air pushed out

Intercostal muscles move ribs down

Diaphragm muscle relaxes and pushes up

Breathing out

Your lungs are basically two sponge-like structures in your chest that fill up with air:

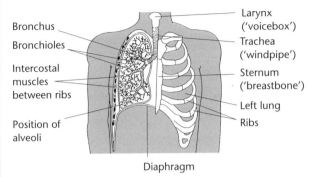

The human chest cavity

- Oxygen diffuses over the moist surface of the air sacs (or *alveoli*) which in turn help oxygen diffuse into the blood in the capillaries

- Here it combines with **haemoglobin** in the *red blood cells*, to make a new substance called oxyhaemoglobin

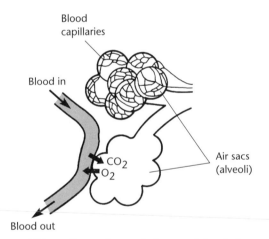

Oxygen diffuses from air sacs into your blood stream

- The blood is pumped by the *heart* muscle to the rest of the body through *arteries* and eventually *capillaries*

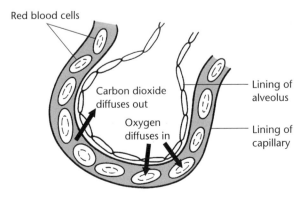

Inside one capillary

- The oxygen diffuses into your cells and carbon dioxide from the cells diffuses into your blood and is carried back to the lungs

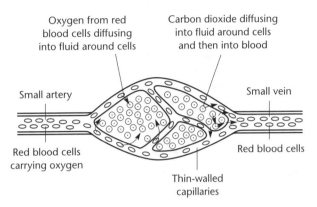

Oxygen and carbon dioxide transport

CHECKPOINT

Cross out the wrong words in these sentences.

When you breathe in, the ribs move *down and in/up and out*. The diaphragm *flattens/pushes up* and air is *pushed out/rushes in*.

↔ *Aerobic respiration, Anaerobic respiration, Diffusion action, Excercise, Pulmonary artery and vein, Respiration*

BROWNIAN MOTION

Brownian motion was first noticed by a scientist called Robert Brown. He noticed that when he looked at pollen grains in water through a microscope they were 'jiggling around' in a random way. This was explained in later years by another scientist who said that the strange movement was due to the very much smaller water **particles** (water **molecules**) hitting the pollen grains and making them move. This can also be seen in a 'smoke cell' where the bits of smoke are being moved by the air molecules striking them.

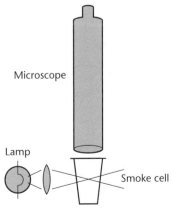

Smoke cell to show Brownian motion

This odd movement could only be explained by assuming that air (**gas**) and water (**liquid**) were made of particles and that these particles were moving, striking the much larger pollen grains or smoke and causing them to move slightly.

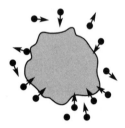

Smoke particle is bombarded by air molecules

*Remember: You cannot see the water or air molecules even with the most powerful microscope, they are far too small, but you **can** see the effect they have on the much, much larger pollen grains or 'bits' of smoke.*

*✦ **Diffusion, Gas, Kinetic theory, Liquid, Solid***

CANCER

One of the commonest causes of death in Western society is from some form of cancer. A cancer is caused by a group of **cells** in the body that begin to grow abnormally and destroy healthy cells. It is thought that environmental factors such as **smoking**, **alcohol** and **radiation** can increase the risk of cancer developing. Cancers can be caused in most parts of the body, e.g. the lungs, the large intestine, the skin and the breasts. Prevention of cancer may be helped by reducing the amount of fats in the diet and by increasing the intake of fresh vegetables.

Radioactivity

CAPILLARIES

Capillaries are the smallest blood vessels and carry blood to all the cells in the body. They have very thin walls so that substances, such as **oxygen**, **carbon dioxide**, glucose and waste products can be exchanged between the **blood stream** and the **cells** in the body.

Artery, Blood system, Vein

CARBOHYDRATES

These are a family of compounds that include **sugars** and **starches**. All carbohydrates contain **carbon**, hydrogen and oxygen. The name carbohydrate is obtained from the terms *carbo-* meaning carbon, and *hydrate*, meaning hydrogen and oxygen present, in the proportions they are in water.

Examples of carbohydrates are:

● **Sugar**: found in fruit, cakes, jam, soft drinks and sweets

● **Starch**: found in bread, cereals, potatoes, pasta and rice

Carbohydrates are manufactured by plants, during the process of **photosynthesis**, to produce simple sugars. The plant then converts these into more complex molecules, such as starch and cellulose.

When we eat plant material as food, it provides us with a source of carbohydrate, which in turn is broken down inside our bodies to provide energy.

Balanced diet, Energy from food

CARBON

Carbon is an **element** (it contains only one type of atom), chemical symbol C, that has two crystalline forms:

● **diamond**: one of the hardest substances known

● **graphite**: in this form carbon will conduct electricity

Carbon is also found in coal, coke and charcoal. Carbon is a good **reducing agent**, in that it will 'grab' oxygen from many other compounds, e.g. it will remove oxygen from iron oxide, leaving iron.

Allotropes, Blast furnace

Carbon compounds

Carbon is an unusual element, since it can form a very large number of different substances that consist of long carbon chains, or rings of carbon atoms. It is this ability for carbon atoms to link with each other that make it almost unique (silicon has a similar ability). There is a branch of chemistry called *organic* chemistry, devoted to the study of just these compounds:

● All living things consist of carbon compounds; proteins, starches and cellulose

● Sugars consist of carbon chains or rings

● All the substances found in **crude oil** consist of rings or chains of carbon compounds

● All man-made polymers (plastics) consist of long carbon chains

Addition polymers, Hydrocarbons

Carbon cycle

Carbon is breathed out, as **carbon dioxide**, by all animals and plants. Whenever **fossil fuels** (such as coal, oil or gas) are burnt, carbon dioxide is also released into the **atmosphere**.

Green plants take in carbon dioxide during the day time, and combine the carbon dioxide with water to make **carbohydrates**. This process is known as **photosynthesis** and it releases oxygen as a waste product.

The plants are eaten by animals and the carbon, in the form of carbohydrates, proteins and fats, is used to make the cells of the animals. As the animals **respire**, the carbohydrates are broken down to form carbon dioxide and water. The carbon is released as carbon dioxide to the atmosphere, completing the carbon cycle.

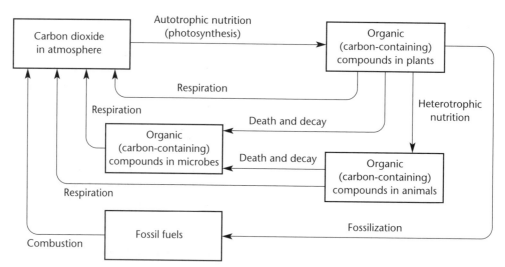

The carbon cycle

-⊹- **Greenhouse effect**

Carbon dating

-⊹- **Radioactivity – uses**

CARBONATES

Carbonates belong to a group of substances called **salts**. All carbonates contain the **carbonate** ion which is negative and a positive **ion** (metal).

Carbonate ion

Examples of the carbonate ion, CO_3^{2-}, are zinc carbonate ($ZnCO_3$), copper carbonate ($CuCO_3$) and calcium carbonate ($CaCO_3$).

Most carbonates are not soluble; the exceptions being sodium, potassium and lithium. Metal carbonates can be thought of as **bases**; they will react with **acids** to produce salt and water and **carbon dioxide**.

-⊹- **Limestone**

CARBON DIOXIDE CO₂

Carbon dioxide is:

- colourless
- odourless
- more dense than air
- dissolves slightly in water to produce a weakly acidic solution

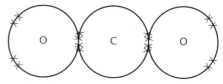

Structure of carbon dioxide

Carbon dioxide is:

- A gas made up of **molecules** that contain one atom of **carbon** and two atoms of oxygen (formula CO_2)
- The only gas that will turn limewater cloudy or 'milky'; this can be used as a test for the gas
- Given off when **fossil fuels** and plant materials are burnt when carbonates are heated
- Released into the atmosphere by the respiration of animals and made use of by plants during **photosynthesis**

> *Remember: The level of carbon dioxide in the atmosphere is about 0.03–0.04 per cent.*

-⊹- **Carbon cycle, Greenhouse effect**

CARNIVORES

-+- *Ecosystem, Food chains and food webs*

CATALYSTS

A catalyst is a substance that changes the rate of a **chemical reaction**; the catalyst itself remains unchanged at the end of a reaction and can be re-used. Catalysts are often used to *speed up* reactions, but they can also be used to slow them down.

Gas reactions and catalysts

One way in which catalysts are thought to work in reactions involving gases by the surface of the catalyst providing sites where the reacting **molecules** 'meet'. The **transition metals** are often used as catalysts in this way in industrial processes.

Manufacture of ammonia

$$N_2 + 3H_2 \rightleftharpoons 2NH_3$$

Iron is used as a catalyst; nitrogen and hydrogen are adsorbed onto the surface where they come into contact and react. In the gas state they are often moving too fast, so that when they collide they bounce off each other without reacting.

Manufacture of sulphuric acid

One stage involves the production of sulphur trioxide from sulphur dioxide:

$$2SO_2 + O_2 \rightleftharpoons 2SO_3$$

Vanadium (V) oxide is the catalyst and works in a similar way to that described above.

Pollution control on cars

Petrol engines in cars burn petrol (a **hydrocarbon** fuel) and produce **carbon dioxide** and water as waste products. In addition, carbon monoxide and some oxides of nitrogen are produced, which **pollute** the **atmosphere**. Catalytic converters are now fitted to the car exhaust systems of all new cars. The device contains a metal catalyst with a large surface area. As the hot exhaust gases such as **sulphur dioxide** and nitrogen dioxide, pass over the catalyst, the pollutant gases are converted into carbon dioxide and nitrogen.

Antioxidants

Certain chemicals can be added to foods, such as crisps, to slow down the natural oxidation of foods, which would result in loss of flavour and decay. These chemicals (antioxidants) are acting as catalysts. Here they are reducing the rate of a chemical reaction.

> *Remember: Catalytic converters in car exhausts are a good technological application of catalysts.*

Enzymes

These are biological **catalysts** and enable chemical reactions to take place in living things. For example, the enzyme salivary **amylase** aids the breakdown of starch to sugar.

-+- *Acid rain, Enzymes, Reversible reactions*

CATHODE

The cathode is the name given to a negative **electrode** either in an **electrolysis** cell or an **electrical cell** (battery).

In electrolysis

The cathode and **anode** (the positive electrode) are attached to an electrical source (e.g. battery or power-pack) and dipped into an **electrolyte** (liquid or solution containing **ions**). A current flows through the electrolyte when positive ions (**cations**) are attracted to the cathode. At the cathode these ions are converted to **atoms**:

$$M^+ + e^- \rightarrow M$$

The cathode must conduct electricity and is usually carbon (graphite) or a metal.

> *Remember: The cathode is the negative electrode and attracts positive cations.*

In an electrical cell

When two different metals (which act as electrodes) are placed in an **electrolyte** and are connected together externally, e.g. with a wire, they produce an electric current (a flow of electrons). The cathode (the *negative* electrode) will be the metal that has the greatest tendency to lose electrons (higher in the reactivity series). In the dry cells (batteries) that we buy, the cathode is often made of zinc.

-+- *Cell – electrical, Electrolysis*

CATHODE RAY OSCILLOSCOPE (CRO)

A CRO can be used as a visual **voltmeter** for measuring **voltage**. A bright spot is produced on the oscilloscope screen by a beam of **electrons**. The position of the spot can be altered by the voltage across the CRO. When the time-base control is adjusted, the dot moves across the screen and draws a visual graph of the voltage against time.

-+- *Alternating current, Direct current*

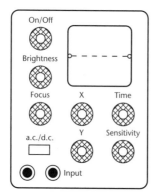

Control panel of a cathode ray oscilloscope

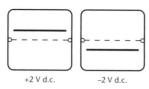

+2 V d.c.   –2 V d.c.

The waveform of a direct current (d.c.) supply

The waveform of an alternating current (a.c.) supply

CATION

A positively charged ion. Metal atoms tend to form cations. During **electrolysis** cations are attracted to the **cathode**, the negative electrode. Examples of some cations are shown below:

Some common cations		
Name of ion	*Symbol*	*Charge on ion*
Copper	Cu^{2+}	2+
Sodium	Na^{+}	1+
Calcium	Ca^{2+}	2+
Aluminium	Al^{3+}	3+
Ammonium	NH_4^{+}	1+

⤙ *Anions, Anode, Cathode, Electrolysis,
Ionic bonding, Solubility*

CELL – BIOLOGICAL

Cells are the basic units that make up all living organisms (plants and animals). A cell is basically a very tiny fragment of cytoplasm surrounded by a cell membrane. The cell's activities are controlled by a **nucleus** which contains genetic material in the form of **chromosomes**.

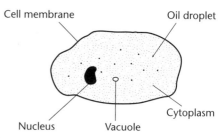

A typical animal cell

⤙ *Meiosis, Mitosis, Nucleus*

CELL – ELECTRICAL

The difference in tendency of **metals** to form **ions** can be very useful. If a pair of different metals is placed in a solution containing ions and the metals are linked by a wire, then **electrons** will flow through the wire. This means that a **current** is flowing through the wire, and there is a **voltage** between the two metals. This arrangement is called a simple cell.

All electrical cells contain three things:

● a + terminal (the positive electrode or **anode**)

● a – terminal (the negative electrode or **cathode**)

● a solution containing ions through which electricity can pass (**electrolyte**)

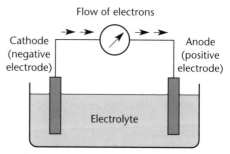

A simple electrical cell

The voltage that is produced between the two metals generally depends on their relative positions in the **reactivity series**:

● If the metals are *far apart* in the reactivity series, then a *large* voltage is produced

● If the two metals in the pair are *close together*, then a *small* voltage is produced

For example:

Metal pair	Voltage produced
Magnesium–copper	Large voltage
Iron–zinc	Small voltage

Dry cells (**batteries**) that you can buy to use in a torch, consist of metal pairs in an electrolyte, except that one of the metals is replaced by carbon (in the form of graphite). In normal dry cells, the electrolyte is a weak acid, in the form of a paste. Alkali batteries have electrolytes that are alkalis (e.g. potassium hydroxide), the positive electrode often being a mixture of carbon and manganese oxide.

-+- *Electrolysis, Electromotive force, Reactions of metals*

CELSIUS SCALE (°C)

This is a scale of temperature that has 100 degrees (divisions) between the lower fixed point of 0 °C and the upper fixed point of 100 °C:

- The *lower* fixed point is the temperature at which ice melts and changes to water

- The *upper* fixed point is the temperature at which pure water boils and changes to steam

-+- *Kelvin, Kinetic theory*

CERAMICS

Ceramics are materials that are made from clays and have been heated at some stage of their manufacture, such as pottery, bricks, etc. They consist of giant structures of silicon and oxygen atoms (silicates).

Ceramics are useful because they are: strong (in compression); hard; non-conductors of heat and electricity; can withstand very high temperatures, and are chemically inert. They are also relatively easily cleaned.

-+- *Composite material, Glass*

CHARACTERISTICS OF LIVING ORGANISMS

-+- *Life processes, Organ systems*

CHEMICAL EQUATIONS

A chemical equation is a way of describing what is happening in a **chemical reaction**. It tells us:

- What is reacting

- What products are formed

- How much of each substance is required

A chemical reaction always follows the general pattern: reactant(s) → product(s).

There may be one or more reactants and one or more products, but the **mass** of the reactants at the beginning will be the same as the mass of the

products at the end. In an equation representing the reaction, you will have the same number of **atoms** (represented by their chemical **symbols**) on the left as you will have on the right-hand side.

> *Remember: All that is happening in a chemical reaction is a rearrangement of the atoms of the reactants to form the products.*

Writing chemical equations

It may help to demonstrate with actual examples:

Example 1

Sodium reacts with chlorine to form **sodium chloride**:

- Step 1: Write the equation in words:

  sodium + chlorine → sodium chloride

- Step 2: Write each substance as a formula:

  $Na + Cl_2 \rightarrow NaCl$

  Sodium is an element (Na); reactive gaseous elements are diatomic (Cl_2); the formula for sodium chloride is $NaCl$ ($Na^+ Cl^-$)

- Step 3: Imagine the reaction as particles:

  $Na + Cl_2 \rightarrow NaCl$

  Ⓝa + ⒸlⒸl → ⓃaⒸl

- Step 4: Balance the equation:

  There are two Cl on the left, so there must be two Cl on the right. The only way to obtain this is to have two NaCl on the right, as follows:

  2NaCl   ⓃaⒸl
            ⓃaⒸl

  $Na + Cl_2 \rightarrow 2NaCl$

  Ⓝa + ⒸlⒸl → ⓃaⒸl
                ⓃaⒸl

  Now we must have two Na on the left to balance the equation:

  $2Na + Cl_2 \rightarrow 2NaCl$

  Ⓝa + ⒸlⒸl → ⓃaⒸl
  Ⓝa   ⓃaⒸl

  Four atoms   Four atoms

The equation is balanced.

> *Remember: When balancing an equation NEVER change the actual formulae.*

Example 2

Magnesium reacts with hydrochloric acid to produce magnesium chloride and hydrogen:

- Step 1: Write the equation in words:

magnesium + hydrochloric → magnesium + hydrogen
acid   chloride

- Step 2: Write each substance as a formula:

$$Mg + HCl \rightarrow MgCl_2 + H_2$$

- Step 3: Imagine the reaction as particles:

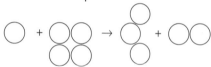

- Step 4: Balance the equation:

$$Mg + 2HCl \rightarrow MgCl_2 + H_2$$

CHECKPOINT

Fill in these circles to show the particles involved in step 4 of the above equation.

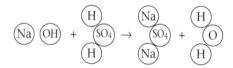

Five atoms   Five atoms

Example 3

Sulphuric acid *neutralizes* sodium hydroxide:

- Step 1: Write the equation in words:

sodium + sulphuric → sodium + water
hydroxide   acid   sulphate

- Step 2: Write each substance as a formula:

$$NaOH + H_2SO_4 \rightarrow Na_2SO_4 + H_2O$$

- Step 3: Imagine the reaction as particles:

Na OH + $\overset{H}{\underset{H}{SO_4}}$ → $\overset{Na}{\underset{Na}{SO_4}}$ + $\overset{H}{\underset{H}{O}}$

- Step 4: Balance the equation:

$$2NaOH + H_2SO_4 \rightarrow Na_2SO_4 + 2H_2O$$

This example also shows that we can regard some groups of *particles* as one unit which is not usually changed in a chemical reaction, e.g. the sulphate ion SO_4^{2-}. Other examples where we can do this are hydroxide ion (OH^-); nitrate ion (NO_3^-); and sometimes carbonate ion (CO_3^{2-} in displacement reactions) and hydrogen carbonate ion (HCO_3^-). More unusual ions are sulphite ion (SO_3^{2-}) and (nitrite ion NO_2^-).

-**•**- *Ionic equations, Mole, Molecule, Salts, State symbols, Valency*

CHEMICAL FORMULA

A chemical formula for a compound shows the ratio of **atoms** present in that **compound**. Each atom has a combining power that is called the **valency**. The valency of an atom depends on the number of electrons in its outer shell and hence its position in the **periodic table**.

-**•**- *Atomic structure, Molecule*

CHEMICAL REACTIONS

Chemical reactions are interactions between particles (**atoms**, **molecules** or **ions**) that involve the 'breaking' and 'making' of chemical bonds. There is a general pattern:

reactants   → products
(starting materials) (new materials)

> *Remember: In a chemical reaction, new substances are always formed which have a different set of properties to those of the reactants.*

Mass stays the same. In any chemical reaction the total mass of the products is always the same as the total mass of the reactants. The reason for this is that chemical reactions only involve the rearrangements of the particles involved.

$$A B + C \rightarrow A C + B$$

You can think of this in the same way as dismantling a Lego model of a house and a garage and using the same bricks to build a small factory and storehouse. This allows us to write **chemical equations** and to make calculations for particle interactions, e.g. the mass of reactants needed to produce 1 kg of a certain product (this is invaluable in the chemical industry). Energy is always involved in a chemical reaction:

Activation energy

Not all substances will react with each other but many do. Some combinations of reactants need a 'push' to get them going – usually in the form of heat – this is referred to as the activation energy. During a reaction sometimes heat is given out (**exothermic**) and sometimes heat is taken in (**endothermic**).

Rate of reaction

Chemical reactions take place at different rates, and this rate (speed) can be measured. Often ways are needed to control the rate of these reactions, either to speed them up or to slow them down (this is important in the chemical industry).

✦ *Catalysts, Covalent bonding, Ionic bonding, Mole, Neutralization, Rates of reaction*

CHEMICAL SYMBOL

There are approximately 100 different **elements** (different **atoms**) and each one has a chemical symbol.

Each chemical symbol is either one capital letter (often the first letter of the name) or a capital letter followed by a small letter. Here are some examples: carbon, C; chlorine, Cl; zinc, Zn; sodium, Na; potassium, K; oxygen, O.

✦ *Atomic number, Periodic Table*

CHLORIDE

Chlorides belong to a group of substances called **salts**. All chlorides contain the chloride **ion** which is negative, and a positive ion (metal or ammonium). Examples of compounds that contain the chloride ion (Cl^-) are: **sodium chloride**, $NaCl$; zinc chloride, $ZnCl_2$; magnesium chloride, $MgCl_2$; ammonium chloride, NH_4Cl.

Most chlorides are soluble in water; the exceptions are silver and lead. Small amounts of chlorides (mostly calcium and magnesium) can be found in tap water, whereas sea water contains much larger quantities of chlorides (as sodium and potassium salts).

✦ *Halogens*

CHLORINE

Chlorine is a halogen, group 7 **element** (contains only one type of **atom**) with **chemical symbol** Cl.

It is a green, poisonous gas that contains chlorine **molecules** (Cl_2). It is quite soluble in water, with which it reacts to produce an acidic solution that also has a bleaching action. In fact the smell you get from bleach is that of chlorine gas which is given off by the bleach. Chlorine also acts as an antiseptic (kills germs) and so is added to swimming pools in the form of a **solution**.

✦ *Chlorofluorocarbons, Electrolysis, Halogens, Periodic table*

CHLOROFLUOROCARBONS

Chlorofluorocarbons, known as CFCs, are a group of **compounds** that contain **carbon**, **chlorine** and fluorine **atoms**, and that have boiling points at just below room temperature. They are not flammable and have low toxicity. This makes them ideal for use in **aerosols** and refrigerators. They are also used in the manufacture of plastic packaging. Unfortunately, they have been linked to damage of the **ozone layer**, which protects us from harmful **ultraviolet rays**.

Uses of CFCs

Aerosol use

CFCs are used as the propellant gas in some aerosols; their use has been banned from 1992.

Refrigeration use

CFCs are used in refrigerants; they are the liquids that circulate in the black pipes at the back of the fridge. They take the heat away from the inside of the refrigerator.

Plastic packaging manufacture

CFCs are used as 'blowing' or foaming agents to make rigid or flexible plastic foam. Some of the boxes used by fast-food chains to hold hamburgers or for egg packaging use CFC rigid foam.

There are about a dozen different CFCs in use today, some of which are more harmful to the ozone layer than others; companies are beginning to use the less harmful CFCs or to look for alternatives. The European governments have agreed to eliminate the use of CFCs by the year 2,000.

✦ *Greenhouse effect, Pollution*

CHROMATOGRAPHY

Chromatography is a technique for detecting the parts of a mixture by separating them.

Paper chromatography

A drop of **solution** of the mixture to be separated is placed on a type of blotting paper (called chromatography paper) and then dipped into a **solvent**. As the solvent soaks up through the paper it carries the mixture with it, but because different substances dissolve at different rates, the solvent carries some parts of the mixture further than others, so separating them. This can be seen if a dot is made with a black felt-tip pen on chromatography or filter paper and then dipped into a solvent such as water. The colours that make up the black (e.g. purple, red, blue, green, etc.) will separate. This technique can be used to separate a mixture of **amino acids** or **proteins**.

CHROMOSOMES

Normal human body cells have 23 pairs of chromosomes in the **nucleus**; every 23 pairs carry instructions for the whole human body. Each chromosome holds the information for many chemical reactions and is made of complex molecules of deoxyribonucleic acid (DNA), e.g. the instructions for making the enzyme salivary **amylase** and the Rhesus blood antigens are thought to be part of the same chromosome.

✦ *Gene, Meiosis, Mitosis, Monohybrid inheritance, Mutations*

CIRCUIT BREAKERS

-+- *Magnetic circuit breakers*

CIRCUIT SYMBOLS

See bottom of page for diagram.

-+- *Current electricity, Parallel circuit, Series circuit*

CLONING

When new individuals are produced by *asexual reproduction*, the cells in the parent's body divide by *mitosis*. This means that all the offspring are genetically identical to the parent and to each other. They are described as clones. Cloning has been used to produce genetically identical plants that all have the same characteristics, e.g. high yield and resistance to disease.

More recently, a cloning technique has been developed that allows a clone of a mammal, such as a sheep, to be produced. The *zygote* (fertilized egg) is removed from the ball of cells that normally surrounds it, and a body cell is inserted in its place. This body cell divides by mitosis and eventually forms an embryo and fetus. If it is allowed to develop fully, it will be a genetically identical copy of its parent. Cloning in this way could have advantage if a particular organism had been genetically engineered to produce an important protein. It would be cost-effective to be able to produce identical copies of these organisms.

-+- *Genetic engineering, Selective breeding*

COKE

Coke is made by heating coal in the absence of air so that it does not burn. This drives off substances

contained in the coal that tend to produce a lot of smoke when they burn. The result is coke, which burns with almost no smoke. Coke is used as a *reducing agent* in the *blast furnace*.

-+- *Fossil fuels, Reduction*

COMBUSTION

Combustion (burning) is a *chemical reaction* that involves a substance reacting with oxygen:

- Some *metals* will burn in air to produce metal oxides; how easily they do this depends on how reactive the metal is:

  magnesium + oxygen → magnesium oxide

- Fuels are substances that give out a lot of energy when they burn; their reactions are strongly *exothermic*. The fuels react with the oxygen in the air. The *fossil fuels* we use (coal, gas and oil) contain carbon and hydrogen and are referred to as *hydrocarbons*. The products of combustion are *carbon dioxide* and *water*.

- Coal is mainly *carbon*:

$$\text{carbon} + \text{oxygen} \rightarrow \text{carbon dioxide}$$
$$C \quad + \quad O_2 \quad \rightarrow \quad CO_2$$

- Natural gas is *methane*:

$$\text{methane} + \text{oxygen} \rightarrow \text{carbon dioxide} + \text{water}$$
$$CH_4 \quad + \quad 2O_2 \quad \rightarrow \quad CO_2 \quad + 2H_2O$$

Combustion in action

Natural gas is often considered to be a very suitable fuel for greenhouses. This is because it not only produces heat but also *carbon dioxide*, which the plants can use, as well as water, to keep the atmosphere humid.

However, if a limited amount of air is present, then carbon monoxide (CO) will be produced. This gas is

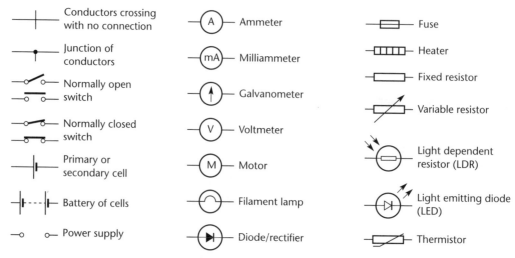

Some conventional symbols for electrical circuit diagrams

poisonous because it latches on to haemoglobin in the *blood*, forming carboxy-haemoglobin, and prevents the blood from carrying oxygen around the body. For this reason it is important to keep a room well ventilated when coal or gas is being burned.

> *Remember: Complete combustion occurs when there is a plentiful supply of oxygen. Incomplete combustion occurs when a fuel burns in a limited amount of oxygen, producing carbon monoxide, a poisonous gas.*

⊹ **Greenhouse effect**

COMPETITION

When two organisms both require the same resource, such as food, space, light and water, they can be said to be competing with each other. Sometimes competition occurs between members of the same **species**, and sometimes between members of a different species.

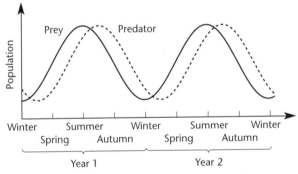

How the *population* of a *predator* increases and decreases as the population of the *prey* goes up and down.

⊹ **Adaptation, Biological control, Predator – prey**

COMPOSITE MATERIALS

Composite materials are those that are **mixtures**. Concrete is a composite material because it is a mixture of cement, sand and gravel.

Fillers are often added to a polymer to give it extra strength, e.g.:

● Glass fibres are added to a thermosetting plastic to give it enough strength to be used to make the glass fibre hulls of boats

● Military aircraft have wings made up of a composite material containing carbon fibres, which are much lighter than metal

● Many modern cars are made using a glass reinforced plastic for the bonnet lids and boot lids

⊹ **Ceramics, Glass**

COMPOUNDS

Compounds are substances that contain more than one type of **atom**, chemically joined. The particles in a compound might be **molecules** or **ions**. A compound can be chemically split into simpler substances.

For example:

● Water is a compound, it consists of water molecules. Each water molecule contains two atoms of hydrogen and one atom of oxygen. Water can be split by **electrolysis** into hydrogen and oxygen

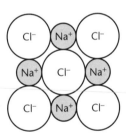

Sodium chloride

The melting points and boiling points of compounds, and whether they conduct electricity when molten				
Compound	*Relative molecular mass*	*Conduct when molten*	*Melting point (°C)*	*Boiling point (°C)*
Ammonia	17	No	−78	−34
Carbon dioxide	44	No	−111	−78
Calcium carbonate	100		decomposes when heated	
Calcium oxide	56	Yes	2600	2850
Copper (II) chloride	135	Yes	620	990
Copper (II) sulphate	160		decomposes when heated	
Glucose	180	No	146	decomposes
Hydrogen chloride	36.5	No	−114	−85
Lead (II) chloride	278	Yes	501	950
Silicon dioxide	60	No	1610	2230
Sodium Chloride	58.5	Yes	801	1413
Water	18	No	0	100

- Sodium chloride is a compound, it consists of sodium and chloride ions. There is one sodium ion for every chloride ion. It can be split by **electrolysis** into sodium and chlorine

> *Remember: All metal compounds conduct electricity when molten.*

-**-** **Chemical formula, Giant structures**

CONDENSATION

Condensation is the **liquid** formed as a result of cooling a **gas**; e.g. in a warm room there may be a lot of water vapour that, when it reaches the cold glass of a window, condenses out to form water droplets.

-**-** **Evaporation, Water cycles**

CONDUCTION

Conduction is the transfer of **energy** through a substance without the substance itself moving. Heat energy is conducted as a result of **particles** vibrating in a solid conductor, such as metals or non-metals. Energy is transferred through a substance from where the temperature is higher to where the temperature is lower.

Conductor	Insulator
Copper	Wood
Iron	Sulphur
Aluminium	Polythene
Carbon	Rubber
Sea water	Paraffin
Sulphuric acid	Propanone

> *Remember: Metals are good conductors of heat but non-metals are poor conductors and are called insulators.*

CHECKPOINT

Underline **three** substances in this list that are good conductors of heat:

air   aluminium   copper   glass   iron   polystyrene

-**-** **Convection, Radiation**

CONTINENT DRIFT

-**-** **Plate tectonics**

CONVECTION

Convection is the movement of **particles** in **liquids** and **gases**. When gases and liquids flow energy is carried away from places where the temperature is higher to where the temperature is lower. Hotter, less dense, liquids rise up; colder, denser fluids sink down to take the place of the hotter fluids. A convection current is produced as a result of the continuous movement of the fluids.

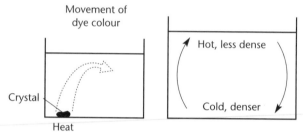

Using potassium permanganate to see convection currents

You may have studied convection currents by placing a crystal of potassium permanganate in a beaker of water. As you gently heat the water containing the crystal, the liquid becomes less dense and rises. Colder, denser water sinks to take its place.

CHECKPOINT

Complete these sentences by using these words:

energy   gases   high   lower   particles

Convection is the transfer of heat .... by the movement of .... in liquids and ....
Energy is carried away from where the temperature is .... to where it is ....

-**-** **Conduction, Diffusion, Radiation**

CORONARY ARTERY DISEASE

The coronary arteries are very small **arteries** that supply the muscle of the **heart** with oxygenated **blood**. When the diameter of these arteries becomes narrower, the blood supply is reduced and the person feels a cramp-like pain in his/her chest. Part of the heart muscle may die if it is deprived of oxygen and this puts more strain on the rest of the heart muscle.
   Two factors contribute to coronary heart disease:

- Cholesterol fat builds up on the inside of the coronary arteries
- Blood clots can stick to the cholesterol and stop the blood flowing

Exercise can help to reduce the risk of coronary artery disease by improving the functioning of the heart. A **balanced diet**, which reduces the amount of fats, can prevent cholesterol building up, stopping **smoking** and limiting **alcohol** intake can also help reduce the risk of heart disease.

✛ *Blood system, Breathing*

CORROSION

Corrosion is a **chemical reaction**. Corrosion of a metal will only take place if the **metal** is in contact with a **solution** containing **ions**. When the metal corrodes, it loses **electrons** to form positive ions:

metal atom – electron(s) → metal ion
$$M(s) \quad - \quad e^- \quad \rightarrow \quad M^+$$

Metals corrode at different rates, depending on their position in the **reactivity series**; magnesium will corrode more quickly than copper because magnesium is *higher* in the reactivity series and has a greater tendency to form ions.

Corrosion of iron

Iron will corrode (rust) when it is in contact with water and air. The water is acting as a weak **electrolyte** (a solution containing ions) because it contains dissolved substances. Iron will corrode much more quickly when in contact with sea water, because sea water is a much stronger electrolyte (it contains a larger amount of dissolved salts). This is a real problem for ships; also cars that are kept near the sea tend to corrode more quickly than those kept inland.

The reaction of iron corrosion is as follows:

$$Fe(s) - 3e^- \rightarrow Fe^{3+}(aq)$$

Corrosion can be a greater problem with structures built of more than one metal. For example, if the steel plates of a ship's hull are riveted together with brass rivets, then the steel will corrode much more quickly than if the rivets were made of steel. This is because:

● The sea water is acting as the electrolyte

● A simple cell is set up between the iron (steel) and the copper (in the brass). The iron has a greater tendency to form ions than the copper so will corrode much more rapidly

Rates of corrosion

The rate of corrosion of a metal therefore depends on:

● The position of the metal in the reactivity series

● The concentration of the electrolyte with which the metal is in contact

● The nature of any other metal with which it is in contact

● The temperature of the metal (this is why car exhausts corrode quickly) – a higher temperature speeds up chemical reactions

Preventing corrosion

● *Surface coating*: This is the simplest method of preventing metals from corroding, by either painting the metal or covering it with some other covering such as a polymer layer that is bonded to the surface. Some oil rigs in the North Sea are protected in this way.

● *Sacrificial protection*: This is where one metal is in contact with a more reactive one that corrodes first, e.g. galvanizing.

● *Electroplating*: This is a method of preventing corrosion by covering one metal with a less reactive metal.

✛ **Electroplating, Reactions of metals, Zinc**

COULOMB

✛ **Current electricity – current and charge**

COVALENT BONDING

Atoms can have stable arrangements if their outer **electron** shells are filled. Atoms join together, forming bonds, in order to achieve this. When this happens by the sharing of electrons, it is called covalent bonding.

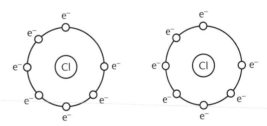

Two chlorine atoms, each with seven electrons in their outer shell

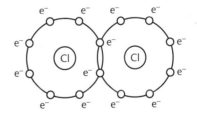

Each chlorine atom now appears to have a full outer shell: shared electrons

Covalent bonding

In elements

Non-metal atoms will combine to form **molecules** by sharing electrons in their outer shells. The exception to this are the atoms in group 0, the noble gases, which have stable electron arrangements already.

Two hydrogen atoms will join together to form a hydrogen molecule, by sharing their electrons. Each atom can then be considered to have a filled electron shell (two electrons). The shared pair of electrons is called a covalent bond and can be shown as a line between the two atoms '–'. The molecule is represented as H_2, or H–H.

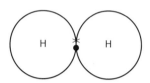

A covalent bond between two hydrogen atoms

An oxygen molecule is formed in a similar way but because each oxygen molecule has six electrons in its outer shell (electron configuration 2,6), it has two 'spaces' to be filled. It does this by each atom sharing *two* of its electrons. This forms a double covalent bond. The molecule is represented as O_2, or O=O.

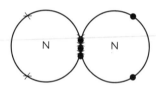

A double covalent bond between two oxygen atoms

Similarly, nitrogen atoms will pair up to form nitrogen molecules but this time by forming a *triple* covalent bond. Each covalent bond is a shared pair of electrons. The nitrogen molecule is represented as N_2, or N≡N.

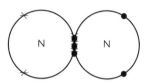

A triple covalent bond between two nitrogen atoms

CHECKPOINT

Complete these sentences.

Covalent bonds are formed when atoms share ....
Atoms become stable when their .... electron shells are filled. Oxygen atoms have six electrons in their outer shell. They form a .... covalent bond by sharing .... electrons with another oxygen atom and forming a .... of oxygen.

In compounds

Non-metal atoms exist in the free state as **molecules** because in this way they can have stable electron arrangements. Non-metal atoms

A water molecule

will combine with other non-metal atoms to form molecules. The resulting compounds are called covalent compounds, e.g. water, H_2O.

Some common covalent compounds

The table shows the molecular structure of some common covalent compounds. Remember, *each* line represents a shared pair of electrons – a covalent bond.

Name	Formula	Structure
Carbon dioxide	CO_2	O=C=O
Ammonia	NH_3	H, N, H, H
Sulphur dioxide	SO_2	O=S=O
Methane	CH_4	H—C—H
Ethane	C_2H_6	H—C—C—H
Ethene	C_2H_4	C=C

Molecular structure of some common covalent compounds

Properties of covalently bonded molecules

The covalent bond between atoms in a molecule is strong; however, the forces holding the molecules together are weak. This means that covalently bonded substances are often gases or liquids, or solids with relatively low melting points. These substances have low melting points, low boiling points, do not conduct electricity and do not usually dissolve in water.

✦ Ionic bonding, Periodic table, Valency

CRACKING

Cracking is a term used in the petrochemical industry for breaking long **hydrocarbon** molecules down into shorter, more useful chains; e.g. an alkane. Ethane (C_2H_6) is passed through a cracking tower with heated steam to produce the smaller ethene (C_2H_4) molecule and alkene.

✦ Hydrocarbons

CRUDE OIL

Crude oil (petroleum) and natural gas **methane** are formed by the effects of heat and pressure on the remains of animals and plants that were trapped in sediments millions of years ago.

Crude oil is a mixture **hydrocarbons**, **compounds** that contain only **carbon** and hydrogen. Crude oil can be separated **fractional distillation** into different fractions, such as petrol, paraffin and diesel oils, which are used as fuels:

- Smaller hydrocarbon molecules, such as liquid gas, petrol, petrol and paraffin have lower boiling points, are very flammable and are very volatile

- Larger hydrocarbon molecules, such as fuel oil, grease and bitumen have higher boiling points, burn with smoky flames and are less volatile

---

CHECKPOINT

Complete these sentences.

Crude oil is a mixture of .... It can be separated into fractions by .... Some of the fractions are used as .... The heavier molecules are split into smaller molecules by ....

-+- **Fossil fuels**

CRUST

The Earth's crust is a hard outer layer about 70 km thick around the **Earth**. It consists mostly of **metamorphic rocks** and some **sedimentary** and **igneous** rocks. Many of the rocks contain minerals, which exist either as pure elements, such as gold, or as mineral ores, such as malachite (copper carbonate).

The Earth's crust, as well as the sea and **atmosphere**, are the source of all raw materials used in manufacturing processes. Rocks in the Earth's crust contain mixtures of minerals from which useful substances can be made; e.g. **limestone** (calcium **carbonate**) is extracted from the Earth by quarrying and used for:

- buildings

- neutralizing acidity in lakes

- making cement, which can be mixed with water, sand and rock to make concrete

The Earth's crust contains large plates of rock, forming the continents, which float on the molten mantle. Mountain building and **volcanoes** can occur when two of these plates meet, whereas **earthquakes** can occur when the plates slide past each other.

-+- **Plate tectonics, Rock cycle**

CURRENT ELECTRICITY

Electric current is the flow of charged particles around a circuit of conducting material, such as metals. In metal **conductors**, these charged particles are **electrons**, which are part of the metal **atoms**. The energy given to the electrons to push them round the electrical circuit is transferred from electrical power sources such as batteries, solar cells and generators, to components in a circuit, such as lamps, resistors, bells and motors.

> *Remember: The energy transferred makes things happen in the circuit, such as heat, light and sound.*

How to measure current in a series and parallel circuit

Current is measured in **amperes** (amps, A) by using an **ammeter** in the circuit; the current will depend on the number of components, e.g. the number of cells (voltage).

Current and charge

When an ammeter measures that 1 A (one ampere) of current is flowing, it means that in one second, 1 C of charge is passing that point. One *coulomb* is the amount of charge transported by an electric current of 1 A in 1 s. It is about the same charge as 6.2×10^{18} electrons. A household lamp uses about 2 A of current. This means that 2 C/s are used. The relationship between the amount of electrical charge, current and time is shown by:

$$\begin{array}{ccccc} \text{charge} & = & \text{current} & \times & \text{time} \\ \text{(coulomb, C)} & & \text{(ampere, A)} & & \text{(seconds, s)} \\ Q & = & I & \times & t \end{array}$$

For example, if 10 A flows for 5 s then 50 Ω have passed through a point in the circuit.

Note also that the amount of current flowing is charge divided by time.

CHECKPOINT

How many joules of electrical energy are changed to light and heat when a current of 2 A flows for 20 s through a lamp that has a potential difference (pd) of 12 V?

-+- **Parallel circuit, Series circuit**

CYTOPLASM

-+- **Cell – biological**

DAY

A day is the time taken for the **Earth** to spin on its own axis, about 24 h.

- **Seasons, Year**

DEAMINATION

Deamination is the process of breaking down excess **amino acids** in the liver. **Urea** is produced as a waste product and is removed from the blood by the **kidney**, and passed out of the body in the **urine**.

- **Proteins**

DECOMPOSERS

- **Bacteria, Food chains and food webs, Nitrogen cycle**

DENSITY

The density of a substance is the **mass** of the substance divided by its volume: units are kilograms per metre cubed (kg/m^3) or grams per centimetre cubed (g/cm^3).

$$\text{density} = \frac{\text{mass}}{\text{volume}} \text{ or } D = \frac{M}{V}$$

Each substance has a different density and this fact can help to identify a substance:

- The density of a substance is *high* if a *large* mass occupies a *small* volume; e.g. steel and lead

- The density of a substance is *low*, if it has a *small* mass occupying a *large* volume; e.g. **gases**

DIABETES

Diabetes is caused by a lack of sufficent **insulin**. This results in a increase in the **glucose** concentration in the blood. The **kidneys** are unable to absorb all the glucose and some glucose appears in the **urine**. Diabetics can control their condition by low-sugar diets and by regular injections of insulin.

- **Hormones**

DIALYSIS

Using a **partially permeable membrane** to separate substances. Kidney machines use flat tubes of cellophane as partially permeable membranes.

- **Kidney, Osmosis**

DIAPHRAGM

- **Breathing**

DIET

- **Balanced diet, Carbohydrates, Fibre, Minerals, Proteins, Vitamins**

DIFFRACTION

When waves pass through a small opening or around the edge of an obstacle, they change the shape of their wavefront so that they spread out from the edges. You may have seen this in a ripple tank. The **velocity**, **frequency** and **wavelength** do not change. This effect is known as diffraction. The amount of diffraction depends on the size of the gap and the wavelength of the wave.

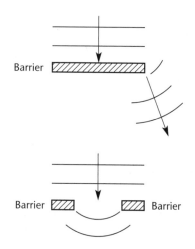

Barrier

Barrier   Barrier

Remember: Light and sound waves can be diffracted.

- **Reflection, Refraction**

DIFFUSION

Diffusion means mixing; **gases**, **liquids** and even **solids** can mix together (diffuse) if left alone even without anyone stirring them.

Types of diffusion

Diffusion in gases

When the top is removed from a bottle containing ammonia you can smell the ammonia (which is a gas) even if you are some distance away. The ammonia has mixed with the air and spread out.

When the equipment, shown in the diagram, is set up and left for a short time, a white ring appears in the tube. This white substance is ammonium chloride, which is formed when the gas ammonia meets the gas hydrogen chloride. This could only happen if the gas particles had **kinetic energy** and were able to spread out and mix. Notice the white ring where the gases meet is *not* in the centre. Which gas spreads out the fastest? Does this tell you which has the lightest particles?

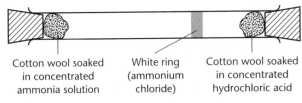

Cotton wool soaked in concentrated ammonia solution

White ring (ammonium chloride)

Cotton wool soaked in concentrated hydrochloric acid

Diffusion in gases

Diffusion in liquids

Diffusion can also occur in liquids. This can be shown by placing a crystal of potassium permanganate in a beaker of water. The diffusion takes place more slowly than between gases because the particles have less energy. They are moving more slowly and are closer together.

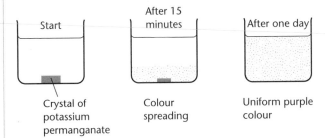

Start

After 15 minutes

After one day

Crystal of potassium permanganate

Colour spreading

Uniform purple colour

Diffusion in liquids

Diffusion in solids

Diffusion can take place in solids although this takes place even more slowly. This can be shown by placing a coloured crystal in some gelatin; after a day or two the colour has spread through the gelatin.

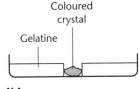

Coloured crystal

Gelatine

Diffusion in solids

The only way to explain all these results is to assume that substances are made of **particles** and that these particles have kinetic energy (are moving).

Diffusion in action

Atmospheric pollution

Diffusion can be a nuisance: it is because of diffusion that pollutant gases can spread throughout the atmosphere, e.g. from car exhausts, power stations and **aerosols**.

In the lungs

Gaseous exchange in the alveoli of the lungs takes place by diffusion. Diffusion of particles takes place from where there is a *higher* concentration to where there is a *lower* concentration. Particles will diffuse until they are evenly distributed:

Diffusion of particles in the alveoli		
	Concentration of gas in blood flowing to alveoli	*Concentration of gas in air in alveoli*
Oxygen	Low	High
Carbon dioxide	High	Low

➪ *Breathing, Convection, Osmosis*

DIGESTION

The food that you eat contains large **molecules** that have to be broken down into smaller, soluble molecules so that they can pass through the wall of your gut into your blood stream. The process of breaking down the large, insoluble molecules is described as 'digestion'. In your body you make chemical **catalysts**, called **enzymes**, that speed up the rate of breakdown of your food. The diagram shows the human digestive system in detail.

Stages of digestion

Stage 1

The process of digestion starts in your mouth when your teeth crush and chew the food that is mixed with saliva. The saliva contains an enzyme called **amylase** that starts to break down or digest the large molecules of **starch**.

Stage 2

The food is then swallowed and goes to your stomach for about 3 or 4 h. The stomach lining secretes a dilute **acid** to create an acidic environment so that the enzyme *pepsin* can break down the large **protein** molecules into smaller molecules.

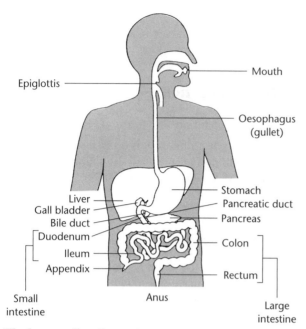

Epiglottis
Mouth
Oesophagus (gullet)
Liver
Gall bladder
Bile duct
Duodenum
Ileum
Appendix
Small intestine
Anus
Stomach
Pancreatic duct
Pancreas
Colon
Rectum
Large intestine

The human digestive system

Stage 3

The partly digested food is then passed into the small intestine, where enzymes from the pancreas continue the process of digestion.

- Starch is eventually converted into small molecules of glucose

- Protein is broken down into amino acids

- Fats are broken down into fatty acids and glycerol by lipase; bile secreted by the liver, neutralizes the hydrochloric acid from the stomach and breaks up the large globules of fat into smaller droplets

Stage 4

The small molecules are then absorbed through the lining of the small intestine into the blood stream.

Stage 5

The undigested food and other waste products then pass into the large intestine where water is absorbed and faeces are formed.

Stage 6

The faeces then pass out of the body through the rectum and anus.

Eating a good amount of **fibre** (roughage) in your diet each day helps you to pass faeces out of your body at regular intervals. If you do not eat sufficient fibre in your diet then you become constipated and it is difficult to pass the faeces out of your body.

> ### CHECKPOINT
>
> Complete the missing words in the passage.
>
> Digestion is the breaking down of .... insoluble molecules to small .... molecules. Biological catalysts called .... speed up the rate of breakdown. The salivary glands in the mouth secrete an enzyme, salivary .... that digests large molecules of starch into smaller molecules. Acid is secreted in the .... to give an acid pH so that another enzyme, pepsin can break down ....

✦ *Balanced diet, Food tests, Hydrolysis*

DIODE

A diode is a device that allows current to flow in one direction only. It is an example of a device that uses **resistance**. It has a *high* resistance in one direction and a *low* resistance in the other direction. Diodes are used to change **alternating current** to **direct current.** When a diode is placed in a circuit, the alternating current flows in only one direction and half-wave **rectification** occurs.

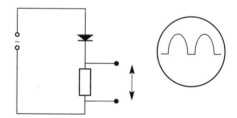

The pattern produced on a CRO when a diode is placed in the circuit

✦ *Ohms law – current and voltage*

DIPLOID

✦ *Fertilization*

DIRECT CURRENT

Direct current is electric current that flows in one direction only, as produced by **electric cells** (batteries), and **dynamos**.

> ### CHECKPOINT
>
> Explain the difference between direct current and alternating current.

✦ *Alternating current*

DISCONTINUOUS VARIATION

-+- *Variation*

DNA (DEOXYRIBONUCLEIC ACID)

-+- *Chromosomes*

DOMINANT ALLELE

A dominant allele is the allele that is expressed in the appearance of an individual when both dominant alleles are present, or when the dominant and *recessive* alleles are present: e.g. if a person has the dominant allele for brown eyes and the recessive allele for blue eyes, then the person appears to have brown eyes. The dominant allele is given a capital letter symbol.

-+- *Gene, Heterozygous, Homozygous, Monohybrid inheritance*

DOUBLE GLAZING

-+- *Insulation*

DOUBLE INSULATION

Some electrical appliances are totally enclosed in a plastic, insulated casing, so that there is no chance of someone getting an electric shock when they touch the appliance if it is faulty. Hairdriers, electric drills and vacuum cleaners are usually made like this.

-+- *Magnetic circuit breakers, Mains electricity*

DRUGS

Drugs are chemical substances that either affect your body cells, or affect viruses and bacteria inside your body. Drugs are usually taken for medical reasons, but some drugs, such as heroin, are taken to produce a pleasurable sensation in the person. This can lead to drug addiction and death.

● Some drugs are prescribed by a doctor to help a person maintain good health: e.g. *insulin* is given to someone who has *diabetes* and is unable to control the amount of sugar in his/her blood.

● Some drugs are widely available but do *not* require a prescription: e.g. nicotine is an addictive drug found in cigarettes. People who are addicted to nicotine have to smoke more and more cigarettes to produce the same effect on their bodies, and this can have a dangerous effect on their health. Pregnant women who are addicted to nicotine may give birth to small-sized, underdeveloped babies.

-+- *Alcohol, Solvent abuse*

DYNAMO

A dynamo is a simple *generator* that transforms mechanical *energy*, e.g. produced by pedalling a bicycle, into electrical energy. As the coil of the dynamo is turned inside the poles of a permanent *magnet*, a current flows in the coil.

-+- *Direct current, Electromagnetism, Induced current*

EAR

The ear drum detects the compressions and rarefactions (changes in density) of the air that are caused when **sound waves** are produced from a vibrating source. The vibrations of the ear drum are passed through the three small bones or ossicles in the middle ear. The fluid in the cochlea (inner ear) then vibrates and impulses are passed via the auditory nerve to the **brain**.

Fluid-filled canals to help your balance

4 Auditory nerve carries impulses to the brain

1 Sound waves enter the ear tube

3 Fluid in the inner ear vibrates

2 Three small bones vibrate

The structure of the ear

✛ *Longitudinal waves, Nervous system, Receptors, Reflex arc*

EARTH

The Earth is a spherical planet of about 12,757 km diameter. It takes 365.25 days to orbit the Sun at a distance of about 150,000,000 km from the Sun.

The Earth is surrounded by an **atmosphere** about 400 km deep. The outer, solid part of the Earth is the **crust**, about 70 km deep, consisting of large sections of rock called plates. These plates are moved very slowly by the currents that flow in the mantle (a thick layer of very hot rocks). Where the plates move *against* each other, pressure builds up and may cause cracks (faults) to appear on the surface, and violent shaking movements (**earthquakes**). The crust contains **igneous**, **metamorphic** and **sedimentary** rocks.

The crust covers the mantle, a thick layer of very hot rocks, that in turn surround the core, which is made of very hot dense rocks under extreme pressure.

Much of the evidence for the layered structure of the Earth comes from the behaviour of earthquake shock waves as they reach different zones. There are two types of earthquake waves:

- P waves (pressure waves) are **longitudinal waves** that travel very quickly through the Earth – they travel more quickly through the core than the mantle

- S waves (shake waves) are **transverse waves** that only travel through solids

An analysis of the behaviour of these shock waves has indicated the main regions of the Earth.

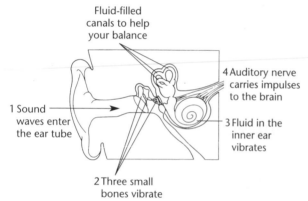

Crust between 70 and 40 km thick,

Soil is formed on the surface

Under the ocean the crust is only about 7 km thick

Mantle about 2,870 km thick – possibly two rigid layers with a molten layer in between

Outer core – liquid metal, mostly iron and nickel, about 2,190 km thick

Inner core – a solid metallic substance about 2,680 km in diameter

Structure of the Earth

✛ *Plate tectonics, Rock cycle, Seasons, Solar system, Year*

EARTHQUAKE

Earthquakes are caused when the plates of the Earth's **crust** are displaced, either along a fault line or by volcanic action. The earthquake produces shock waves that are felt as vibrations of the Earth's surface. Earthquakes and **volcanoes** mostly occur in well-defined zones, usually at the boundaries of the different sections of the Earth's crust: e.g. around the coast of the Pacific Ocean. Other main earthquake areas are in a zone stretching from the Mediterranean through the Middle East, to the Himalayas, Indonesia and South China.

Some of the visible effects of earthquakes are buildings falling down and large cracks appearing in the roads. In mountainous regions earthquakes can be responsible for causing avalanches of snow, and in the oceans very large tidal waves can be produced. In 1985 a very powerful earthquake in Armenia destroyed whole towns and killed many thousands of people.

✛ *Plate tectonics*

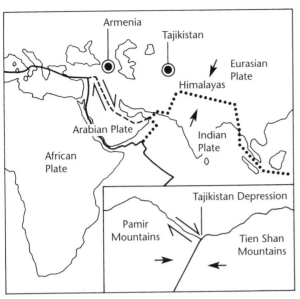

A powerful earthquake occurred in Armenia in 1988

EARTH WIRE

In a **three-pin plug** the earth wire is coloured green and yellow, and is connected to the earth pin at the top of the plug. The purpose of the earth wire is to make sure that electricity flows to earth, if for any reason the appliance becomes faulty. This may happen if the live wire touches part of the metal casing of the appliance.

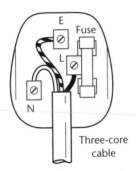

How the earth wire is connected in a three-pin plug

*Remember: If the earth wire was **not** connected, then electricity would flow to a person who touched the metal casing of the appliance.*

✛ *Fuse, Magnetic circuit breakers*

ECLIPSE OF THE MOON

An eclipse of the **Moon** (lunar eclipse), occurs when the **Earth** stops the **Sun's** rays from reaching the Moon.

✛ *Earth, Eclipse of the Sun, Year*

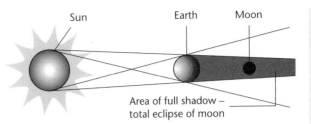

Eclipse of the Moon

ECLIPSE OF THE SUN

An eclipse of the **Sun** (solar eclipse), happens when the **Moon** passes between the Sun and the **Earth**, so the Sun appears to be covered.

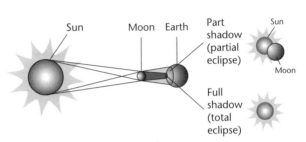

Eclipse of the Sun

CHECKPOINT

What happens during a total eclipse of the Sun:

(a) the Sun is between the Earth and the Moon,
(b) the Earth is between the Sun and the Moon,
(c) the Moon goes behind the Sun,
(d) the Moon is between the Earth and the Sun?

✛ *Earth, Eclipse of the Moon, Year*

ECOSYSTEM

An ecosystem is all the living (**biotic**) and non-living (**abiotic**) factors in a specific area such as woodland, a pond or lake, a hedgerow, a sand dune, a beach or a garden. The living components of an ecosystem are the **producers**, **consumers** and **decomposers**.

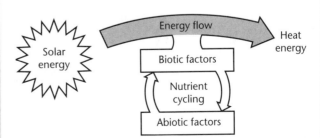

How biotic and abiotic factors interact in an ecosystem

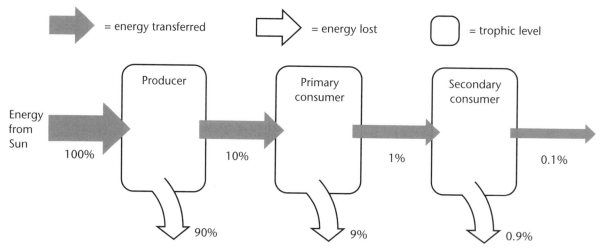

➡ = energy transferred   ⇨ = energy lost   ☐ = trophic level

| Energy from Sun | Producer | Primary consumer | Secondary consumer |

100%   10%   1%   0.1%

90%   9%   0.9%

Energy is lost at each stage of the food chain

Energy transfer through the ecosystem

Energy is transferred at each stage of the food chain from the producer to the consumers, the herbivores and carnivores. About 10 per cent of the available energy is transferred at each stage of the food chain. The other 90 per cent is lost by **life processes** such as respiration, excretion and movement.

For example, when a cow eats grass:

● about 60 per cent of the energy taken in is excreted

● about 30 per cent is used up in respiration, growth and movement

● about 10 per cent is available for human consumption

One hectare of land produces enough food for cows to feed 10 people, or enough grain to feed 100 people.

> *Remember: The amount of living material or biomass is reduced at each stage of the food chain.*

✦ **Biomass, Food chains and food webs, Pollution**

EFFECTOR

An effector is usually a muscle or gland that responds to a stimulus: e.g. when you touch a hot object it is the muscles of your upper arm that contract to move your hand away from the heat.

✦ **Receptor, Reflex arc**

ELECTRIC CELL

✦ **Cell – electrical**

ELECTRIC MOTORS

Electric motors are devices that transfer electrical energy to **kinetic energy**, in other words, they produce motion.

When a current is passed through a length of copper wire that is placed in the field of a strong magnet, the wire moves upwards at 90° to the direction of the **magnetic field**. If the current direction is reversed, then the force on the current is reversed and the wire moves in the opposite

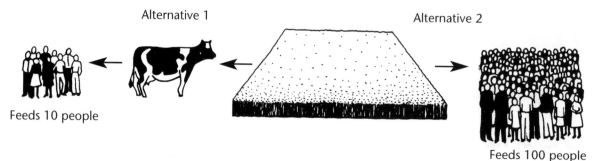

Alternative 1

Alternative 2

Feeds 10 people

Feeds 100 people

The alternative ways in which the corn produced by one hectare of land could be used

direction. The direction of force is always at right angles to the current direction and the field direction. The size of the force can be increased by:

- Increasing the strength of the magnetic field
- Increasing the size of the current

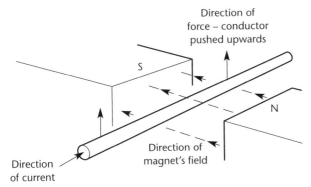

The direction of force is at right angles to the current direction and field direction

Simple motors

- A simple motor contains several coils of wire, wound on a core, which is pivoted on an axle between two permanent magnets.
- The coil is connected to a power supply by two carbon contacts called brushes.
- These are held in position against two halves of the commutator, which is a split ring made of copper.
- When a direct current is passed through the coil, the magnetic field created is attracted to the opposite poles of the permanent magnets and this causes the coil to spin in a clockwise direction.
- When the N and S poles of the coil lie opposite the S and N poles of the permanent magnets the coil should stop turning, but it carries on spinning because the two brushes now press against the opposite half rings of the commutator.

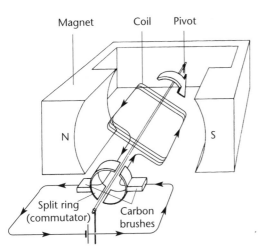

The construction of a simple electric motor

- The current now flows in the opposite direction and this results in the N and S poles of the coil being reversed.
- The coil then spins round to the S and N poles of the permanent magnets, and once again the current direction is reversed as the coil is about to stop.

More complex motors

Real motors that are used in everyday appliances such as electric drills, washing machines and food mixers usually have several coils, each of which may have its own commutator. The purpose of these is to produce a smoother and more powerful turning effect, and allows the motor to run more evenly without stopping. The coils are usually wound on a soft iron core, called an armature that increases the strength of the magnetic field.

> *Remember: A magnetic field is produced by a current in (1) a straight wire and (2) in a solenoid (a coil). The d.c. electric motor is a result of the interaction between the magnetic force around a current-carrying wire and an external magnetic field.*

CHECKPOINT

1. The diagram shows a horizontal wire placed between the poles of two magnets.

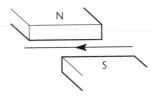

What will happen when an electric current is passed through the wire?

2. State **one** application of this effect.

✛ *Electromagnetism, Induced current*

ELECTRICITY

✛ *Alternating current, Current electricity, Direct current, Generators, Mains electricity, Parallel circuit, Series circuit, Transmission of electricity*

ELECTRODE

An electrode is a positive or negative terminal in an electrolysis cell or an electrical cell (dry cell, battery, etc.):

● The negative electrode is called the **cathode**

● The positive electrode is called the **anode**

✛ *Anion, Cation, Electrolysis*

ELECTROLYSIS

If electricity is passed into a **solution** or molten substance containing **ions** (both states where the ions are free to move) then:

● The positive ions (**cations**) will be attracted to the *negative* electrode (**cathode**)

● The negative ions (**anions**) will be attracted to the *positive* electrode (**anode**)

Electrodes are rods that carry the current to the liquid and where ions are converted into **atoms**. The end result is that electrolysis breaks down compounds containing ions into their **elements**.
An electrolysis cell always contains:

● A *positive* electrode, or **anode**

● A *negative* electrode, or **cathode**

● An electrolyte (a liquid containing ions, for example, an **aqueous solution** of an ionic substance or a molten ionic substance)

The anode and cathode are connected to an electrical power source. The electricity is conducted through the liquid electrolyte by the ions themselves moving.

> *Remember: The positive ions (cations) are attracted to the negative electrode, cathode. The negative ions (anions) are attracted to the positive electrode, anode.*

● At the cathode, the positive ions (metal or hydrogen) *gain* an electron and become atoms:

$$M^+ + e^- \rightarrow M$$

The metal is deposited as a layer on the cathode, any hydrogen is released as molecules of the gas.

● At the anode, the negative ions *lose* electrons and become atoms (which may combine to form molecules):

$$X^- - e^- \rightarrow X$$

CHECKPOINT

1. Complete the table using these words:

anion   anode   cathode   cation

Electrode	Positive	Negative
Electrode	....	....
Ion	....	....

2. (a) Which ion is attracted to the cathode?
   (b) What happens to the ions at the cathode?

3. During the electrolysis of sodium chloride, what product is formed at (a) the positive electrode, (b) the negative electrode?

4. What do you understand by 'electrolysis'?

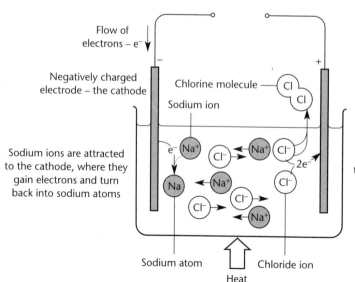

The reactions occurring in the electrolysis of molten sodium chloride

Examples of electrolysis

Aluminium extraction

Aluminium is extracted from its ore by electrolysis. The ore **bauxite** (mainly aluminium oxide) is first concentrated by removing the impurities. The concentrate (alumina) is then dissolved in molten cryolite at about 1,000 °C to give a solution that provides free-moving aluminium ions. Aluminium oxide has a melting point above 2,000 °C, so melting the oxide to provide free-moving aluminium ions is not practical. The anodes and cathodes are made of carbon. Aluminium, when it is formed, is molten and is tapped off from the bottom of the cell.

The following reactions are occurring in the electrolysis cell:

- At the cathode: $Al^{3+} + 3e^- \rightarrow Al$
- At the anode: $2O^{2-} - 4e^- \rightarrow O_2$

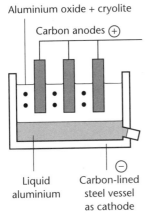

The electrolysis of alumina to extract aluminium

> Remember: All metals above aluminium in the reactivity series are normally extracted by electrolysis because they are too reactive to be reduced by carbon. Sometimes metals lower down such as zinc are extracted by electrolysis.

Purification of copper

One use of electrolysis is to purify copper:

- the positive electrode (**anode**) is made of impure copper
- the negative electrode (**cathode**) is made of a thin plate of pure copper (greased to allow the deposits of pure copper to be peeled off)
- the electrolyte is an aqueous solution of copper (II) sulphate

During electrolysis, the copper present in the impure copper anode dissolves into the electrolyte and is plated onto the pure copper cathode The deposit of pure copper is peeled off and the cathode is reused.

> Remember: This an example of how a metal can be purified by electrolysis.

✛ *Redox reactions*

ELECTROMAGNETIC RELAY

An application of the principle of **electromagnetism** is the electromagnetic relay. The relay is a simple switch operated by an electromagnet in which a small *input* current controls a larger *output* current:

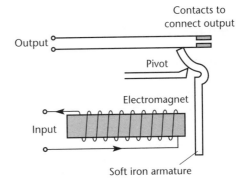

An electromagnetic relay

- The input current causes the electromagnet to become magnetized
- The electromagnet attracts a soft iron armature that closes the contacts and causes a greater current to flow through the output circuit
- The output circuit controls a device such as a motor
- When the input current stops, then the output current is switched off and the motor stops

ELECTROMAGNETIC SPECTRUM

These are a group of **transverse waves** that have electric *and* magnetic properties. They are all produced by changing **magnetic fields** and electric fields, and travel at the very high **speed** of 300 000 000 m/s (see the table on the next page).

Position, relative wavelength and frequency of the different electromagnetic waves				
Type of wave	Uses	Source	Wavelength	Frequency
Radio wave	Radio communication, television	Radio transmitters	long	low
Microwaves	Satellite communication, radar, microwave ovens	Electronic circuits		
Infrared	Electric fires, ovens, remote control devices	Any hot object		
Visible light	Electric lights, optical fibres	Very hot objects		
Ultraviolet	Sunbeds, fluorescent lamps, security devices	Extremely hot objects glowing gases		
X-rays	Used in hospitals to photograph bones, at airports to check luggage	X-ray tubes		
Gamma-rays	Kill cancer cells, irradiation of food and equipment	Radioactive metals	short	high

Electromagnetic and mechanical waves

The chart below summarizes the main points of difference between electromagnetic waves such as **radio waves**, and mechanical waves, such as **sound waves**.

Differences between electromagnetic and mechanical waves	
Electromagnetic	Mechanical
Transverse waves	Longitudinal waves
Travel through a vacuum, do not need a material medium	Need a material such as air in which to travel
Travel very fast (3×10^8 m/s)	Much slower speed (300 m/s approximately)

CHECKPOINT

The chart shows the position of some of the waves in the electromagnetic spectrum.

Microwaves	Visible light	X-rays	P

What type of radiation is at position, P: (a) gamma; (b) infrared; (c) radio; (d) ultraviolet?

✦ **Microwaves. Radiation, Radio waves, X-rays**

ELECTROMAGNETISM

Electromagnetism is the study of the relationship between **electricity** and **magnetism**. A **magnetic field** is produced around a coil of wire whenever an electric **current** flows through the wire. Plotting compasses or iron filings can be used to show this magnetic effect.

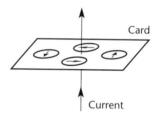

Plotting compasses can be used to show the magnetic field around a current flowing through a wire

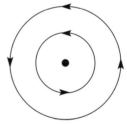

The pattern produced for a single wire carrying current – the current is flowing upwards out of the page

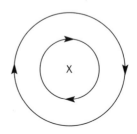

The pattern produced for a single wire carrying current – the current is flowing downwards into the page

These magnetic fields are fairly weak, and the effect can be increased by using a coil of wire called a *solenoid*. When the wire is coiled around a soft iron bar (called a *core*), the magnetic effect is more powerful, depending on the size of the current and the number of turns on the coil.

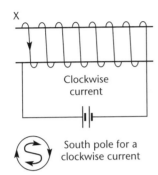

The current flows in a clockwise direction around the X end of the core

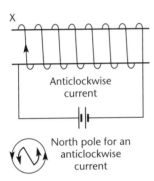

The current flows in an anticlockwise direction around the X end of the core

- When the current flow at end X of the core is in a *clockwise* direction, this end becomes a south pole
- When the current flow at end X is in an *anticlockwise* direction, this end becomes a north pole

The polarity changes by reversing the direction of current.

Remember: Reversing the current in an electromagnet reverses the direction of the magnetic field around it.

-+- **Electric motor, Generator, Magnets and magnetic fields, Transformers**

ELECTROMOTIVE FORCE E.M.F.

In an electric circuit, the electromotive force (e.m.f.) is the force that drives an electric **current** around a circuit and makes the current flow. The e.m.f. is produced by a power supply, e.g. an **electrical cell,** battery, generator or 'mains'. The e.m.f. is divided so that each part of the circuit has a share of the **voltage** to drive the current through it. This share of e.m.f. across each part of the circuit is the **potential difference** (p.d.). If you add all the voltages round the circuit, you will find that they add up to the voltage of the supply. The e.m.f. is usually given the symbol E, and is measured in volts.

Remember: The e.m.f. is the total of all the potential differences in a complete circuit.

-+- **Voltmeter**

ELECTRON

An electron is one of three **particles** found in an atom (the others being **proton** and **neutron,** which are found in the **nucleus**). Electrons have very little mass (about 1/2,000 that of a proton) and carry a *negative* charge. They orbit the nucleus of an atom in shells that take up most of the space of the atom. Each shell can only take a certain number of electrons.

Chemical reactions between atoms are a result of interactions between the electrons in an atom, so chemical activity depends on the numbers of electrons in the outermost shells of an atom.

Remember: There are always the same number of **electrons** in an atom as **protons**.

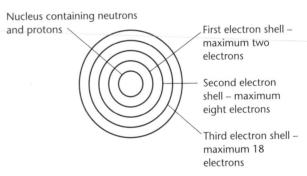

Electron shells

-+- **Atomic structure, Electrostatics, Ionic bonding, Ions, Periodic table, Valency**

ELECTROPLATING

Electroplating is a method of preventing **corrosion** by covering the surface of a metal to be protected with a thin layer of another metal that does not corrode. This is done by placing the metal to be plated in an **electrolysis** cell connected as the **cathode**.

Examples of electroplating to prevent corrosion are 'tin cans' (steel coated with a thin layer of tin), and chromium-plated bumpers on cars. Electroplating can also be used to produce cheaper products of precious metals, such as silver and gold (hence the term gold-plated or silver-plated). The main bulk of the object may be steel, coated with a thin layer of gold or silver giving the appearance of being made of solid gold or silver. Electroplating also ensures a thin, even coat of the metal.

-✧- *Transition metals*

ELECTROSTATICS

- Positive and negative electrostatic charges are produced on materials by loss and gain of **electrons**

- There are forces of attraction between *unlike* charges and forces of repulsion between *like* charges

Electrostatic charges are generated in everyday situations: e.g. synthetic fabrics rubbing together. If a charge builds up on an object and causes a voltage (p.d.) between the object and earth, a spark can jump across the gap from the object to any earthed conductor. This could be extremely dangerous. For example, when putting petrol in a petrol tank of a car, a spark could jump from the car to the fuel pumps.

-✧- *Atomic structure*

ELEMENT

All substances can be classified according to the types of **particles** they contain and how these particles are joined (chemically bound or not). Substances can be classified as either:

- element
- compound
- mixture

Elements cannot be broken down into simpler chemical substances and contain only *one* type of atom. Their particles may be single **atoms** or **molecules**:

- Hydrogen is an element; hydrogen gas contains hydrogen molecules

- Copper is also an element; copper contains copper atoms

> Remember: All metals are good conductors of electricity.

-✧- *Alkali metals, Halogens, Noble gases, Periodic table, Transition metals*

EMBRYO

The embryo develops from the fertilized egg or **zygote**. It develops by cell division into a fully developed offspring, which in humans is called the foetus. In plants the embryo develops from a fertilized ovule (egg cell) and grows into a new plant.

-✧- *Fertilization, Hormones – fertility treatment, Mitosis, Reproduction, Sexual reproduction*

ENDOTHERMIC

Energy is always involved in a **chemical reaction**; the substances reacting sometimes *take in* energy and sometimes *give out* energy.

Endothermic reactions are those in which energy in the form of heat is transferred from the surroundings, to the substances; in other words heat is *taken in*; often the products are cooler than the reactants were. Energy is needed for any chemical reaction to take place; first to break any bonds and then to reform new chemical bonds. If the energy required to break the chemical bond is *greater* than the energy released when new bonds are formed, then the reaction is endothermic.

Photosynthesis is an example of an endothermic reaction. When many substances dissolve in water the 'reaction' is often endothermic.

CHECKPOINT

What is meant by the statement: 'an endothermic reaction occurs when nitrogen reacts with hydrogen to produce ammonia'?

-✧- *Activation energy, Exothermic*

ENERGY

Energy is the ability to do work. The unit of energy is the **joule**, J. There are different forms of energy: **potential** (stored), **kinetic** (motion), heat (thermal), light, **electrical**, chemical, **nuclear**.

Energy can be transferred from one form to another, but the total amount of energy remains unchanged. The total quantity of energy entering a system is equal to the total quantity of energy leaving the system: e.g. in a hydro-electric power station the kinetic energy of the water is converted into electrical energy and heat energy. The energy efficiency of the power station is therefore equal to the quantity of useful energy given out, divided by the total quantity of energy input:

$$\text{energy efficiency} = \frac{\text{quantity of useful energy given out}}{\text{total quantity of energy input}}$$

CHECKPOINT

What is the efficiency of a motor that is supplied at 100 W and has a power output of 60 W?

Energy from food

The **blood system** carries the small molecules of **glucose** and **amino acids**, together with **oxygen**, to every cell in your body. A chemical process called **respiration** takes place in the cells to release the energy from the food:

food + oxygen → carbon + water + energy
dioxide

The **carbon dioxide** and **water** are carried by the blood to your **lungs** and breathed out. The energy is used by your cells for the various functions of the cells. Muscle cells need energy for contraction, gut cells need energy for secretion and **absorption**.

You may have investigated the energy released from different foods by letting them burn under a measured volume of water, and measuring the change in temperature. High energy foods are usually fats, such as butter and oils, and **carbohydrates**, such as potato, bread and sugar.

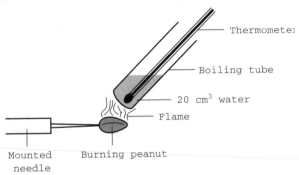

Finding out how much energy is released when a peanut is burned

✦ *Food chains and webs, Pyramid of biomass, Pyramid of numbers, Respiration*

ENERGY TRANSFER THROUGH THE ECOSYSTEM

✦ *Ecosystem, Food chains and food webs, Pyramid of biomass, Pyramid of numbers*

ENVIRONMENT

The environment describes the surroundings where an organism lives, including all the living **(biotic)** and non-living **(abiotic)** factors that affect an **organism**. The living and non-living factors interact to produce a balanced **ecosystem**. The main

environments are the sea, the rivers and lakes, and the land, which contain several **habitats**.

✦ *Biosphere, Pollution*

ENZYMES

Many chemical reactions take place in living things (often in the cells). These reactions are controlled by biological **catalysts** enzymes.

Enzymes are **protein molecules** that consist of long chains that can be folded and coiled into different shapes. Each enzyme has its own special shape; it is this shape that causes the enzyme to act as a catalyst. The reactant molecule(s) on which it acts, fits the enzyme like a key in a lock.

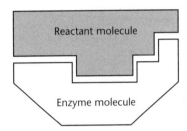

The lock and key principle

Properties of enzymes

Enzymes have unique properties:

● They are specific; because the way an enzyme works depends on its shape it will only work for *one* molecule or reaction

● They will only work within a small temperature range: e.g. enzymes in the human body will only work around normal body temperature (37 °C)

● They are very sensitive to pH changes and will only work within small pH ranges, e.g. pH 6–7

● They can help *large* molecules break into *smaller* ones, help small molecules join to form larger ones, or help atoms rearrange within a molecule

Enzymes in action

● Enzymes take part in every part of the **digestive** process, helping to break large molecules into smaller ones so they may pass through the gut wall into the blood stream: e.g. an enzyme in saliva called **salivary amylase** breaks down starch into smaller sugar molecules.

● **Yeasts** contain enzymes that help convert sugar into **alcohol** in the process of brewing.

● Enzymes are becoming increasingly important in industry: e.g. in the manufacture of **biodegradable** dressings for wounds, in biological washing powders and in new food sources such as mycoprotein.

CHECKPOINT

1. State **two** properties of enzyme-catalysed reactions.

2. Describe **two** examples of the use of enzymes in industry.

‑✛‑ **Acids – acids in action, Digestion**

EROSION

Erosion describes the way in which the **Earth's** surface is being worn away (eroded) by weathering agents such as wind, ice or frost, changes of temperature, chemical action, or the action of living organisms. The result of erosion is to form much smaller **particles** that are then carried by wind or water and eventually form soil.

‑✛‑ **Rock cycle, Sedimentary rocks, Weathering**

EVAPORATION

If a bowl of water is left on a windowsill the water will eventually disappear; a puddle of rain will also eventually disappear; we say the water has evaporated. The same is true of liquids other than water.

In a beaker of a liquid (e.g. water) the particles (water molecules) will have different energies, some fast-moving molecules will have enough energy to escape the surface of the water. This is evaporation. When the molecules escape the surface, they bump into air molecules and some might even travel back into the liquid. The more molecules that escape the surface and become vapour (gas form), the more chance that any newly escaped molecules will be knocked back into the water.

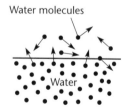

Water molecules

Water

Molecules escape from the surface of the water

We can *increase* the speed of evaporation in several ways:

●   Blowing across the surface of the water, removing the vapour molecules as they are formed (this is why blowing across a cup of tea will cool it down).

●   Heating, thereby giving more molecules the energy to escape. If enough energy is transferred to the water, *all* the molecules will be able to escape. We call this boiling; water boils at 100 °C at sea-level.

●   By reducing the air pressure, allowing the molecules to escape more easily. This is why water will boil at a lower temperature on mountains (less air pressure) than at sea-level.

‑✛‑ **Body temperature, Condensation, Kinetic theory, Transpiration**

EVOLUTION

This describes the way in which different **species** of organisms have developed and changed over a very long period of time.

CHECKPOINT

In the struggle for survival, those organisms that are best suited to the environment survive to pass on their genes to the next generation.

List **three** features of a prey animal, such as a rabbit, that would give it an advantage over other rabbits when escaping from a predator, such as a fox.

‑✛‑ **Fossil record, Natural selection, Mutation, Variation**

EXCRETION

Excretion is the removal of waste products formed in the body by metabolic processes. For example:

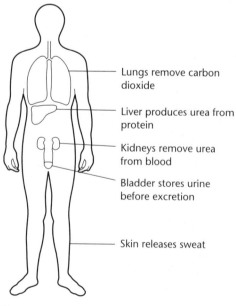

Lungs remove carbon dioxide

Liver produces urea from protein

Kidneys remove urea from blood

Bladder stores urine before excretion

Skin releases sweat

Excretion

- The liver breaks down excess **amino acids** during the process of **deamination** and produces **urea**, a waste product.

- Urea is carried in the blood stream to the kidneys, where it is removed from the blood and passed out of the body in the urine.

- The skin also removes some urea during sweating.

- The **lungs** remove **carbon dioxide**, a waste product produced by the cells during **respiration**.

CHECKPOINT

What is the function of the excretory system:

(a) to control body temperature,
(b) to remove harmful waste produced by the body,
(c) to get rid of undigested food from the body,
(d) to transport oxygen to all cells in the body?

⊹ **Homeostasis, Life processes, Organ systems**

EXERCISE

Your muscles need more **energy** when they are working harder during vigorous exercise. Your **heart** rate increases to pump **blood** carrying glucose more quickly to your cells, and your rate of **breathing** increases so that more oxygen is taken in to release the energy from the glucose. More **carbon dioxide** is produced, which is removed by the increased rate of breathing. People who are fit generally have a lower heart rate and therefore a lower pulse rate than people who are unfit, because exercise develops the heart muscle, just like any other muscle. Fit people and non-smokers get back to their resting pulse rate more quickly than unfit people and smokers.

Remember: Regular exercise, eating a good well-balanced diet without too much fat, and not smoking, can reduce the risk of heart disease.

⊹ **Aerobic respiration, Anaerobic respiration, Balanced diet, Coronary artery disease, Smoking**

EXOTHERMIC

Energy is always involved in a **chemical reaction**; the substances reacting sometimes *take in* energy and sometimes *give out* energy.

Exothermic reactions are those in which energy in the form of heat is transferred to the surroundings, in other words heat is *given out* – often the products are warmer than the reactants were. Energy is needed for any chemical reaction to take place, at first bonds have to be broken and then new chemical bonds are formed. If the energy required to break the chemical bonds is *less* than the energy released when new bonds are formed, then the reaction is exothermic.

All **combustion** and **neutralization** reactions are exothermic.

Remember: Energy is needed to make and break bonds:
- *The breaking of bonds is endothermic, energy is taken in, e.g. dissolving potassium chloride in water*
- *The making of bonds is exothermic, heat energy is given out, e.g. adding a small volume of water to anhydrous copper sulphate.*

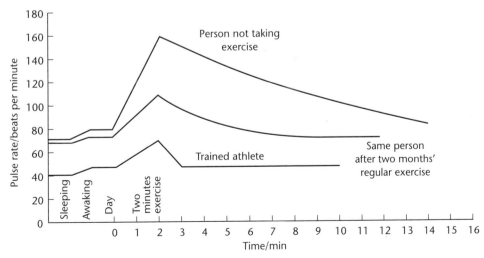

The effect of regular exercise on heart rate

-+- *Activation energy, Endothermic*

EXTRACTION OF METALS

Many **metals** are found as ores in the Earth's crust. The most abundant metal in the Earth's crust is aluminium, yet it was one of the last to be discovered. Why should this be so? The reason for this lies in the reactivity series.

Metal	Approximate date of first use
Gold, silver, copper	5,000 BC
Tin	2,500 BC
Iron	1,200 BC
Zinc	BC–AD
Aluminium	AD 1825

If we compare the dates of discovery with the **reactivity series** we can see that one is the reverse of the other. In other words, the first metals discovered were those with the *least* tendency to form ions. Gold, silver and small amounts of copper can be found in their native state, i.e. as the metals themselves. Other metals only exist in the **Earth's crust** as compounds, i.e. the metals are present as metal ions, chemically bonded with other substances. The more reactive a metal (the higher in the reactivity series) the more stable it becomes as a compound, so that it is difficult to extract it from its ore.

> Remember: The way in which a metal is extracted from its ore is related to its reactivity.

-+- *Blast furnace, Electrolysis – examples, Reduction*

EYE

Light is refracted, or bent, as it enters the eye through the transparent *cornea*. It is then refracted even more by the convex lens of the eye, and focused on the retina at the back of the eye. The retina consists of light-sensitive cells called rods and cones that are connected to the **brain** by nerve fibres. The cells are sensitive to red, green and blue light. When these cells are stimulated by light, an impulse is sent to the brain, via the *optic nerve*. The brain then forms images as a result of the impulses it receives. The lens is able to adjust to looking at objects that are close to or far away. This is known as *accommodation*. The chart shows a summary of the main parts of the eye:

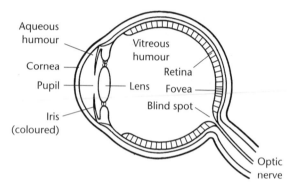

The function of the main parts of the eye

Cornea	Refracts (bends) the light entering the eye
Aqueous humour	Supplies nutrient to the lens and cornea
Iris	Controls the amount of light entering the eye by adjusting the size of the pupil
Pupil	The aperture that allows light into the eye
Lens	Refracts the light rays and changes shape to allow for fine focusing
Ciliary muscle	Controls the shape of the lens
Suspensory ligaments	Attach lens to ciliary muscle
Vitreous humour	Maintains the shape of the eye
Retina	Contains light-sensitive cells that convert light energy into a nerve impulse
Fovea	Very sensitive region of retina where most light is focused
Optic nerve	Carries impulses to the brain where they are interpreted

Accommodation

The ciliary muscles control the shape of the lens so that the eye can see objects that are near or far away. This is known as accommodation:

- To focus light from *distant* objects on the retina the lens needs to be thin and this is brought about by the contraction of the radial ciliary muscles.

- To focus light from *near* objects on the retina the lens becomes thicker due to contraction of the circular ciliary muscles. This action is a reflex action and some of the ability of the lens to change shape is lost with age.

CHECKPOINT

State which part of the eye does each of the following:

(a) controls the amount of light entering the eye,
(b) changes shape to allow for focusing on near and far objects,
(c) contains light-sensitive cells,
(d) carries impulses to the brain.

-⊹- ***Ears, Nervous system, Receptors, Reflex arc, Refraction***

FAULT

The pressure of the Earth causes the rocks in the crust to break or fault.

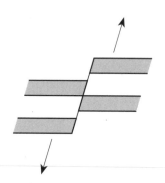

Fault

Earthquakes happen near large faults (e.g. the San Andreas Fault) as two plates in the **Earth's crust** move past each other, aided by lubrication of a small proportion of molten material. Sudden fracturing releases energy, causing vertical and horizontal vibrations. Volcanic eruptions occur at weak places in the Earth's crust, as molten rock forces its way to the surface. In this area, lava runs from long fractures or fissures to form basalt plateaus.

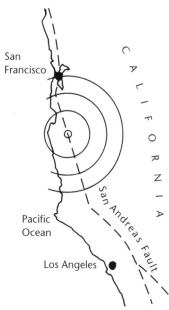

The San Andreas Fault

✛ **Earth, Plate tectonics, Volcano**

FERMENTATION

Micro-organisms can live and grow without the need for oxygen (**anaerobic respiration**). When they do this they sometimes produce products that are useful; this process is called fermentation. For example, **yeast** (a micro-organism) when added to fruit juices, in the absence of air digests the sugars creating **alcohol** as a waste product and releasing **carbon dioxide**.

Fermentation in action

Beer, bread and wine making are all a result of fermentation by yeasts. Lactic acid **bacteria** convert milk into yoghurt and micro-organisms are needed to convert milk into cheese. Fermentation of some moulds and bacteria produce antibiotics, while others can produce industrial chemicals such as acetone and glycerol.

✛ **Bacteria**

FERTILIZATION

Fertilization is the fusion or joining of the male and female **gametes**. In mammals, the nucleus of the sperm cell penetrates the egg cell and the **chromosome** number is restored to its diploid or full number. The fertilized egg (**zygote**) begins to develop into a new individual by **mitosis**.

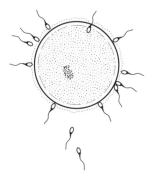

Only one sperm enters the egg and fertilizes it

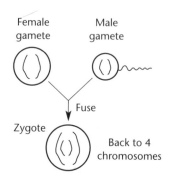

Restoration to the diploid number

✛ **Embryo, Ovary, Reproduction, Sexual reproduction, Testis**

FERTILIZERS

When plants grow they take certain substances from the air (e.g. **carbon dioxide**) and from the soil (water and **minerals**). The supply of minerals in the soil has to be replaced each season; this can happen by adding organic manure, by growing other plants and digging them in, or by adding chemical fertilizers.

Fertilizers contain **salts** (compounds) and provide plants with the **minerals** (elements) they need. **Nitrogen** is by far the most important of these, followed by phosphorous and potassium. Because these elements are needed by plants, salts containing these are manufactured in large quantities and sold as fertilizers. Examples are ammonium nitrate, ammonium phosphate and potassium chloride. Fertilizers containing these three salts are called N, P, K fertilizers because they provide nitrogen (N), phosphorus (P) and potassium (K). These are the three elements that need replacement in the soil more than others.

Manufacture of fertilizer

- **Ammonia** is reacted with oxygen, in the presence of a **catalyst** to form nitrogen monoxide

- Nitrogen monoxide is reacted with water to produce nitric acid

- Nitric acid is neutralized by ammonia to produce ammonium nitrate fertilizer

Effect of fertilizers on the environment

When fertilizers are washed into rivers and lakes, they can cause the water plants to grow rapidly. Due to overcrowding and lack of light, these plants then die and are decomposed by **bacteria** that use up most of the available oxygen in the water. Any fish living in the river or lake then die as they are unable to obtain enough oxygen. This process is described as eutrophication.

⁂ **Food production, Minerals, Nitrates – nitrates in drinking water, Nitrogen cycle**

FIBRE

Fibre (roughage) is the part of your food that is essential for regular bowel movements. You are unable to digest the cellulose fibres of green plants such as apples, leafy vegetables and wheat and so it passes through the gut undigested. Fibre is essential to provide the muscles of the gut with some bulk to push against during **peristalsis** and helps to form soft faeces that can be eliminated easily from your gut. Eating fibre as part of a **balanced diet** prevents constipation and is thought to prevent some types of bowel cancer.

⁂ *Digestion*

FOETUS

⁂ *Embryo*

FOOD CHAINS AND FOOD WEBS

When you studied an **ecosystem** you were probably able to identify the main **species** of plants and animals, and to find out what was feeding on what:

- A food chain simply shows how an animal obtains its food directly from another animal or plant. The arrows show the *direction* of transfer of *energy* from one trophic level to the next:

Producer	Primary consumer	Secondary consumer	Tertiary consumer

Oak (leaves) ➝ Caterpillar ➝ Shrew ➝ Owl

A simple food chain

- Food webs are more complicated, as they show how one animal may be feeding on *several* others to obtain food, or how one plant may have several differents animals feeding on it.

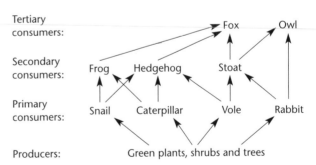

In a food web one animal feeds on more than one source of food

Remember: The arrow shows the direction of energy transfer.

At the beginning of the food chain are the **producers** or green plants that manufacture food by **photosynthesis**. The **consumers** obtain energy from the producers. Feeding on the producers directly are the **herbivores** and feeding on the herbivores are the **carnivores**. **Omnivores** feed on both producers and consumers.

Producers

At the start of all food chains and webs are the green plants, called the *producers*. Green plants make their own food by using solar energy from the Sun in the process of **photosynthesis**. Plants convert **carbon dioxide** and water into carbohydrates, which are then converted into plant protein, oils and fats.

Consumers

These are all the animals in the food chain, and can be divided into herbivores and carnivores:

● The *herbivores* are the *primary consumers*. They obtain their energy by feeding directly on green plants, or producers. For example, sheeps, cows and rabbits are herbivores.

● The *carnivores*, which obtain their energy by feeding on the herbivores, are the *secondary consumers*. Some carnivores obtain their energy from other carnivores, and these are described as *tertiary* or *third level consumers*; e.g. a hawk or fox that feeds on other carnivores in the food chain.

● Some animals feed on a *mixed diet* of plants and animals, and these are described as *omnivores*. They feed at more than one level in the food chain.

Decomposers

When plants and animals die, all the nutrients that are stored in their bodies are recycled by decomposers such as **bacteria** and **fungi**. These organisms break down the bodies of dead animals and plants and release **nutrients** such as nitrogen into the soil.

CHECKPOINT

1. The diagram shows a food web.

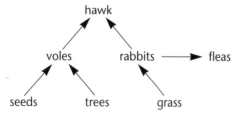

Which of the following is a primary consumer:

(a) fleas; (b) grass; (c) hawks; (d) rabbits?

2. In any food chain only some of the energy from the producers is transferred to the next trophic level:

(a) What happens to most of the Sun's energy falling on grass?

(b) When a cow eats grass, much of the energy is lost from the food chain. Suggest two processes in which energy is lost from the cow to the surroundings?

FOOD PRODUCTION

It is estimated that about 30 per cent of the world's land area can be cultivated; the rest is either too dry, too steep or otherwise unsuitable. Of the land being cultivated about half is used for growing crops, the rest is used for pasture or forest. Due to the increasing world **population**, yields of food from the land and sea have to be increased.

In the developed world, agricultural yields are improved by use of:

● **Fertilizers** to increase grain yields

● **Pesticides** to control **predators** and disease

● Herbicides to reduce competition from weeds

● **Selective breeding** and **genetic engineering** to produce disease-resistant high-yielding strains

● Irrigation to increase yields

These techniques are usually expensive and usually not available to farmers in developing countries.

In the harvesting of animals it is essential that quotas are agreed as to how many organisms are removed each year to allow a breeding population to remain to build up numbers for the following year. The oceans offer vast food resources, especially fish, which are an excellent form of protein, but in large-scale fishing in the sea, a minimum mesh size for fishing nets allows smaller fish to escape. If too many organisms are removed at the same time the population declines rapidly and consequently fewer organisms are available for another year.

CHECKPOINT

Describe **two** ways in which yields of food from land can be increased.

✦ **Food chains and food webs, Plant hormones**

FOOD TESTS

These tests help to identify the different type of foodstuff that may be present in a sample of food: e.g., to find out if **starch** is present in potato, add iodine solution to the potato. The brown colour of

Food tests		
Food type	Substance used	Positive result
Starch	Iodine solution	Blue–black colour
Reducing sugar	Add Benedict's solution and warm tube gently	Green–red colour
Protein	Add sodium hydroxide solution, then a few drops of copper sulphate solution	Violet colour appears
Fat	Rub food onto filter paper	A translucent grease/stain forms

iodine changes to blue-black, showing starch is present (see the above opposite).

⊹ Balanced diet, Digestion

FORCE – BALANCED AND UNBALANCED

There are three basic laws of motion:

1. An object will remain at rest or will continue to move at the same speed in a straight line unless it is acted on by a force. This means that once an object is moving it will keep on moving unless something stops it or changes its motion. For example, the force of **friction** will slow down the rate at which objects move. An aircraft moves by the force of the engines pushing the aircraft forwards, which is equal to the force of friction, which creates a drag effect. These two forces balance each other so the aircraft moves at constant speed.

2. The rate of change of **momentum** is equal to the applied force. This means that how much an object accelerates or decelerates depends on the size of the force acting on the object. This relationship is expressed as

    force = mass × acceleration

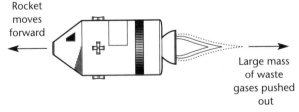

Rocket moves forward

Large mass of waste gases pushed out

The rocket accelerates due to the force of the gases being pushed out

3. Action and reaction are equal and opposite. This means that when a force acts, an equal force acts in the *opposite* direction. For example, **gravity** is exerting a force on you to pull you *down*, but your muscles are exerting an upward force to make you stand *up*.

⊹ Free-fall, Gravitational potential energy

FORCE AND ACCELERATION

When an object is at rest, a *force* such as a push or a pull must be exerted on the object to make it move. More force is required to make it go faster or to accelerate. The amount of force required depends on the **mass** of the object and is given the following formula:

$$\text{force (N)} = \text{mass (kg)} \times \text{acceleration (m/s}^2)$$
$$F = ma$$
$$\text{or } a = \frac{F}{m}$$

The amount of **acceleration** produced depends on two factors:

● The size of the force, measured in Newtons (N)
● The mass of the object, measured in kilograms (kg)

Remember: If the force doubles, or the mass is halved, then the acceleration is doubled.

⊹ Free-fall, Vehicle-stopping distance

FORCE AND EXTENSION

When a force, such as a hanging **weight**, is applied to a metal wire or spring, they stretch or extend. The greater the force, the greater the extension. Hooke's Law states that the extension of the spring is proportional to the force applied, provided that the force is not enough to stretch the spring permanently. If the elastic limit is exceeded, the spring will not return to its original shape and will be deformed.

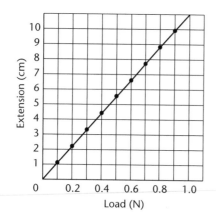

A graph of extension against stretching force

FOSSIL

A fossil is the remains of an organism or the shape of an organism preserved in rocks. Fossils are usually found in **sedimentary rocks** and are studied by palaeontologists to find out what animals and plants may have looked like millions of years ago. The hard outer parts of the animals are usually preserved, whereas the soft tissues will have decayed before being fossilized.

Fossil record

Fossils provide evidence for **evolution**: e.g. based on fossilized remains that have been found, it is thought that the modern-day horse evolved from a small, dog-sized ancestor.

✦ *Natural selection*

Recent ▲

Name	Skull	Fore limb	Hind limb	Teeth Top view	Side view	Height (cm)
Equus						150
Pliohippus						125
Meryohippus						100
Mesohippus						60
Eohippus						28
	Hypothetical ancestor with five toes on each foot and monkey-like teeth					

Ancient

Fossils and evolution

FOSSIL FUELS

Coal, oil and gas are described as fossil fuels. Fossil fuels contain **carbon** and hydrogen. They were formed millions of years ago by the effect of heat and pressure on decaying plants and animals. The chemical **energy** in the cells of the plants and animals became trapped into the coal and oil, and this energy is released as heat and light when the fuel (for example, methane gas) is burned:

fuel + oxygen → carbon + water + heat
dioxide

$$CH_4 + 2O_2 \rightarrow CO_2 + 2H_2O + \text{thermal energy}$$

When fuels burn they may also produce oxides of sulphur and **nitrogen**, as well as carbon monoxide. These waste products are one of the main causes of **pollution**: e.g. **sulphur dioxide** dissolves in water vapour in the air to cause **acid rain**, which damages trees, and harms animal life in rivers and lakes.

What makes a good fuel? There are a number of factors that affect why a certain fuel is used for a particular job:

- The cost of the fuel
- How easy it is to transport and to store
- Whether it is solid, liquid or gas
- How easily it ignites and burns
- How much pollution is caused
- How much energy is released when it burns

The chart below shows how much energy in millions of **joules** (or megajoules, MJ) is released when 1 kg of fuel is burned:

Gas	55 MJ/kg
Oil	44 MJ/kg
Coal	29 MJ/kg
Wood	14 MJ/kg

Gas releases the most energy, but takes up much more space than 1 kg of oil, and is more bulky to transport and to store. Oil is easier to transport and store but costs more than gas to buy. Wood is much cheaper, but is bulky to store and releases less heat than the other fuels.

-*+*- *Generation of electricity, Greenhouse effect, Hydrocarbons*

FRACTIONAL DISTILLATION

Fractional distillation is a process used in industry and in laboratories to separate liquids of different boiling points. It is used in the chemical industry to separate **crude oil** into 'fractions', mixtures of liquids with similar boiling points:

- The liquids with *high* boiling points have large, heavy particles

- The liquids with *low* boiling points have small, light particles

The heavier particles need more energy to help them escape the surface of the liquid.

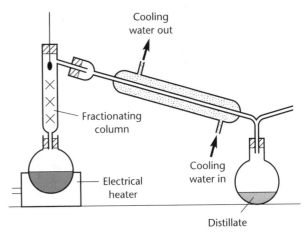

Fractional distillation

-*+*- *Hydrocarbons*

FREE-FALL

An object that is allowed to fall freely near the Earth's surface has a constant **acceleration** of 10 m/s²: e.g. if two objects, one of 5 kg and one of 20 kg, were dropped from a weather balloon, they would both have the same acceleration. The larger object would need more force to accelerate its greater **mass**.

Both the 5 kg object and 20 kg object would have the same acceleration

The *faster* an object moves through a gas or liquid the *greater* the force of **friction** that acts on it. Air resistance *increases* as the speed increases so the acceleration of the object is reduced. Air resistance (exerted upwards) equals the weight of the object (acting downwards). The resultant force eventually reaches zero and the body falls at constant velocity, which is its *terminal velocity*. Factors affecting the terminal velocity are:

- the shape of the object (streamlined objects move faster)

- air resistance (drag), which opposes the motion of a falling object: e.g. air resistance allows a parachute to slow down a falling sky-diver

> *Remember: Terminal velocity is the constant velocity reached by falling objects in air and fluids.*

CHECKPOINT

1. What forces act on a falling object?

2. When does a falling object reach terminal velocity?

3. How can a skydiver change his or her terminal velocity?

The force that is acting on free-falling objects is the force of **gravity** caused by the Earth's gravitational field. This is described as the **weight** of the object:

weight = mass × gravitational field strength

The weight of an object depends on how far it is from the Earth's centre. The *gravitational pull* of the Earth is decreased the further away an object is, so the weight is reduced. At the Earth's surface, the force acting on 1 kg is 10 N. Therefore: the weight of the 5 kg mass is 5 × 10 = 50 N, and the weight of the 20 kg mass is 20 × 10 = 200 N

$$\text{acceleration} = \frac{\text{force}}{\text{mass}}$$

For the smaller object:

$$a = \frac{50}{5} = 10 \text{ m/s}^2$$

For the larger object:

$$a = \frac{200}{20} = 10 \text{ m/s}^2$$

(assuming negligible air resistance)

✥ *Forces – balanced and unbalanced*

FREQUENCY

The frequency of the wave is the number of complete cycles per second, measured in **hertz** (Hz). Imagine standing on a beach and counting the waves as they come towards you. This would give you the frequency of the waves.

A low frequency wave with a high amplitude

~~~~~

A high-frequency wave with a low amplitude

✥ *Amplitude, Speed, Wavelength*

FRICTION

Friction is a **force** that resists motion. When you push an object to start it moving, the object will eventually slow down and stop due to the force of friction. When travelling in a car, friction between the tyres and the roads is essential if the car is going to travel safely and not skid. When riding a bike or motorbike, friction is essential between the brake pads and the wheels, and between the wheels and the road.

Friction energy has to be used to overcome, so there are ways of reducing friction:

- Oil is used in car engines to reduce the friction of the parts rubbing against each other

- Air is used in a hovercraft to reduce the friction between the boat and the water

- Ball bearings are used to reduce the friction between the wheel and the axle of a skateboard

✥ *Free-fall, Kinetic energy, Vehicle stopping-distance*

FUNGI

✥ *Food chains and food webs – decomposers, Micro-organisms, Yeast*

FUSES

A fuse is a thin piece of wire that melts and breaks the circuit if too much **current** is flowing. To find out the correct fuse for a particular appliance use the following formula:

$$\text{current} = \frac{\text{watts}}{\text{volts}}$$

For example, a 60 W table lamp uses 60/240 = 0.25 A, so a 3 A fuse would be the correct one to use. However, an electric kettle using 2,000 W would take a current of 2,000/240 = 8.3 A, so a 13 A fuse is needed.

CHECKPOINT

What fuse should be used in a 50 W video recorder if the mains electrical supply is 250 V? Choose from 3 A, 5 A and 13 A.

✥ *Earth wire, Magnetic circuit breakers, Three-pin plug*

GALAXY

Millions of **stars** make up what is described as a galaxy. Our **solar system** is part of the galaxy known as the Milky Way.

✢ **Sun, Universe**

GAMETES

Gametes are special cells in the body called sex cells:

● Female gametes are produced in the **ovary**.

● Male gametes are produced in a **testis** in animals, or stamen in plants.

Gametes are produced by a process of cell division known as **meiosis** which only occurs in the sex organs. Meiosis reduces the **chromosome** number by half in each cell. All the cells produced by meiosis are different from each other. The other cells in the body are a result of cell division by **mitosis** and are identical to the parent cells with exactly the same **chromosomes**.

The gametes have half of the information content required so two gametes, one male and one female gamete, must fuse at **fertilization** to produce a fertilized ovum. At fertilization each gamete carries only one of each type of chromosome. When fusion has taken place the **zygote** has two full sets of chromosomes, which is normal for an ordinary body cell.

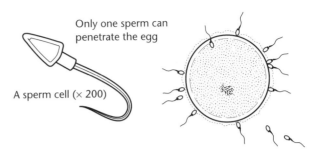

Only one sperm can penetrate the egg

A sperm cell (× 200)

Gametes

✢ **Reproduction, Sexual reproduction**

GAMMA RAYS

✢ **Radioactivity**

GAS

All matter can be classified as either **solid**, **liquid**, or gas. These are called the three states of matter. In a gas the **particles** are moving very fast and are large distances apart. Gases are made up of either single **atoms** or small **molecules**. Gases exert pressure; air is a mixture of gases.

The particles in a gas are moving very fast. When these particles hit something they exert a force on that object. The combined effect of the many millions of particles in a gas acting on an area is its pressure:

pressure = force per unit area

Gas laws

Pressure is measured as force per unit area; the units are **newtons** per square metre (N/m^2):

● The pressure of a gas can be increased by *increasing* its temperature (heating). The gas particles will have more **kinetic energy** so will be moving faster and striking the sides of a container harder and more often.

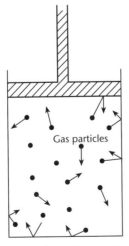

(a) Particles striking the sides of a container create pressure

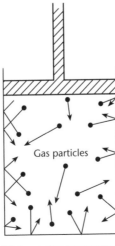

(b) Increasing temperature increases pressure

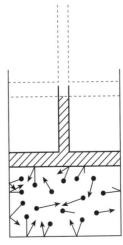

(c) Decreasing volume increases pressure

- The pressure of a gas can also be increased by *reducing* the volume of that gas. The particles in the gas will then be closer together, so they will strike the walls of the container more often.

> *Remember: The volume of a gas is equal to the volume of the container. The volume of a gas can be increased by increasing the temperature.*

These ideas may help you to understand the 'gas laws' or 'gas patterns':

- Pressure (P) α temperature (T) (provided the volume (V) remains the same) P/T = a constant

- Pressure α 1/volume (provided the temperature remains the same) $P \times V$ = a constant

In order to make calculations using these gas 'laws', temperatures are measured on the **Kelvin** scale of absolute temperature. (0 K = –273 °C). 0 K is known as absolute zero; it is the temperature at which particles have *no* kinetic energy.

-+- **Brownian motion, Gas laws, Kinetic theory**

CHECKPOINT

For each choice in italics, cross out the incorrect words:

If a gas is slowly pushed into a smaller space so that its *pressure/temperature* stays the same, its *temperature/pressure* will *decrease/increase* because the particles hit the walls of the container *less/more* often.

GASEOUS EXCHANGE

Gaseous exchange in the alveoli of the lungs takes place by **diffusion**. Diffusion of particles takes place from where there is a higher concentration to where there is a lower concentration. Particles will diffuse until they are evenly distributed.

-+- **Breathing, Diffusion in action – in the lungs**

GEIGER–MÜLLER TUBE

The Geiger–Müller (G–M) tube is an instrument used to detect **radioactivity** and measure the strength of **alpha**, **beta**, and **gamma** rays. Radiation enters the window of the G–M tube and creates argon **ions** and **electrons**. When the ions reach the **electrodes**, they produce a current pulse that is amplified and fed into

a ratemeter from which the average pulse-rate can be determined. The G–M tube is usually connected to a **loudspeaker** that emits a series of clicks in proportion to the strength of the radiation.

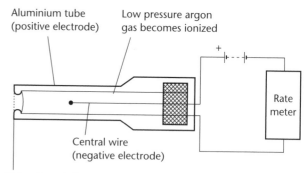

Aluminium tube (positive electrode)
Low pressure argon gas becomes ionized
Rate meter
Central wire (negative electrode)
Thin mica window allows alpha, beta and gamma particles to pass through

Geiger–Müller tube

GENDER

-+- **Puberty, Sex determination**

GENE

The instructions for a particular characteristic, or trait, are called a gene. There are genes for all our characteristics such as eye colour, hair colour and blood type. Each **chromosome** carries many genes, each a certain length of **DNA**. We have two copies of each gene in every normal body cell, one in each of a pair of chromosomes because we inherit one gene from our father and one from our mother of each type. Genes can exist in alternative forms called *alleles*. For example, the gene controlling eye colour has two alleles: one for brown eyes and one for blue eyes. Usually one of the alleles is the dominant allele and one is the recessive allele. We can't see genes, but their effects have been observed and patterns of inheritance discovered by scientists.

> *Remember: A gene is a section of DNA.*

CHECKPOINT

Write these words in order of the size of the structures to which they refer, starting with the cell.

DNA   cell   chromosome   nucleus   gene

Cell → .... → .... → ....
→ ....

◆ *Genetic engineering, Monohybrid inheritance, Mutations, Natural selection*

GENERATION OF ELECTRICITY

Coal, oil, gas and nuclear fuel are used in power stations to heat water and convert it into high pressure steam. The steam is then used to turn huge turbines that spin around. These turbines drive a *generator* that produces an *alternating current* at a *frequency* of 50 Hz and about 25,000 V. The process of *generating electricity* is inefficient and some energy is lost to the environment as heat.

◆ *Fossil fuels, Hydro-electric power, Nuclear power, Transformers, Transmission of electricity*

GENERATOR

A generator transfers *kinetic energy* into electrical energy. It works on the principle that a voltage can be *induced* in a coil when the coil is turned in a *magnetic field* between the poles of two bar magnets. This induced voltage causes a current to flow. There are basically two types of generator:

● A d.c. generator, which produces a one-way *direct* current, such as a bicycle *dynamo*.

● An a.c. generator (*alternator*), which produces an *alternating* current, such as that found in a power station and in a car.

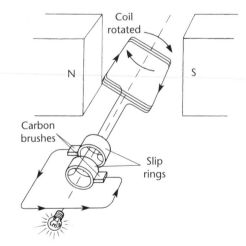

The construction of a simple a.c. generator (alternator)

> Remember: A voltage is induced when there is relative movement between a conductor and a magnetic field, and when the magnetic field through a coil changes.

CHECKPOINT

1. Complete the boxes to show the energy change that takes place in a generator.

.... → ....

2. Explain the principle on which the generator works.

◆ *Electromagnetism, Induced current, Transmission of electricity*

GENETIC ENGINEERING

Genetic engineering involves the transfer of a section of *DNA* from one organism to the DNA of another organism of a different *species*. For example, the *gene* determining production of the *hormone insulin* can be inserted into the DNA of *bacteria* or yeast cells. The transferred gene continues to produce insulin, which can be used in the treatment of *diabetes*. The process is now carried out on an industrial scale to manufacture large quantities of the hormone.

Genes can also be transferred into the cells of animals or plants at an early stage so that they develop certain beneficial characteristics such as resistance to disease. It is also possible to produce genetically identical organisms by a process known as tissue culture, using small groups of cells from a part of a plant to grow a new plant, genetically identical to the parent. There are obvious benefits in agricultural terms to being able to produce many identical plants, say with high resistance to drought or high yields of fruit. However, all the plants produced in this way from one parent could be affected by the same disease or insect pest as they are all the same. In animals, cells from a developing *embryo* can be split apart and each can develop into a new, genetically identical organism.

● Genetic engineering raises many social and ethical issues; e.g.: How far should it be used to produce genetically identical human beings? Should research be carried out using potentially viable human embryos that may later have to be destroyed? Guidance on these issues is being developed in the medical profession.

● On medical grounds, genetic engineering could be used to help treat diseases such as cystic fibrosis and muscular dystrophy. It could therefore help people who have a defect in their immune system and are unable to make a particular protein. The missing gene could be inserted into some white blood cells and the person would then be able to lead a normal life.

Remember: Genetic engineering is the insertion of new genes into the DNA of bacteria, using enzymes, to make genetically altered cells that produce useful substances, e.g. human insulin.

✦ *Cloning, Food production, Selective breeding*

GEOTHERMAL ENERGY

Geothermal energy is an example of an **alternative** source of energy. Using geothermal energy, there are basically two ways of producing the steam required to drive the turbines that generate electricity.

● One method, used in Cornwall, is to use the heat that is trapped in hot **granite** rocks deep in the Earth to heat up water and convert it into steam.

● Another method is to drill a deep well to release steam from hot underground water that occurs in **volcanic** areas.

In both cases the steam can then be used to drive **generators** and produce **electricity**.

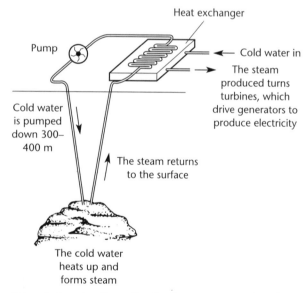

Heat exchanger

Pump

Cold water in

The steam produced turns turbines, which drive generators to produce electricity

Cold water is pumped down 300–400 m

The steam returns to the surface

The cold water heats up and forms steam

Using hot water from the Earth to generate electricity

● An advantage of geothermal power is that it is non-polluting and is not likely to run out.

● A disadvantage is that very complex and expensive technology is involved in the process.

At present, this form of alternative energy is still under investigation.

✦ *Crust, Generation of electricity, Solar energy, Wave energy, Wind energy*

GIANT STRUCTURES

Giant structures are formed when all the **particles** in a substance are linked together in one giant framework (rather than in small units such as molecules). This gives rise to certain properties. Substances that are giant structures are crystalline, and have high melting points, boiling points, etc.

Elements as giant structures

Carbon forms large numbers of **covalent bonds** between its **atoms**. It can do this in two ways to form diamond or graphite. These two forms of carbon are called **allotropes**, and both are crystalline:

● Diamond is very strong because each carbon atom is linked to four others. A diamond crystal is one giant molecule.

● Graphite is very strongly bonded in layers; each layer is a giant molecule, however, the forces holding the layers together are weak so they slide over each other. This property is made use of in lubricants and in pencils. The pencil 'lead' is really graphite.

● Silicon is in the same group as carbon; it too has similar abilities to form giant structures. The structure of silicon is the same as that of diamond.

CHECKPOINT

1. Name **one** example of a giant structure.
2. State **two** properties of giant structures.

Metals as giant structures

Metals are giant structures. The metal atoms are 'bonded' together in an unusual way. The metal atoms lose some of their outer **electrons** and so become, in effect, positive **ions**. These electrons then move around the atoms freely. The metal atoms/ions are floating in a 'sea' of electrons. The electrons are free to move and are shared by all the atoms. This idea helps to explain many of the properties of metals:

● **High boiling points and melting points**: The attraction between the 'ions' and electrons is strong, so the metals will have high melting points and boiling points and will be strong and hard.

Metal ions floating in a sea of electrons

● **Conduction of electricity**: The ease of movement of electrons will mean that metals will easily conduct electricity when a potential difference is applied across the metal.

Compounds as giant structures

Any **compound** containing ions will form giant structures; each positive ion surrounds itself with as many negative ions as possible and vice versa. The way in which the ions pack together depends on the size of the individual ions and their charge, i.e. 1+, 2+ or 1–, 2–, etc.

In addition, silicon dioxide, a compound of silicon, has a giant structure, the atoms being bonded by **covalent bonds**. We come across this substance quite often; it appears as sand, as quartz in rocks and can be made into **glass**. It is the second most common element found in the Earth's crust (26 per cent), the first being oxygen (50 per cent).

✛ **Bonding**

GLASS

Glass is a very useful material, it is resistant to **corrosion**, is waterproof, does not conduct electricity and can be made transparent. The raw materials are cheap and easily available, such as silica (sand). Glass is made by heating a mixture of oxides and **carbonates** in a furnace, the exact combination depending on the type of glass required. The molten material is then moulded and cooled.

✛ **Ceramics, Composite materials, Recycling**

GLUCOSE

Glucose is a type of **sugar**; its chemical formula is $C_6H_{12}O_6$. Glucose is the sugar that plants first produce in the process of **photosynthesis**, and is then converted to more complex molecules, like sucrose (the sugar we buy from a shop) and starch.

✛ **Alcohol, Balanced diet, Digestion**

GRANITE

A hard, **igneous** rock containing different minerals, such as quartz, feldspar and mica.

✛ **Geothermal energy, Rock cycle**

GRAVITATIONAL POTENTIAL ENERGY

When an object is at rest at a point above the ground it has gravitational **potential energy**. If you hold a book above your desk, the book has gravitational potential energy equal to the amount of **work** that you did to lift it to that height, which is given by force × distance moved.

The gravitational potential energy of an object is mgh, where mg is the upward force needed to lift the object, and h is the vertical height above the ground. (Gravitational field strength g = 10 N/kg.)

For example, if the book has a mass of 2 kg, and is held 3 m high, then the gravitational potential energy is 2 kg × 10 N/kg × 3 m = 60 J.

✛ **Forces – balanced and unbalanced, Gravity, Weight**

GRAVITY

Gravity is the attraction of the **Earth** for **solids**, **liquids** and **gases**. This means that if you drop an object it will always fall, due to the attraction of the Earth for the object. The **Moon** has one-sixth the gravitational attraction of the Earth as it is smaller in size.

✛ **Forces – balanced and unbalanced, Free-fall, Gravitational potential energy, Satellites, Weight**

GREENHOUSE EFFECT

Causes

The **Earth** is surrounded by an **atmosphere** that acts as a 'blanket' keeping it warm. On Earth the average surface temperature is +15 °C, whereas on the **Moon**, which has no atmosphere, the surface temperature is –18 °C. Evidence has shown that the Earth is slowly warming up, caused by changes in the atmosphere. This gradual warming is called the 'greenhouse effect'.

During the last century humans have been adding to the amount of **carbon dioxide** in the atmosphere as a result of burning **fossil fuels** (coal, oil, gas) and burning trees (as a result of deforestation to provide land for growing crops). This has disturbed the balance of carbon dioxide in the atmosphere; it has been estimated to have increased over the last century from a 'pre-industrial' level of 0.27–0.35 per cent today. This in turn has resulted in a slight warming of the Earth. In addition, other man-made gases have been released into the atmosphere that have been shown to add to the problem: e.g. **chlorofluorocarbons** (CFCs), methane, nitrous oxide and ozone. (Be careful – this is an increase in ozone in the lower atmosphere do not confuse it with the **ozone** layer.)

How the greenhouse effect works

- The Earth is warmed by solar **radiation** that passes through the atmosphere and is absorbed by the ground and oceans, warming them up.

- This energy is re-radiated (at a different wavelength) as heat into the atmosphere.

- Carbon dioxide, water vapour and the other gases mentioned absorb this heat energy and then re-radiate it back to the surface.

- Any increase in the amount of carbon dioxide will therefore increase the amount of heat 'trapped', resulting in a gradual warming.

Implications

Many predictions have been made as to the effect that a slight warming of the Earth (1–2 °C) will produce, using many different computer models. Some of the suggestions put forward include:

- A change in climate; some areas will become dryer, some wetter, some warmer. Droughts may occur in parts of the Earth and floods in others.

- Polar ice caps will melt, and this will itself affect the climate.

No one is certain what will happen – only that there will be changes.

-✦- *Carbon cycle, Combustion*

GROUP 1

-✦- *Alkali metals*

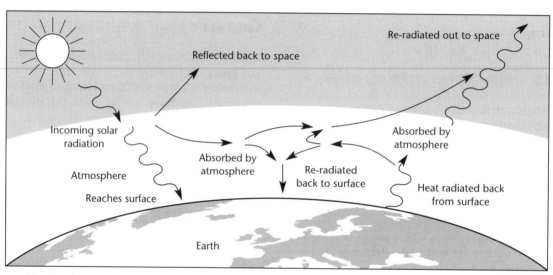

The greenhouse effect

HABITAT

The habitat is the place where an **organism** lives: e.g. the habitat of earthworms is in the soil, the habitat for a crab is on a rocky beach.

✦ *Ecosystem, Environment, Quadrat, Sampling populations*

HAEMOGLOBIN

✦ *Red blood cells, Combustion – combustion in action, Smoking*

HALF-LIFE

After a period of time any radioactive material will decay and become stable (non-radioactive). You cannot predict, however, when any particular nucleus will decay and release its radiation and energy. They decay in a *random* way. Different substances do, however, decay at different rates. The decay rate of any radioactive material is measured in half-lives.

The *half-life* of a radioactive material is the time taken for half the atoms in a radioactive material to undergo decay. For any particular radioactive material, the half-life is constant whatever the conditions, because radioactive decay is unaffected by temperature or pressure. Half-lives can be very long or very short (thousands of years to less than a second): e.g. the half-life of carbon-14 is 5730 years, but for carbon-10 it is only 19 s. If you plot a graph for the decay of any radioactive material it will always follow the same pattern.

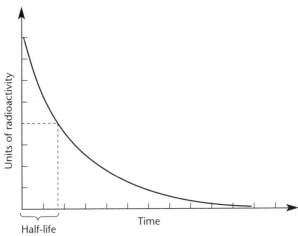

The decay curve for radioactive materials

CHECKPOINT

A radioactive substance has a half-life of 20 years. What proportion of the substance would be left after 40 years?

(a) one-half
(b) one-third
(c) one-quarter
(d) one-sixth

✦ *Background radiation, Nuclear fission, Nuclear power*

HALOGENS

The halogens are a family of **elements** (group 7 of the **periodic table**) that have similar chemical properties.

- Have seven electrons in their outer shell
- Are non-metals
- Consist of molecules made of pairs of atoms
- Form ions with a charge of –1, one electron is added to the outer shell
- Form ionic salts with metals in which the chloride, bromide or iodide ion carries a –1 charge
- Form molecular compounds with other non-metallic elements
- The reactivity decreases down the group as the number of shells increases

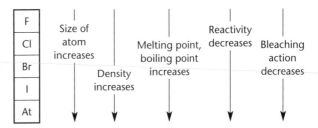

The halogens

Types of reaction

Reaction with metals

The halogens will react with **metals** to form metal halides: e.g. iron will react with chlorine:

$$2Fe + 3Cl_2 \rightarrow 2FeCl_3$$

Remember: The reactivity of the halogens decreases as you move down the group.

Reaction with water

The halogens will react with **water** to form acidic solutions that also act as bleaches. In the same way that the reactivity *decreases* as you *move down* the group, so does the bleaching power of the solutions. The solutions produced from iodine and bromine are weak **acids**, whereas chlorine and fluorine will produce strong acids:

$H_2O + Cl_2 \rightarrow HCl + HOCl$ (chloric acid – bleach)

CHECKPOINT

1. What is formed when one electron is added to the outer shell of the halogens?

2. Why does the reactivity of the alkali metals decrease down the group?

3. What is formed when the halogens react with metals?

Reactivity trends

When halogens react with metals they do so to form **ions:** F⁻, fluoride ion; Cl⁻, chloride ion; Br⁻, bromide ion; I⁻, iodide ion.

The ease with which these atoms form ions depends on the number of **electron** shells the atom has. In order to form an ion the atom has to *gain* an electron. The atom with its outer shell closer to the positive nucleus will find this easiest, because of the strong pulling-power of the positive nucleus. The larger the atom, the further away the outer electron shell, so the less influence the nucleus will have. As you would expect, chlorine is much more reactive than iodine.

Halogen reactivity

	Chlorine	Bromine	Iodine
At room temperature	Gas	Liquid	Solid
Reaction with iron	Very fast	Fast	Slow
Reaction with potassium iodide solution	Reacts	Reacts	No reaction
Effect on indicator paper	Bleaches	Bleaches	Bleaches

-+- **Chlorine**

HEART

The heart is basically two muscular pumps that work side by side. Each side is divided into two chambers:

● an upper atrium

● a lower ventricle

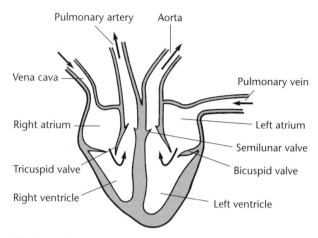

The heart is a powerful pump that pumps blood round the body and to the lungs

● The *right* atrium takes in deoxygenated blood, which has been round the body

● The *right* ventricle pumps the blood to the lungs, via the **pulmonary artery**

● The *left* atrium takes in oxygenated blood from the lungs, via the **pulmonary vein**

● The more muscular *left* ventricle pumps the blood under great pressure around the body, via the aorta, the thick walled main artery

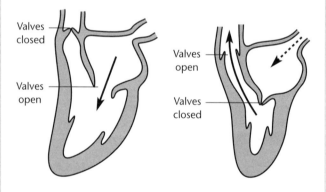

The heart in action: (left) ventricle relaxed: blood is forced from the atrium into the ventricle. Valves at the base of the artery prevent blood flowing 'backwards'. (right) Ventricle contracted: blood is forced from the ventricle and out of the heart. The atrium meanwhile re-fills with more blood. Valves between the atrium and ventricle are closed to prevent blood flowing backwards into the atrium.

Remember: It is important to learn the sequence of blood flow through the heart.

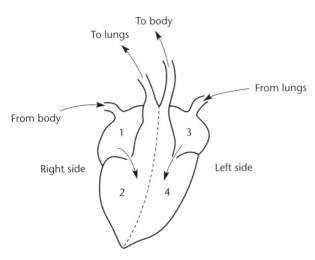

The sequence of blood flow through the heart

-+- *Artery, Blood system, Vein*

HEMATITE

Hematite is an ore of iron that is red in colour and is sometimes referred to as kidney ore because some samples are shaped like kidneys. It is an oxide of iron, chemical composition Fe_2O_3. The iron is extracted from the ore by **reduction** in the **blast furnace.**

-+- **Extraction of metals**

HERBIVORE

-+- **Food chains and food webs**

HERTZ

The hertz (Hz) is the SI unit for **frequency**. One hertz is one cycle every second. The mains current supplied to houses in Europe has a frequency of 50 Hz.

-+- **Alternating current, Mains electricity**

HETEROZYGOUS

This means an individual has both the dominant and recessive alleles for a particular characteristic.

-+- **Homozygous, Monohybrid inheritance**

HIV (HUMAN IMMUNO-DEFICIENCY VIRUS)

The human immuno-deficiency virus lives in body fluids such as semen, **blood** and saliva. The virus can enter a person's body in several ways:

- Through unprotected sexual intercourse with an infected person
- By injecting drugs using an unsterilized needle that has been used by an infected person
- By receiving blood transfusions from an infected person
- By coming into contact with blood from an infected person
- By an infected mother breastfeeding her baby

A person who is exposed to HIV will produce **antibodies** after a few weeks. A positive test for HIV means that the person is infected with HIV. The virus attacks the body's immune system and the person is unable to fight infections such as tuberculosis. There are an estimated 20 million people who are HIV positive. People who are HIV positive may develop the disease called AIDS, the acquired immune deficiency syndrome. About 4 million people already have AIDS, of which 30 per cent are women under 25 and 15 per cent are men under 25. The death rate from AIDS is over 50 per cent.

-+- **Reproduction**

HOMEOSTASIS

Homeostasis is the maintenance of a constant environment within the body. This means maintaining normal levels of the dissolved substances in the blood and tissue fluid, such as **glucose, amino acids**, salts, **hormones** and excretory products, as well as pH and a constant **body temperature**. The advantage of homeostasis to the organism is that the functioning of the body is independent of the external environment. **Osmoregulation** helps to maintain this constant balance within the blood.

> *Remember: Examples of homeostasis are: the kidneys regulate the water content of the body, the lungs remove carbon dioxide, the kidneys remove urea from the blood, the skin regulates body temperature.*

CHECKPOINT

State **two** examples of homeostatic control in the body.

-+- **Breathing, Insulin, Kidney, Pituitary gland, Vasoconstriction, Vasodilation**

HOMOZYGOUS

This means an individual has two identical alleles for a particular characteristic, either both **dominant** alleles or both **recessive** alleles.

-‡- *Heterozygous, Monohybrid inheritance*

HORMONES

Hormones are chemical substances produced in very small amounts by special glands in the body called endocrine glands. Hormones are carried from the gland via the blood stream to their target organ where they have their effect. For example, **oestrogen** is produced in the **ovaries** but has its effect on the development of the breasts and growth of pubic hair. The thyroid gland produces a hormone called thyroxine that controls the rate of metabolism in humans, and therefore controls rate of growth. The thyroid gland is controlled by the 'master gland' of the body, the **pituitary**.

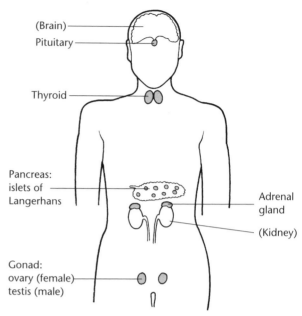

Position of the main endocrine glands in humans (the relative position of some other organs is also shown)

-‡- *Adrenalin, Diabetes, Insulin, Plant hormones, Puberty*

Medical uses of hormones

Fertility treatment

Hormones such as oestrogen are used to increase fertility in women who are unable to produce sufficient eggs from their ovaries. The oestrogen stimulates **ovulation** and increases the number of eggs released. If a woman's oviducts are blocked, then the eggs can be **fertilized** outside her body '*in vitro*'. This means that sperm fertilize the eggs in a glass dish and the resulting **zygotes** are taken from the dish and placed in the woman's uterus where they develop as normal. The use of fertility drugs can, however, lead to multiple births if several **embryos** develop at the same time.

Contraception

Couples who wish to plan when they will have a baby may decide to use some form of contraception. One popular method of contraception is the contraceptive pill, which contains small amounts of hormones, usually oestrogen and progesterone, which prevent an egg being released during ovulation.

-‡- *Menstrual cycle*

Treatment of diabetes

-‡- *Diabetes*

Summary of some of the main hormones in humans		
Gland	*Hormone*	*Effect*
Pituitary	Trophic hormones	Cause other endocrine glands, e.g. ovary and testis, to release their hormones
Ovary	Oestrogen	Promotes the development of female secondary sexual characteristics, e.g. enlargement of breasts, widening of hips
	Progesterone	Maintains the lining of the uterus during pregnancy
Testis	Testosterone	Promotes the development of the male secondary sexual characteristics, e.g. enlargement of genitals, growth of facial hair, widening of hips,
Pancreas (islets of Langerhans)	Insulin	Causes conversion of glucose to glycogen
	Glucagon	Causes conversion of glycogen to glucose

Plants also produce hormones in very small amounts and these help to control the growth of the plant.

HYBRIDS

If two different varieties of animals or plants, each of which has useful characteristics, are allowed to breed together, the offspring are known as hybrids and will possess the characteristics of both the varieties that were cross-bred. The technique of cross-breeding has been used to great advantage in producing disease-resistant plants and high-yielding crop plants. Hybrids such as varieties of corn were introduced to America in the 1930s and resulted in increased yields of up to 50 per cent. You will find that seeds of hybrid flowers and vegetables are very expensive due to the amount of research that has been done in developing the hybrid seeds.

✛ **Monohybrid inheritance, Selective breeding**

HYDRAULICS

Hydraulic machines, such as hydraulic brakes and hydraulic jacks, use liquid pressure to transfer a force from one place to another. They work on three basic properties of liquids:

- They cannot be compressed

- At the same depth, the pressure in the liquid is the same in all directions

- Any change in liquid pressure is transmitted immediately to all parts of the liquid

- A force, F_1 is applied to the smaller piston whose area is A_1.

- This pressure is transmitted through the liquid and is applied to the larger piston, area A_2.

- As A_2 is greater than A_1, a small force applied at the small cylinder is multiplied to become a larger force applied at the larger cylinder.

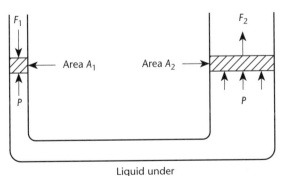

Principle of hydraulic systems

HYDROCARBONS

Hydrocarbons are compounds that contain carbon and hydrogen atoms only. They originate from **crude oil** and are used as fuels and in the manufacture of plastics.

When hydrocarbons are burnt, **carbon dioxide** and **water** are produced.

$$\text{natural gas} + \text{oxygen} \rightarrow \text{carbon dioxide} + \text{water}$$
$$CH_4 \quad + \quad 2O_2 \quad \rightarrow \quad CO_2 \quad + \quad H_2O$$

There are different groups of hydrocarbons.

Alkanes, such as **methane**, CH_4, ethane C_2H_6, propane C_3H_8 and butane, C_4H_{10}:

- are saturated hydrocarbon molecules

- have single covalent bonds between two carbon atoms C–C

Structural formula of ethane, C_2H_6

Alkenes, such as ethene, C_2H_4, propene C_3H_6:

- Are unsaturated hydrocarbon molecules

- Have double covalent bonds between two carbon atoms, C=C

Structural formula of ethene, C_2H_4

Remember: Fossil fuels, such as coal, oil and gas, contain carbon and hydrogen and are hydrocarbons.

-‡- **Addition polymers, Cracking, Crude oil, Fossil fuels**

HYDRO–ELECTRIC POWER (HEP)

The movement of fast-flowing rivers through turbines
in a hydro-electric power station produces electricity.
The **kinetic energy** of the fast-flowing river is used to
turn a water turbine. The turbine is connected to a
dynamo, which generates electricity. Some hydro-
electric power stations work on a system of two
reservoirs, one higher than the other. The water is
pumped back up to the high reservoir from the lower
reservoir during the night when electricity is cheaper.

● Advantages of HEP are that there is no pollution,
  and the source of energy is unlikely to run out.

● Disadvantages are that the power station may be
  very costly to build and maintain and the power
  stations may spoil the appearance of the
  environment.

-‡- **Alternative energy, Generation of electricity,
  Transmission of electricity**

HYDROLYSIS

Hydrolysis is a type of **chemical reaction** in which a
molecule of water reacts with a **reactant**. One

important hydrolysis reaction is that of **starch** (a
polymer), which is broken down into sugars (small
molecules). The hydrolysis product of starch with an
acid catalyst is *glucose*:

$$\text{starch} + \text{water} \rightarrow \text{glucose}$$

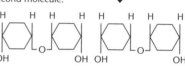

How amylase breaks down starch

If the hydrolysis of starch is catalysed by the enzyme
salivary amylase; the product is *maltose* (another
sugar). This difference in product highlights the
importance of the catalyst in chemical reactions:

$$\text{starch} + \text{water} \rightarrow \text{maltose}$$

Acid hydrolysis

Acids can also catalyse the breakdown of starch but
the product is glucose. The stomach contains
hydrochloric acid that can help break down any
unconverted starch or maltose molecules into
glucose. Glucose molecules are small enough to pass
through the gut wall.

-‡- **Amylase, Digestion, Proteins**

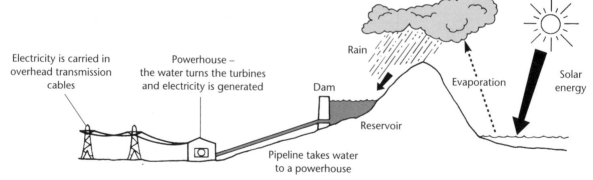

How electricity is generated from hydroelectric power

IGNEOUS ROCKS

Igneous rocks are formed when very hot molten *magma* from the mantle cools and solidifies. The size of the crystals that can be seen in igneous rocks indicates the rate of cooling of the magma. Small crystals are formed when the magma cools rapidly. Granite and basalt are examples of igneous rocks.

-**+**- *Metamorphic rocks, Rock cycle, Sedimentary rocks, Volcano*

INDICATORS

An indicator is a substance, often derived from plant dyes, that tells us whether something is *acid* or *alkaline* by changing colour.

-**+**- *Litmus, pH scale, Universal indicator*

INDUCED CURRENT

When a coil of wire is moved in a *magnetic field* or there is a change in the magnetic field around a coil then a current is *induced* in the coil. Faraday explained this effect by suggesting that an *e.m.f.* was induced in a conductor whenever it cuts magnetic field lines. Three factors increase the induced e.m.f.:

- How fast the magnet or coil is moved
- How many turns there are on the coil
- How strong the magnet is

The size of the induced e.m.f. is directly proportional to the rate at which the conductor cuts the magnetic field lines.

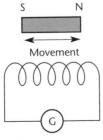

G = galvanometer

Induced current

CHECKPOINT

1. List **three** factors that can affect the size of the induced voltage.

2. State **two** devices that use induction.

-**+**- *Alternator, Electric motor, Electromagnetism, Generator, Transformers*

INFRARED RADIATION

These are *electromagnetic* waves that are radiated by all warm objects including the *Sun*. The infrared rays are invisible and their *wavelength* is just longer than that of visible red light. The upper levels of the *atmosphere* absorb some of the infrared *radiation* from the Sun to prevent the surface of the *Earth* from becoming too warm.

-**+**- *Greenhouse effect, Satellites*

INSULATION

During cold weather, about one-third of the *energy* produced in Britain is used to heat people's homes to a comfortable temperature of about 20 °C. But a percentage of this energy is *lost* through windows, walls, doors and the roof.

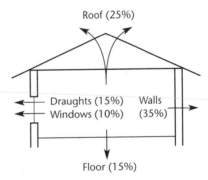

How heat is lost from a house

This loss of heat is reduced by using various ways of trapping *air* to insulate the house. Air is a poor *conductor* of heat and prevents heat escaping from the house. There are four main ways of insulating a house to reduce this loss of heat:

- Roof insulation – by putting a layer of insulating fibre material in the loft of the house. The insulation material traps air in tiny spaces between the fibres.

- Double glazing of windows – putting a second pane of glass in each window so that a layer of air is trapped inside the two panes, which greatly reduces the amount of heat that can escape.

However, most recently built houses have windows that are installed as sealed double-glazed units. These consist of two panes of glass that prevent heat escaping. You may have had 'double glazing' put into some existing windows at home. The old single pane windows are replaced by double pane window units.

● Cavity wall insulation – many recently built houses have walls made of two layers of bricks with a gap in between them. The gap can be filled with insulating foam that traps pockets of air and prevents heat escaping from the house.

● Draught excluders – strips of draught-excluding material can be put around doors and windows to prevent warm air escaping and stop cold air from coming into the room. However, if you burn a **fossil fuel** such as coal, wood or gas you should make sure that there is a good flow of air to prevent the build-up of poisonous fumes.

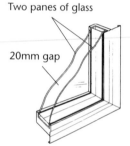

Double glazing of windows

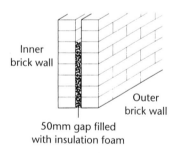

Cavity wall insulation

> Remember: Insulation reduces the transfer of energy from hotter to colder objects. Insulation works by trapping air, a poor conductor of heat.

CHECKPOINT

How does insulation reduce heat loss from a building?

Some information on how heat losses can be reduced in the home, and how much money in heating bills can be saved, is shown in the table below.

Reducing heat loss in the home			
Method of reducing heat loss	% of heat saved	Typical cost in £s	Approx time to recover cost (years)
Double glazing	15	1000	30
Carpet underlay	20	200	8
Draught proofing	25	50	1
Roof insulation	30	150	3
Cavity wall insulation	35	300	5

✦ **Conduction, Convection, Mains electricity – paying for electricity, Radiation.**

INSULIN

Insulin is a **hormone** produced by special cells in the pancreas. It is released when the concentration of **glucose** in the blood increases: e.g. after a meal. The effect of insulin is to decrease glucose concentration by converting glucose to glycogen.

Another hormone, glucagon, is released when the concentration of glucose in the blood decreases: e.g. during exercise. The effect of glucagon is to increase the concentration of glucose by converting glycogen, stored in the liver, to glucose.

> Remember:
>
> insulin
> glucose ⇌ glycogen
> glucagon

CHECKPOINT

Complete these sentences to explain the effect of insulin on the concentration of blood glucose.

When blood glucose levels are high, the pancreas secretes the hormone .... The glucose is converted to .... and stored in the .... When glucose levels fall, glucagon is secreted which converts .... to ....

✦ **Bacteria, Diabetes, Genetic engineering, Homeostasis**

INTESTINE

-✦- *Digestion, Peristalsis*

ION

An ion is a ***particle*** that carries an electrical charge, which might be positive or negative. Each ion has a name and formula. Ions can be derived from single atoms or from combinations. The charge on the ion is shown as a + or – at the top of the symbols. The size of the charge is indicated as a number, e.g. 1+, 2+, 3+, etc., or 1–, 2–, 3–, etc. Examples of ions and their formulae are oxide, O^{2-}; chloride, Cl^-; copper, Cu^{2+}; carbonate, CO_3^{2-}.

In ***compounds*** that contain ions, the overall charge is zero; the positive charge balances the negative charge. This helps when working out the formula for a compound; e.g. a compound made from sodium ions and chloride ions has the formula NaCl. The formula for sodium carbonate is Na_2CO_3; because the carbonate ion has a charge of 2–, two sodium ions $Na+$ are needed to balance this charge.

Ions and the periodic table

- Group 1 elements form ions with *one* positive charge (they have one electron to lose).

- Group 2 elements form ions with *two* positive charges (they have two electrons to lose).

- Group 3 elements form ions with *three* positive charges (they have three electrons to lose).

- Group 7 elements form ions with *one* negative charge (they have one space to fill).

- Group 6 elements form ions with *two* negative charges (they have two spaces to fill).

Some examples of ions formed from metals and non-metals are shown in the table opposite.

-✦- ***Anion, Cation, Ionic bonding, Ionic equations, Periodic table, Valency***

Some atoms and their ions			
Metal atoms	*Group*	*Electrons lost*	*Ion formed*
Lithium	1	1	Li^+
Sodium	1	1	Na^+
Potassium	1	1	K^+
Magnesium	2	2	Mg^{2+}
Calcium	2	2	Ca^{2+}
Aluminium	3	3	Al^{3+}
Non-metal atoms	*Group*	*Electrons gained*	*Ion formed*
Oxygen	6	2	O^{2-}
Sulphur	6	2	S^{2-}
Chlorine	7	1	Cl^-
Bromine	7	1	Br^-
Iodine	7	1	I^-

IONIC BONDING

There is a stable arrangement for electrons in atoms. This occurs when an atom has a *filled outer shell*. All the atoms in group 0 ***(noble gases)*** of the ***periodic table*** have filled outer shells. These atoms do *not* react with other substances, except for a few special cases. All other atoms react in order to fill their outer electron shells. They can do this in two ways:

- By sharing electrons forming ***covalent bonds***

- By transferring electrons forming ***ions***

Electron transfer to form ions

In the reaction between sodium and chlorine atoms, electron transfer has occurred to form ions:

$$Na + Cl \rightarrow Na^+ + Cl^-$$

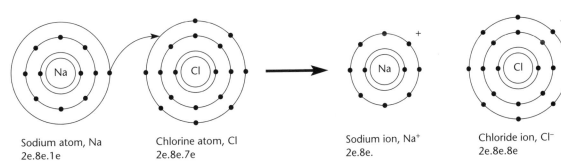

| Sodium atom, Na | Chlorine atom, Cl | Sodium ion, Na^+ | Chloride ion, Cl^- |
| 2e.8e.1e | 2e.8e.7e | 2e.8e. | 2e.8e.8e |

Formation of ions when sodium reacts with chlorine

- The sodium ion has *lost* an electron – we show this as Na^+

- The chloride ion has *gained* an electron – we show this as Cl^-

- Both the ions that are formed have filled outer shells. Once these two ions have been formed they will attract each other because of their opposite charges.

> Remember: Like charges repel; unlike charges attract.

The reason the electron transfer takes place in this direction is because any transfer of electrons takes energy. It is easier to take one electron from sodium than to take seven electrons from chlorine. This results in the general rule:

- Metals form positive ions

- Non-metals form negative ions

> Remember: Positive ions are called **cations**; negative ions are called **anions**.

Properties of ionic compounds

The formation of ions from the reaction between metal and non-metal atoms, results in positively and negatively charged particles that have a strong attraction for each other. These ions form a giant *ionic lattice*, in which each ion is surrounded by as many ions of the opposite charge as possible.

The strong forces of attraction between these ions are referred to as ionic bonds. Such ionic substances have high melting points and high boiling points and are solids at room temperature. Ionic substances will also usually dissolve in water.

Since ionic compounds contain charged particles they will conduct electricity, but only if the ions are free to move. This can happen if:

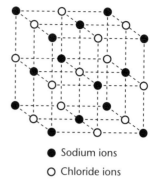

● Sodium ions
○ Chloride ions

The sodium chloride lattice

- The compound is heated until it is molten

- The compound is dissolved in water

-◆- **Bonding, Covalent bonding, Sodium chloride, Valency**

IONIC EQUATIONS

This is a way of showing reactions involving **ions**. They are called ionic equations. In these equations, ions that are unaffected in a reaction are ignored and only those that are affected in some way are written down.

For example, when sodium hydroxide reacts with sulphuric acid, the products are sodium sulphate and water:

$$2NaOH + H_2SO_4 \rightarrow Na_2SO_4 + 2H_2O$$

In this example the sulphate ion (SO_4^{2-}) and the sodium ion (Na^+) are unaffected so we can ignore them. We can rewrite the example as:

$$OH^-(aq) + H^+(aq) \rightarrow H_2O(l)$$

This is the ionic equation that represents the reaction. It is also the general pattern for all **neutralization** reactions.

-◆- **Chemical equations, State symbols**

ISOTOPES

The type of atom is determined by its **atomic number** (number of **protons**). Carbon is carbon because it has six protons. Chlorine is chlorine because it has 17 protons. It is possible, however, for atoms such as these to have different **mass numbers**. This means that they contain different numbers of **neutrons** in their nucleii. These atoms that are chemically the same, but differ in their mass numbers, are called isotopes.

Chlorine has two isotopes:

● Chlorine-35, with a mass number of 35

● Chlorine-37, with a mass number of 37

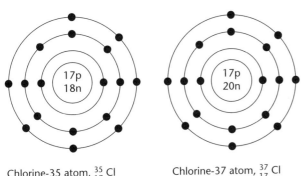

Chlorine-35 atom, $^{35}_{17}$Cl
2e.8e.7e

Chlorine-37 atom, $^{37}_{17}$Cl
2e.8e.7e

Isotopes of chlorine

Both these atoms are identical chemically; the difference in their mass number is due to different numbers of neutrons in their nucleus. In chlorine gas the proportion of these isotopes is always the same. There are three chlorine-35 atoms for every one chlorine-37 atom. The *average* atomic mass for chlorine is therefore:

$$\frac{35u + 35u + 35u + 37u}{4} = 35.5u$$

where u is the atomic mass unit

Different **elements** have different proportions of isotopes (some of which may be radioactive). The **relative atomic mass** of an element is based on the average mass of all the atoms in the element and will not be a whole number.

CHECKPOINT

Complete this sentence.

Isotopes have the same number of .... and different numbers of .... in their nuclei.

◆ **Radioactivity**

JOULE

One joule of **work** is done when a force of 1 N moves an object through a distance of 1 m. The symbol for the joule is J.

⊹ *Newton, Power, Watt*

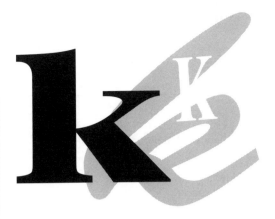

KELVIN

This is the SI (International System) unit of temperature, symbol K. Note that 1 K = 1 °C. The *lower* fixed point is 273 K and the *upper* fixed point is 373 K.

✦ *Gas – gas laws*

KIDNEY

The kidneys are located in the abdomen and, when seen in section, consist of two separate layers – the outer, *cortex* and inner, *medulla*. Within the medulla are *nephrons*, where salts, such as urea, are passed from the blood into the **urine**.

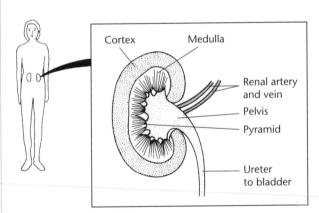

Position and structure of kidneys

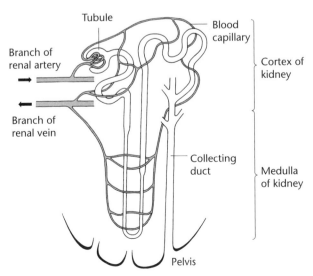

Structure of kidney tubule

The excretion of urea from the blood is concerned with **osmoregulation**, controlling the amount of water present in the blood:

● The renal *artery* carries the blood containing urea, water and salts to the kidney. Molecules such as water, glucose, salts, amino acids and urea, are small enough to be forced under pressure into the tubule. About 99 per cent of this fluid is reabsorbed into the blood, i.e. most of the water all of the glucose and some salts are replaced into the blood.

● The renal *vein* carries blood, which has had the urea removed, away from the kidney. The urine is carried by the ureter to the bladder and then outside the body by the urethra. The kidneys remove about 1,500 ml of urine per day.

✦ *Amino acids, Dialysis, Homeostasis, Organ system*

KINETIC ENERGY

Kinetic **energy** is the energy associated with motion. The kinetic energy (E) of a moving object depends on the **mass** (m) of the object and its **velocity** (v), as stated in the formula:

$$E = \tfrac{1}{2}mv^2$$

● If a person of mass 60 kg is travelling with a velocity of 2 m/s then.

$$E = \tfrac{1}{2} \times 60 \times (2\text{m/s})^2 = 120 \text{ J}$$

● If the same person is travelling *twice as fast* at 4 m/s, then:

$$E = \tfrac{1}{2} \times 60 \times (4 \text{ m/s})^2 = 480 \text{ J}$$

The kinetic energy has increased by *four* times, as the speed has *doubled*. If the mass of the person doubled to 120 kg, and the speed stayed at 2 m/s, the kinetic energy would be doubled:

$$E = \tfrac{1}{2} \times 120 \times (2\text{m/s})^2 = 240 \text{ J}$$

These ideas about kinetic energy are very important when applied to real-life situations such as the **vehicle-stopping distances** of cars. When a car brakes to a stop, the kinetic energy is transferred to the brakes and the road. The amount of energy transferred is equal to the force of the brakes × the distance taken to stop:

● If one car has *twice the mass* of another car, but is travelling at the *same speed*, it will have *twice* the amount of energy and need twice the stopping distance.

● If two cars have the *same* mass but one is travelling at *twice the speed* of the other car, it will have *four* times the amount of energy and need *four* times the stopping distance.

✦ *Friction, Momentum*

KINETIC THEORY

All matter can be classified as either **solid**, **liquid** or **gas**. These are called the three states of matter. The view that matter (solid, liquid or gas) is made up of **particles** that are in constant motion is called the kinetic theory. This idea can help us explain several properties of solids, liquids and gases.

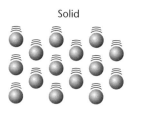

Solid

– Particles are close together

– Particles vibrating, little kinetic energy

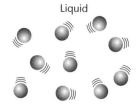

Liquid

– Particles are further apart

– Particles moving, more kinetic energy

Gas

– Particles are far apart

– Particles moving fast, a lot of kinetic energy

Relationships between the particles in solids, liquids and gases

Remember: By adding more energy by heating we can change a solid to a liquid to a gas. By taking energy away by cooling we can change a gas to a liquid to a solid.

- The particles in a gas are moving very fast (they have a lot of kinetic energy) and are a great distance apart.

- The particles in a liquid are moving more slowly and are close together.

- In a solid the particles are very close together and are 'vibrating' rather than moving freely.

This idea is often shown by a piece of equipment similar to that shown in the diagram. The motor turns very fast (providing a lot of energy) and makes the metal spheres imitate a **gas**, but when it is moving more slowly (providing less energy) the spheres imitate a **liquid**.

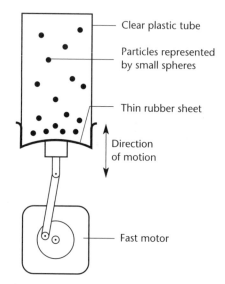

Clear plastic tube

Particles represented by small spheres

Thin rubber sheet

Direction of motion

Fast motor

This equipment imitates the movement of particles

✦ *Brownian motion, Diffusion*

LASERS

The word laser means light amplification by stimulated emission of radiation. Laser light:

- Is a very pure form of very bright light of a single concentrated colour that does not spread out in the way that ordinary visible light does.

- Is very powerful and a beam of light with a power of 1 MW can be used to cut sheets of **metal** or to weld metal together.

- Can be used in hospitals by surgeons who are able to cut and seal without risk of infection. Laser surgery relies on optical fibres, that allow laser light to be transmitted to inaccessible parts of the body, such as a tumour inside the stomach. Two everyday uses of lasers are in compact disc players and bar-code readers at the checkout of a supermarket.

⊹ **Total internal reflection – fibre optics**

LIFE PROCESSES

There are seven life processes common to animals and plants: movement, nutrition, respiration, excretion, growth, reproduction, sensitivity.

⊹ **Breathing, Digestion, Kidney, Muscle, Nervous system, Organism, Organ systems, Skeleton**

LIMESTONE

A **sedimentary** rock made of calcium **carbonate**. It is widely used for building, making cement, **glass** and lime.

⊹ **Acid rain – effects of acid rain, Acids – acidity and the soil, Blast furnace, Crust, Metamorphic rock**

LIMITING FACTORS

The *rate* of **photosynthesis** can be affected by factors such as:

- Light intensity and duration
- **Carbon dioxide** concentration
- Temperature.

If any of these factors is in short supply it limits the rate of photosynthesis and is described as a *limiting factor*. For example, if the intensity of light is too low at dawn and dusk then light becomes a limiting factor on the rate of photosynthesis.

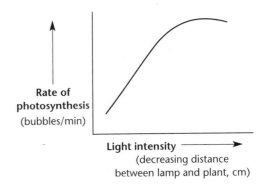

Graph to show the effect of light intensity on the rate of photosynthesis

⊹ **Populations**

LIQUID

All matter can be classified as either **solid,** liquid, or **gas.** These are called the three **states of matter.** In a liquid, the particles are moving and are able to move around each other reasonably freely. Liquids take the shape of whatever they are poured into. Liquids at room temperatures usually consist of small **molecules**. The majority of solids (even those containing **ions** where the particles are strongly held together) will, when heated, melt to form liquids.

⊹ **Brownian motion, Kinetic theory, State symbols**

LITMUS

Litmus is an **indicator** (a dye) that can detect the difference between an **acid** and an **alkali**. It can be used as a **solution**, or as litmus paper. Litmus paper consists of the **solution** soaked onto a type of blotting paper, which must be made wet before using. Litmus paper appears in two forms – red and blue, whereas the solution is a purple colour.

- When litmus turns *red*, acid is present.
- When litmus turns *blue*, alkali is present.

⊹ **pH, Universal indicator**

LONGITUDINAL WAVES

These are waves where the particles of a medium move backwards and forwards, in the same direction as the wave motion. **Sound waves** are longitudinal waves.

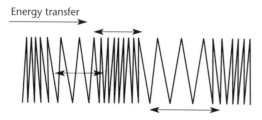

Energy transfer

Energy is being transferred along this longitudinal wave, but the particles are oscillating from left to right

---

CHECKPOINT

Which one of the following is an example of a longitudinal wave:

(a) infrared radiation,
(b) microwaves,
(c) radiowaves,
(d) sound waves?

-+- **Ear, Earth, Transverse wave, Ultrasonic waves**

LOUDSPEAKER

When an ***alternating current*** is passed through the coil, the coil is pushed backwards and forwards, causing the paper cone to vibrate and give out ***sound waves***. The ***frequency*** and ***amplitude*** of the alternating current that flows through the coil affects the type of sound produced.

> *Remember: A loudspeaker transfers electrical energy to sound energy.*

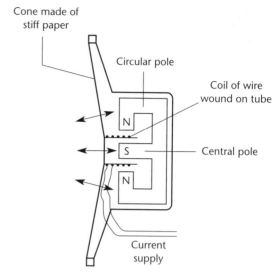

The three main sections of the moving coil loudspeaker

-+- **Microphone**

LUNGS

-+- **Breathing, Respiration**

LYMPHATIC SYSTEM

This is a system of fine tubes running throughout the body that removes excess tissue fluid from around the cells. This fluid (lymph) is returned to the ***blood system*** via a vein near the ***heart***. Lymph nodes are situated along the lymph system to produce lymphocytes – ***white blood cells*** that produce ***antibodies*** to destroy ***bacteria***. The lymph nodes also remove bacteria from the lymph.

MAGMA

Magma is liquid rock at a temperature of about 1,000 °C. It cools to form **igneous rocks** such as granite.

✦ **Earth, Rock cycle, Volcano**

MAGNETIC CIRCUIT BREAKERS

Magnetic circuit breakers are sometimes used instead of **fuses**. They have the advantage that they are very easy to reset after they have broken the circuit.

✦ **Earth wire, Three-pin plug**

MAGNETS AND MAGNETIC FIELDS

Magnets:

- Are solid objects that have a magnetic field around them.

- Attract other magnetic metals such as iron and steel, but don't attract non-magnetic metals such as copper, tin and zinc.

- Are usually made of iron or steel or of magnetic alloys, and can either be *temporary* or *permanent* magnets.

- *Temporary* magnets are usually made of soft iron and lose their magnetism, *permanent* magnets are usually made of steel, or a steel alloy.

The effect of a magnetic field around a magnet can be shown by using a plotting compass to find out which is the north-seeking or N pole of a magnet. The poles of a magnet are the ends of the magnets where the magnetism is strongest. If you place the plotting compass near the end of the magnet, the needle of the compass is repelled from the N-seeking pole as shown in figure (a).

You can also show the magnetic field by shaking iron filings around a magnet. The iron filings line up along the lines of force and produce the patterns shown in figure (b). These patterns show the line of magnetic force. The magnetic field patterns produced between two *attracting* poles and two *repelling* poles can also be seen using iron filings and are shown in figures (c) and (d).

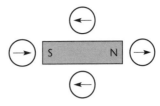

(a) The compass needle is repelled from the N pole of the magnet

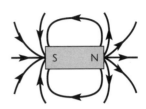

(b) The magnetic field pattern around a magnet

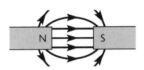

(c) Attraction between unlike poles of two magnets

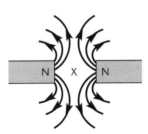

(d) Repulsion between like poles of two magnets

When two magnetic fields come together there is either a force of attraction or a force of repulsion, and as a result there is a possibility of movement.

> *Remember: Magnets have a north (N) and south (S) pole; unlike magnetic poles attract (N–S); like magnetic poles repel (N–N) (S–S); a bar magnet has a magnetic field around it.*

✦ **Electric motors, Electromagnetism, Induced current**

MAINS ELECTRICITY

Three key points to remember:

- The **voltage** of the mains electricity in your home is 240 V.

- The direction of flow changes 50 times per second so its **frequency** is 50 Hz.

● Live and neutral wires carry the mains electricity, and the insulation around the wires is colour coded so you know which is which.

Paying for electricity

The amount of electrical energy an appliance uses depends on how long it is switched on and how fast it uses its energy (power). The **power** is measured in **watts** or kilowatts (1 kW = 1,000 W). How much you pay for electricity depends on:

● How many appliances are in use

● How long they are used for

● What the power rating is of each appliance

The kilowatt hour (kW h) is the basic unit used to calculate the cost of buying electricity. 1 kW h means that 1kW (1,000 W) is being used by an appliance for one hour and costs approximately 10 p:

$$kW\ h = power\ (kW) \times time\ (h)$$

A table lamp rated at 40 W used for five hours uses up $0.04 \times 5 = 0.2$ kW h. The cost of using the table lamp is $0.2 \times 10 = 2$ p

> *Remember: Convert watts to kilowatts when doing these calculations.*

CHECKPOINT

How much would it cost to have a 2 kW electric fire switched on for 2 h if electricity cost 10 p a unit?

✦ **Three-pin plug, Transformers, Transmission of electricity**

MARK – RELEASE – RECAPTURE

This is a method of estimating the size of a **population**; e.g. a population of snails. It involves using a special non-toxic paint or marker pen and following a set sequence:

1. Capture, count and mark a representative sample of a population.

2. Release the animals in the same area.

3. At a later stage, when the marked animals have mixed with the rest of the population, recapture and count the numbers of animals, and record how many of the marked animals are in the second sample.

4. Use the formula below to estimate the total population:

$$\frac{number\ in\ first\ sample \times number\ in\ second\ sample}{number\ of\ marked\ animals\ recaptured}$$

✦ **Ecosystem, Populations, Sampling**

MASS

The mass of an object is the amount of a material measured in kilograms. This amount does not change. An astronaut landing on the **Moon** has the same mass as on **Earth**, but only one-sixth of the **weight**.

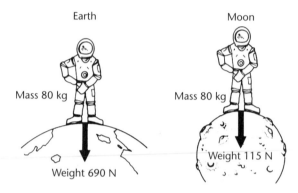

Comparative weight on Earth and on the Moon

✦ **Gravity, Kinetic energy, Vehicle-stopping distance**

MASS NUMBER

The total number of **protons** and **neutrons** contained in the **nucleus** is called the mass number (each proton and neutron has a **mass** of 1u). There are usually about the same number of protons as neutrons in a nucleus.

You can work out the structure of an **atom** from two numbers:

● Atomic number = number of *protons* (= number of *electrons*)

● Mass number = number of *protons* + number of *neutrons*

✦ **Atomic mass, Atomic number, Atomic structure**

MEIOSIS

Meiosis is the process of cell division that takes place in the sex organs to form the **gametes** or sex cells:

● In the human male it occurs in the testis to form sperm, the male sex cell.

● In the human female it takes place in the ovary to form ova (egg cells) the female sex cell

During meiosis the **chromosome** number is reduced to the *haploid* (half) number of chromosomes and four non-identical cells are produced. Meiosis is sometimes described as reduction division.

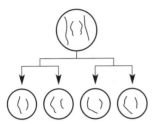

Four new cells, each with only two chromosomes

Meiosis in a cell with four chromosomes

✛ *Mitosis, Mutations, Sexual reproduction*

MENSTRUAL CYCLE

This is a periodic change that occurs in a woman's body about every 28 days. During the first few days of the cycle the extra lining of the uterus breaks down and is released from the body. During the next ten days an egg ripens in the ovary and the uterus lining thickens again. On about the 14th day the egg is released from the ovary during **ovulation**, and this is when **fertilization** can occur. If no fertilization occurs, then the uterus lining breaks down and is released on about the 28th day.

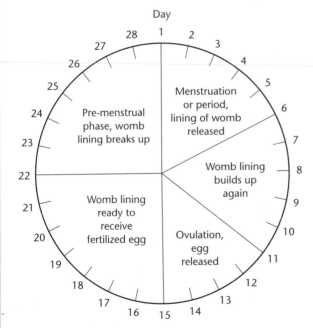

The menstrual cycle

✛ *Hormones, Menstruation, Reproduction*

MENSTRUATION

Menstruation is the passing from a woman's body of the extra lining of the uterus (womb) that has developed. This extra thick lining is developed to receive the embryo after **fertilization**.

If fertilization has not taken place, the lining breaks down and is released as blood and mucus through the vagina. In women this happens about every 28 days, but stops during pregnancy.

✛ *Menstrual cycle, Reproduction*

METABOLISM

This process covers all the **chemical reactions** that take place in an organism. The reactions are usually controlled by **enzymes**.

For example, the release of energy from sugar is a metabolic process whose waste products need to be removed by **excretion**.

✛ *Digestion, Hydrolysis*

METALS

All metals are **elements** (an individual metal contains only one type of atom). Metals exist as **compounds** in rocks; those rocks that contain large quantities of metals are called ores. Metals can be extracted from ores by techniques such as **reduction** using carbon or **electrolysis**. Metals have a number of useful properties:

- Conductors of heat and electricity
- Solids (except mercury)
- Strong, malleable and ductile
- High melting points and densities
- Shiny

There are exceptions to these general properties and different metals exhibit these properties to varying degrees, e.g. copper is used as electrical wiring because it is a better conductor than many. It is important to realize, however, that the choice of a metal for a particular job not only depends on its properties, but also on its cost. (Gold is a better conductor than copper, but is not used in electrical wiring.)

✛ *Extraction of metals*

Metals as elements

All metals are **elements** and are grouped on the left-hand side of the **periodic table**. The common everyday metals are found in the block referred to as the **transition metals**. Metals are **giant structures** in

which the metal **atoms** exist as positive **ions** in a sea of **electrons**. This gives rise to their characteristic physical properties of strength, hardness and the ability to conduct electricity.

In many of their reactions, metal atoms form positive ions, the charge on the ion depending on the metal's position in the periodic table.

Group	Charge on ion	Formula	Metal
1	1+	Na^+	Sodium
2	2+	Ca^{2+}	Calcium
3	3+	Al^{3+}	Aluminium

The transition metals can form ions with different charges; they are said to have variable **valency**. In **compounds**, the charge on the metal ion is indicated by roman numerals. Transition metal compounds are often coloured.

Compound	Colour	Formula	Metal ion
Copper(II) sulphate	Blue	$CuSO_4$	Cu^{2+}
Iron(II) sulphate	Green	$FeSO_4$	Fe^{2+}
Iron(III) oxide	Red	Fe_2O_3	Fe^{3+}
Copper(I) oxide	Red	Cu_2O	Cu^+
Copper(II) oxide	Black	CuO	Cu^{2+}

CHECKPOINT

Suggest why a metal, such as gold, was discovered over 8,000 years ago but metals such as iron, were only extracted from their ores about 4,000 years ago.

-⧩- *Acids*

METAL OXIDES

Metal oxides are formed when metals are heated strongly in air or oxygen. They are also formed when metals are left exposed to the atmosphere and rain (when the metals **corrode**). They all contain the oxide **ion**, O^{2-}. How easily the oxides form depend on the metal's position in the **reactivity series**: e.g.:

magnesium + oxygen → magnesium oxide

$$2Mg \quad + \quad O_2 \quad \rightarrow \quad 2MgO$$

All metal oxides are **bases** and react with **acids**, neutralizing them:

magnesium + hydrochloric → magnesium + hydrogen
oxide   acid   chloride

$$MgO \quad + \quad 2HCl \quad \rightarrow \quad MgCl_2 \quad + \quad H_2$$

Most oxides are not soluble in water; those that are soluble react with the water to form hydroxides and are called **alkalis**. For example, the oxides of sodium, potassium and calcium will react with water to form hydroxides.

-⧩- *Alkali metals*

METAMORPHIC ROCKS

Metamorphic rocks are formed from the action of pressure and heat on both **igneous** and **sedimentary rocks**. Movements of the **Earth's crust** break up sedimentary rocks and push them down into the hotter areas of the Earth where metamorphic rock is formed: e.g. **limestone**, a sedimentary rock is changed into marble by intense heat and pressure; compressed mud can be changed into slate.

-⧩- *Rock cycle*

METHANE

Methane is a colourless, odourless **gas** that burns, producing a lot of heat. It is found in oilfields and bubbles up through swamps, marshes and rubbish tips – in fact any area where dead material is rotting down. Natural gas from the North Sea is methane (for safety reasons a smell is added to the methane so that people can detect leaks, etc.).

Methane is a **hydrocarbon** and has the chemical formula CH_4. When methane burns it produces **carbon dioxide** and **water**:

$$CH_4 + O_2 \rightarrow CO_2 + 2H_2O$$

If, however, methane burns in a *limited* supply of air, carbon monoxide will be produced which is highly poisonous.

MICRO-ORGANISMS

Micro-organisms (microbes) are **bacteria**, **fungi** and **viruses**.

- Viruses are very small simple structures that lack a nucleus, cytoplasm and cell membrane. They are very infectious and cause many diseases such as influenza, polio, etc.

- Fungi are important in the decomposition of dead organisms, and are also important in the food industry, e.g. in baking and brewing.

-⧩- *Nitrogen cycle, Nutrient cycles, White blood cells*

MICROPHONE

A microphone is a device for converting a pattern of sounds into electrical impulses. In the microphone is a thin metal sheet called a diaphragm that vibrates

when **sound waves** hit it. These vibrations push against carbon granules in the microphone and alter the **resistance** of the granules. A variable current is then passed to the receiver, which changes the electrical input into sound waves.

> Remember: A microphone transfers sound energy into electrical energy.

-**+**- **Loudspeaker**

MICROWAVES

Microwaves are radio waves that have a very short wavelength. They are used for **radar** and telephone and television links on an international basis, via geostationary **satellites**.

One common use of microwaves is in cooking food. The microwaves cook the food by heating the water molecules in the food, and also destroy **bacteria**.

-**+**- **Electromagnetic waves**

MINERALS

Minerals required by humans

Minerals are important substances in a **balanced diet** as they are needed for the formation of complex **molecules** in the body.

Mineral	Needed for	Deficiency causes	Source
Phosphorus Calcium	Bones and teeth formation	Brittle bones and teeth	Milk Cheese Fruit
Iron	Haemoglobin formation	Anaemia (insufficient haemoglobin	Liver Eggs Spinach
Iodine	Growth hormone (thyroxin) formation	Goitre (swollen thyroid glands)	Seafood Salt

Minerals required by plants

An understanding of the need for mineral salts has important implications for the agricultural industry. The yield of a particular crop can be limited if an essential mineral is lacking from the soil.

Monoculture is practised by some agriculturists where the same crop is planted over a large area. In these areas, **fertilizers**, either organic or inorganic,

must be added to the soil to provide essential mineral salts and hence produce maximum yields.

Mineral	Needed for	Symptom due to lack of mineral
Nitrogen	To make amino acids, proteins and DNA	Small leaves, thin weak stems
Phosphorus	To make DNA and cell membranes, and for enzyme systems	Poor root growth, small leaves
Magnesium	To make chlorophyll	Yellow leaves

-**+**- **Acid rain, Nitrates, Salts – salts in action, Transport in plants**

MITOSIS

Mitosis is the process of cell division that takes place in all the body cells except the sex cells. Each **chromosome** in the **nucleus** of the **cell** replicates to form two chromosomes. The nucleus then divides into two and two identical daughter cells are produced containing the full or *diploid* number of chromosomes.

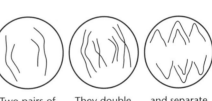

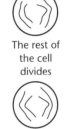

The rest of the cell divides

Two pairs of chromosomes   They double   and separate into two groups

Two new cells, each with four chromosomes

Mitosis in cell with four chromosomes

-**+**- **Asexual reproduction, Cell – biological, Embryo, Gametes, Meiosis, Mutations**

MIXTURE

Mixtures are substances that contain various amounts of **elements** and/or **compounds** mixed together. They can be physically separated: e.g. a mixture of iron and sulphur can easily be separated with a magnet.

> Remember: Air is a mixture of gases. The gases are not chemically combined.

MOLAR SOLUTIONS

Chemical reactions often take place in **solution**, so if we need information about the numbers of particles present we need to know the concentrations of the reactants in solutions.

Concentrations are given in moles per cubic decimetre (mol/dm^3); a solution which contains 1 mol/dm^3 contains 1 mol per dm^3 (litre). This is often expressed as a 1 M solution (one molar). Thus a 2 M solution contains 2 mol/dm^3. A 1 M solution of sulphuric acid contains 1 mol of H_2SO_4, or in other words, 98 g of H_2SO_4/dm^3.

We can use this information to work out the number of moles present in a solution: e.g. how many moles are present in 25 cm^3 of a 2 mol/dm^3 solution of NaOH?

$$\text{No. of moles} = \text{concentration} \times \text{volume (in } dm^3)$$
$$= 2 \times 25/1,000$$
$$= 0.05 \text{ mol}$$

Note: 25/1,000 converts the volume from cubic centimetres to cubic decimetres.

We can use a similar method to calculate the concentration of solutions: e.g. 25 cm^3 of a 2 mol/dm^3 solution of sodium hydroxide exactly reacts with 10 cm^3 of sulphuric **acid**. What is the concentration of the sulphuric acid? First, look at the equation of the reaction:

$$2NaOH + H_2SO_4 \rightarrow Na_2SO_4 + 2H_2O$$

Now, from the question, the number of moles of NaOH used is:

concentration × volume
$$= 2 \times 25/1,000 = 0.05 \text{ mol}$$

From the equation, 2 mol of NaOH react with 1 mol of H_2SO_4; so 0.05 mol of NaOH reacts with 0.025 mol of H_2SO_4.

Then, using the information that:

No. of moles = concentration × volume
$$0.025 = \text{concentration} \times 10/1,000$$
$$2.5 = \text{concentration}$$

The concentration of H_2SO_4 = 2.5 mol/dm^3.

MOLE

There are two facts that apply to any chemical change:

- The total mass of the *products* equals the total mass of the *reactants*
- The total number of atoms in the *products* equals the total number of atoms in the *reactants*

These two facts allow us to make calculations involving **chemical reactions**. To do this satisfactorily, we need a method of counting the number of **particles** present. The mole is an internationally agreed physical quantity. One mole of a substance contains as many particles of that substance as there are atoms of carbon in 12 grams of carbon-12.

When large amounts of coins are handed into the bank they do not count them individually but instead they weigh them. In order to convert the weight of the coins to a number, the bank needs to know certain facts:

- How much do 100 1p coins weigh?
- How much do 100 2p coins weigh, etc.?

We can apply the same principle to particles, because each atom has its own distinct mass: **relative atomic mass**. However, the number we use – the mole – has to be very much larger than 100, since the mass of each atom is very small. Converting numbers to mass is very simple.

Moles of atoms

The **relative atomic mass** of an atom, contains one mole (1 mol) of atoms:

Atom	Atomic mass	Mass of 1 mol of atoms (g)
Hydrogen	1	1
Carbon	12	12
Oxygen	16	16
Chlorine	35.5	35.5
Sodium	23	23

So in 32 g of oxygen we have 2 mol of atoms, and in 8 g of oxygen we have 0.5 mol of atoms.

CHECKPOINT
What is the mass of oxygen contained in 36 g of pure water:
(a) 16 g, (b) 32 g, (c) 48 g, (d) 64 g?

Moles of molecules

The molecular mass contains 1 mol of molecules:

Molecule	Molecular formula	Mass of molecule	Mass of 1 mol of molecules (g)
Oxygen	O_2	32	32
Water	H_2O	18	18
Carbon dioxide	CO_2	44	44
Hydrogen	H_2	2	2

For example, for water (H_2O), the mass of the molecule = $2 \times H + O = 2 \times 1 + 16 = 18\,g$.

> *Remember: the mass of a molecule is found by adding the individual atomic masses.*

So in 36 g of water there are 2 mol of molecules, while in 16 g of oxygen there is 0.5 mol of molecules.

Moles of ionic compounds and ions

The same rules apply for formulae representing **ionic** compounds and for individual ions:

Compound or ion	Formula/ion	Formula mass/mass of ion	Mass of 1 mol (g)
Hydrochloric acid	HCl	36.5	36.5
Sodium hydroxide	NaOH	40	40
Sulphuric acid	H_2SO_4	98	98
Sulphate ion	SO_4^{2-}	96	96
Chloride ion	Cl^-	35.5	35.5

> CHECKPOINT
>
> 4.14 g of lead reacts with 3.20 g of bromine. What is the formula of lead(II) bromide (Pb 207, Br 80)?

Using the mole idea

What mass of magnesium chloride is produced when 12 g of magnesium reacts with excess hydrochloric acid? Note that 'excess' means that you have more acid than you need, so the mass of this compound is not a restriction and can be ignored.

From the equation of the reaction:

$$Mg + 2HCl \rightarrow MgCl_2 + H_2$$

We can see that *one* mole of magnesium produces *one* mole of magnesium chloride. To calculate the amount of magnesium chloride:

● **Step 1**: Convert masses to moles. The atomic mass of magnesium is 24, the mass of 1 mol of magnesium is 24 g.

The number of moles in 12 g of Mg = 0.5.

● **Step 2**: Use the equation. 1 mol of Mg produces 1 mol of $MgCl_2$, so 0.5 mol of Mg produces 0.5 mol of $MgCl_2$.

● **Step 3**: Convert moles to mass.

1 mol of $MgCl_2$ has a mass of 95 g, so 0.5 mol of $MgCl_2$ has a mass of $0.5 \times 95\,g = 47.5\,g$.

Answer: 47.5 g of $MgCl_2$ is produced.

> CHECKPOINT
>
> What mass of calcium oxide can be formed by heating 10 g of calcium carbonate until it all decomposes (Ca = 40, C = 12, O = 16)?

MOLECULAR MASS

⊹ *Mole*

MOLECULE

All matter is made up of **particles**; there are three different types: **atom**, **molecule** and **ion**. The molecule is a particle that contains two or more atoms chemically joined together. Molecules can contain the same type of atom, or different atoms chemically joined (bonded). Each molecule has a name and a **chemical formula** to represent which atoms are joined together.

For example, each molecule can be represented by a formula.

Molecule	Name	Formula
Ⓗ–Ⓗ	Hydrogen	H_2
Ⓗ⸱Ⓞ Ⓗ	Water	H_2O

The numbers show the proportions of each atom present. They refer to the atoms immediately *before* the number, which is always written below the line (subscript). For example, glucose (a sugar) – $C_6H_{12}O_6$ – contains six atoms of carbon, 12 atoms of hydrogen and six atoms of oxygen.

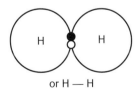

or H — H

The hydrogen molecule

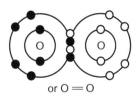

or O $=$ O

The oxygen molecule

93

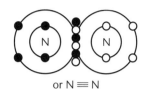

or N ≡ N

The nitrogen molecule

-╬- *Chemical equations, Giant Structures, Mole*

MOMENTUM

The momentum of an object is a product of its mass and its *velocity*: e.g. an object with a mass of 10 kg moving with a velocity of 5 m/s has a momentum of 50 kg m/s.

-╬- *Forces – balanced and unbalanced, Vehicle-stopping distance*

MONOHYBRID INHERITANCE

It is over 100 years since an Austrian monk, Gregor Mendel, established the basic laws of inheritance. Since then the science of genetics has become well established. Our understanding of genetics has developed to a point where we can now create new organisms by *genetic engineering*, that is by transferring genes from one organism to another.

Two pure-bred *homozygous* organisms (animals or plants), one carrying *dominant* alleles for a particular characteristic and the other carrying *recessive* alleles, will produce *heterozygous* offspring. These will have the characteristic appearance of the dominant allele, as shown in (a).

If two *heterozygous* individuals reproduce, then the offspring are produced in a ratio of three to one; in other words:

● 75 per cent have the characteristic of the dominant allele

● 25 per cent have the characteristic of the recessive allele, as shown in (b).

Parent's genotype	BB	×	bb
	(black)		(brown)

Gametes   Ⓑ   ⓑ

Gametes	Ⓑ
ⓑ	Bb

Offspring genotypes   Bb

all black

(a) Homozygous parents

F_1 genotype	Bb	×	Bb
	(black)		(black)

Gametes   Ⓑ   ⓑ   Ⓑ   ⓑ

Gametes	Ⓑ	ⓑ
Ⓑ	BB	Bb
ⓑ	Bb	bb

Offspring genotypes	BB	Bb Bb	bb
	black	black	brown
Ratio 3 : 1		75%	25%

(b) Heterozygous parents

CHECKPOINT

In a species of plant, red flowers were dominant to white flowers. Pure-breeding, red-flowered plants were crossed with pure-breeding, white flowered plants. What proportion of red-flowered and white-flowered plants will be produced in the first generation of offspring (F_1):

(a) all red-flowered plants,
(b) all white-flowered plants,
(c) a 3 : 1 ratio of red-flowered to white-flowered plants,
(d) equal number of red-flowered and white-flowered plants?

MONOMER

Polymers, which are long chain molecules, can be made by combining together much smaller molecules called monomer units.

Plants build up *starch* (a polymer) by combining glucose molecules (monomers) together. The plant manufactures glucose by *photosynthesis*. Many man-made polymers have been produced, e.g.

● *Monomer*: ethene, chloroethene, tetrafluoroethene

● *Polymer*: polyethene (polythene), PVC, PTFE

-╬- *Addition polymers, Alkenes*

MOON

The Moon is a *satellite* that takes 28 days (a lunar month) to orbit the *Earth*. The Moon is held in its orbit by *gravitational* attraction between it and the Earth and the distance between the Earth and the Moon is approximately 384–400 km. The Moon also rotates on its own axis every 28 days so the same side of the Moon faces Earth all the time. The Moon has no *atmosphere* and no *water*.

The diagram shows how the different phases of the Moon appear when the Moon is viewed from Earth. When the Earth is between the **Sun** and the Moon we can see all the light from the Sun that is *reflected* by the Moon, and the Moon therefore appears to be a full Moon.

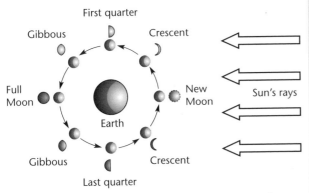

How the different phases of the Moon are caused

-+- *Eclipse of the Moon, Eclipse of the Sun, Tidal energy, Tides*

MOTION

-+- *Force – balanced and unbalanced*

MOTORS

-+- *Electric motors*

MUSCLE

Muscles are tissues which are a collection of muscle cells that have the ability to contract. Skeletal muscles are fixed to the **skeleton** where they are able to bring about movement.

-+- *Organ systems*

MUTATIONS

When **chromosomes** are copied during **mitosis** and **meiosis** there is a possibility for mistakes to be made. These mistakes are known as mutations and can effect either single **genes** or whole chromosomes. Exposure to **radiation**, such as gamma-rays, **X-rays**, **ultraviolet rays**, and chemicals, such as mustard gas and LSD, can increase the rate of mutation. Mutation in body cells may result in **cancer**.

Gene mutations

Gene mutations are usually harmful and may cause genetic diseases. An example would be the recessive albino gene that prevents the formation of the dark skin pigment melanin. Albino animals are not protected from the Sun's ultraviolet rays.

Some mutant genes are helpful and can improve an organism's chance of survival, for instance, the recessive sickle-cell gene, that affects the red blood cells in humans, can give some immunity to malaria. The sickle-cell gene can be harmful if a child gets it from both parents. This is one of some 3,000 known genetic diseases and there are now genetic counsellors to help potential parents assess the risk of giving birth to a child with an inherited genetic disease, such as cystic fibrosis, muscular dystrophy and haemophilia. About 5 per cent of children admitted to hospitals in the UK are suffering from genetic diseases.

Chromosome mutations

Chromosome mutations occur when chromosomes are altered during meiosis; bits may be broken off or added to chromosomes and sometimes whole chromosomes may be lost or gained. The faulty **gametes** that are produced may be **fertilized** and produce **zygotes** with damaged chromosomes, or too few or too many chromosomes. An extra number 21 chromosome in humans produces a Down's Syndrome child with a low mental age and very characteristic facial features, which led to the previous name for this genetic disorder – mongolism. You may indeed know of a Down's person who has developed useful skills through special training and is a happy member of a family. Such diseases can now be detected in the early stages of pregnancy by taking a sample of fluid from the amniotic fluid in the womb and examining some of the embryo's cells.

> *Remember: Mutations are a source of genetic variation.*

CHECKPOINT

List **three** causes of mutation.

-+- *Evolution, Mohybrid inheritance, Radioactivity, Selective breeding, Variation*

NATURAL SELECTION

Natural selection is the theory we use to explain *evolution*. Darwin's voyage around the world in the 1830s aboard HMS Beagle provided the key for him to develop and refine his theory in the years that followed.

Darwin's observations were that:

- Organisms produce large numbers of offspring

- The offspring vary considerably

- Many offspring die before adulthood

- Many offspring do not survive to breed

- They die because they can't overcome problems – starvation, being eaten by predators, being fatally injured, suffering from disease, etc.

Darwin described this as a struggle for survival against a harsh *environment*. Scientists today call the difficulties 'selection pressures'. It is these pressures that determine which individuals survive. Those best adapted survive to pass their *genes* on to the next generation. Hares that can run fastest will escape the fox and so genes for powerful leg muscles will be 'selected' and over many generations the performance of the species will be enhanced.

If the environment changes, the process of natural selection allows the *species* to adapt to the new situation, the most advantageous *variations* surviving to breed. Without *variation* a species is very likely to become extinct.

The Peppered Moth is a good example of natural selection in that the colour of the moths has changed in recent times. The darker, mutant moths became more common in industrial areas when the Industrial Revolution polluted the environment with soot and smoke. The dark moths were still rare in the countryside, which was unpolluted, and where the lighter form of moth was dominant. Camouflage is the key to understanding this phenomenon;

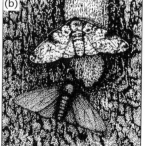

predators could easily find light-coloured moths on soot-covered trees around cities, and so selection favoured the dark genes. In the countryside the reverse was true. Now that industrial pollution is less severe the situation should change again with the light-coloured form becoming dominant both in cities and in the countryside.

Year	Percentage of each form	
	Dark	Pale
1848	1	99
1894	99	1

✦ *Adaptation, Evolution, Monohybrid inheritance, Mutation, Selective breeding, Variation*

NERVOUS SYSTEM

The following table presents a comparison of the nervous and hormonal control systems.

The nervous and hormonal control systems		
Aspect of comparison	Nervous control	Hormonal control
Message	Nerve impulse	Hormone
Route	Nervous system	Blood system
Transmission	Rapid	Slow
Origin of message	Receptor	Endocrine gland
Destination of message	Effector	Target organ(s)
Speed and duration of effect	Immediate, brief	Delayed, prolonged

✦ *Ear, Eye, Hormones, Organ systems, Reflex arc*

NEUTRALIZATION

A neutral solution is one that has a *pH* of 7; e.g. pure water. Neutralization is a *chemical reaction* that involves an *acid* and a *base*, the result of which is a *salt*. The base in the reaction could be either a metal oxide, a metal hydroxide, or a *carbonate*. Examples of these reactions are as follows:

hydrochloric + magnesium → magnesium + water
  acid   oxide   chloride

hydrochloric + sodium → sodium + water
  acid   hydroxide   chloride

hydrochloric + calcium → calcium + water + carbon
  acid   carbonate   chloride   dioxide

In all cases both the acid and base have been neutralized.

-+- *Acids – acids and digestion, Universal indicator – following an acid/alkali reaction*

NEUTRON

The neutron is a subatomic particle found in the nucleus of an **atom**. It has a mass unit of lu and no charge.

Some atoms, e.g. chlorine atoms, can have different numbers of neutrons in their nuclei; these are known as **isotopes**. It is fast-moving neutrons that cause chain reactions in nuclear reactors.

> *Remember: There is no set rule for determining the number of neutrons in an atom as there is for **protons** and **electrons**, but a good rule of thumb is that there are about the same number of neutrons as protons.*

-+- *Atomic structure, Nuclear fission, Nuclear power, Radioactivity*

NEWTON

This is the unit of measurement for a **force**; symbol N. A force of 1 N gives an **acceleration** of 1 m/s^2 to a mass of 1 kg.

-+- *Force and acceleration*

NITRATES

Nitrates are chemical **compounds** (**salts**) that contain the nitrate ion, NO_3^-, e.g. copper nitrate, $Cu(NO_3)_2$. All nitrates are **soluble** in water, and are used in many manufacturing processes, especially of **fertilizers** and explosives. Consequently, nitrate production is very important.

Manufacture of nitrates

Nitrate manufacture starts with the Haber process, in which hydrogen and **nitrogen** from the air are combined to produce *ammonia*:

$$N_2 + 3H_2 \overset{\text{catalyst}}{\underset{\text{heat}}{\rightleftharpoons}} 2NH_3$$

The ammonia is then **oxidized** to produce nitric acid, from which a variety of nitrates are obtained.

-+- *Reversible reactions*

Nitrates as fertilizers

Nitrates are important as fertilizers because plants need nitrogen to build **proteins**. Plants take in nitrates from the soil though their roots. A build-up of nitrates in river water has been blamed on farmers using nitrate fertilizers instead of using more traditional methods such as organic fertilizers (manure) from cows, pig manure, etc. Scientists have shown that the increased rise in nitrate levels is not only due to use of fertilizers, but also to changes in farming practice. When land is left bare in winter, the rain washes out the natural nitrates in the soil, as well as nitrates applied by farmers.

-+- *Minerals – minerals required by plants, Salts – salts in action*

Nitrates in drinking water

Too much nitrate in the drinking water cannot only make babies ill, but has also been linked to increases in stomach cancer (although there is no firm evidence for this). A major problem of nitrates in the rivers and lakes is that they cause increased growth of water plants and algae, which clog waterways. When these plants die they are decomposed by bacteria, which in doing so use up the oxygen in the water. The fish are deprived of oxygen and subsequently die. This process is described as entrophication.

CHECKPOINT

Complete these sentences:

Ammonia can be reacted with .... in the presence of a .... to form nitrogen monoxide, which is reacted with water to form .... The nitric acid is neutralized by .... to produce .... fertilizer.

-+- *Nitrogen cycle, Pollution*

NITROGEN

Nitrogen is a colourless, odourless gas that makes up about 78 per cent of the **air** around us. Nitrogen gas contains nitrogen **molecules** (N_2). Nitrogen itself is not very reactive, but it is needed by plants in the form of **nitrates** (NO_3^-) to grow.

-+- *Ammonia, Nitrogen cycle, Reversible reactions*

NITROGEN CYCLE

Plants such as peas, beans and clover, are able to absorb **nitrogen** gas from the air through special swellings on their roots called nodules. These nodules contain nitrogen-fixing **bacteria** that take in or 'fix' the nitrogen as **nitrates**. The nitrates are then used by plants to make **proteins**. The proteins are taken in by animals when they eat the plants, and are returned to the soil when animals and plants are decomposed by **bacteria** and **fungi** that live in soil. The **decomposers** form ammonium compounds, which are converted into nitrates by nitrifying bacteria.

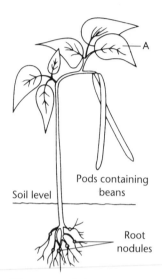

A bean plant with root nodules containing nitrogen-fixing bacteria

Farmers often plant peas, beans or clover to help increase the amount of nitrates in the soil, instead of adding nitrogen in the form of nitrate **fertilizers**. The peas, beans and clover can then be ploughed back into the soil, and the nitrates can be used by other plants to make proteins. Some nitrates are lost from the soil when denitrifying bacteria convert the nitrates into nitrogen gas, which is released into the air. However, some nitrates are added to the soil when lightning converts nitrogen into nitrates.

> ### CHECKPOINT
>
> 1. Why is decomposition important in the nitrogen cycle?
>
> 2. Name **two** types of organisms that are decomposers.

NOBLE GASES (INERT GASES)

The noble gases are a family of **elements** in the **periodic table** (group 0), sometimes referred to as the inert gases. These gases show no chemical reactivity (with a few exceptions) because they have stable filled outer electron shells or orbitals. They do not form **molecules** but exist as separate **atoms**. The gases have various uses, depending on their inert behaviour.

For example:

- *Argon* is used to fill light bulbs – inert argon does not react with a hot-wire filament in the way that oxygen would.

- *Helium* is used in airships – it is lighter than air but is not inflammable, unlike hydrogen.

- *Neon* is used in street-lamps and gives a characteristic pale blue glow.

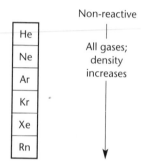

The noble gases – group 0

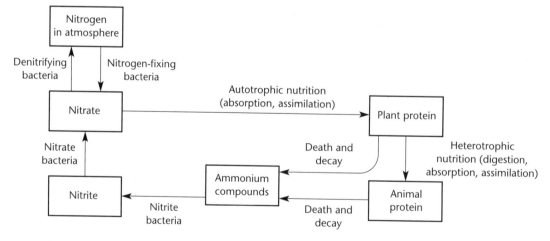

The nitrogen cycle

> Remember: Helium, neon and argon are colourless, unreactive gases at room temperature.

> Remember: The main advantage of nuclear fusion over nuclear fission is that it produces far less radioactive by-products and could use readily available deuterium (an isotope of hydrogen).

CHECKPOINT

1. Why are the noble gases in group 0 of the periodic table?

2. What property is shared by the noble gases?

3. Name **two** examples of the noble gases and state **one** use of each example.

 Air

NUCLEAR FISSION

The **atoms** of radioactive material have unstable nuclei that break down releasing energy, either as radiation (**gamma rays**) or as **kinetic energy** from **alpha** and **beta** particles. Nuclear fission is a process in which a radioactive nucleus splits into fragments; this occurs naturally in some elements that have very large unstable nuclei. When this happens often a few **neutrons** are released as well.

The nucleus of a rare form of uranium (uranium-235) will break down, at the same time releasing a few neutrons. These fast-moving neutrons can then strike another nucleus. When this happens the second nucleus will also immediately break down, releasing yet more neutrons. Each fission (breakdown) produces more neutrons, which in turn cause other breakdowns. This is called a chain reaction, and can happen very quickly. Each time a nucleus breaks down, a large amount of energy is released; this results in a rapid rise in temperature of the uranium and its surroundings. This type of reaction takes place in a nuclear reactor, which is fed with concentrated uranium-235.

 Nuclear fusion, Nuclear power, Radioactivity

NUCLEAR FUSION

Nuclear fusion is the opposite of **nuclear fission**. In nuclear fusion, energy is released when small nuclei are joined to form larger nuclei. This process is happening all the time in the **Sun**, and is the source of the Sun's energy. Scientists and technologists have been trying to produce nuclear fusion reactors on Earth for a long time but have still not overcome two major problems:

- Bringing the particles together fast enough
- Building a 'container' for the reaction that can withstand the high temperatures involved

 Nucleus – nucleus of an atom, Radioactivity

NUCLEAR POWER

The source of energy for nuclear power comes from the energy stored in the nuclei of a particular type of **uranium**, uranium-235, which has 92 **protons** and 143 **neutrons** in the nucleus. In a nuclear power station, the uranium is in the form of fuel elements in the reactor core.

During **nuclear fission**, the uranium nuclei are hit by slow-moving neutrons and the uranium **nucleus** splits into two smaller parts, giving out energy in the process. The neutrons that are released from the uranium nucleus are then used to split more uranium-235 nuclei in a chain reaction. In the nuclear reactor, this reaction is controlled by control rods, made of boron, which absorb neutrons. The heat produced by the reaction is carried away by a coolant liquid to a heat exchanger where it is used to generate steam that drives turbines to generate electricity

Nuclear power is an important source of energy as an alternative to fossil fuels. One of its main *disadvantages* is that the waste products are highly radioactive and are therefore very difficult to dispose of safely.

Two *advantages* of nuclear power are:

- There are adequate supplies of uranium to last for a very long time
- Nuclear power stations do not release gases such as sulphur dioxide and carbon dioxide that can harm the environment

The accident at the nuclear reactor in Chernobyl, USSR, in 1986 was caused by the control rods being removed too far from the reactor core, so that the nuclear fission reaction produced large amounts of heat that could not be removed quickly enough from the reactor. The heat caused an explosion that exposed the top of the reactor core to the atmosphere, and ejecting large amounts of radioactive debris. Some of the radioactive substances were carried by strong winds across into Europe, where heavy rainfall caused contamination of areas of Scotland, the Lake District and North Wales.

 Alternative energy, Generation of electricity, Pollution, Radioactivity

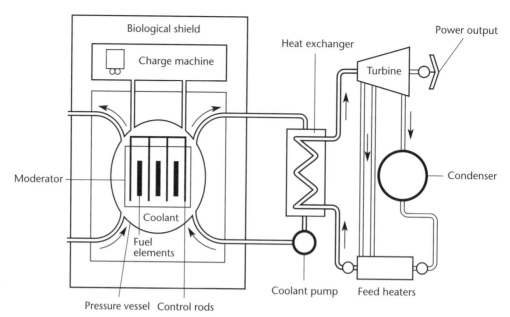

A simplified diagram of a nuclear power station

NUCLEUS

Nucleus of an atom

The nucleus of the **atom** is positively charged, takes up a very small amount of space, yet contains nearly all the **mass** of the atom. It is the breakdown of radioactive nuclei that give rise to **radioactivity** (nuclear radiation).

Within the nucleus are found sub-atomic particles, namely **protons** and **neutrons** The proton has a mass of 1u and a charge of +1; the neutron has a mass of 1u but carries no charge.

Nucleus of a cell

The nucleus of a cell controls the activities of the cell. It contains the **chromosomes** and is surrounded by a nuclear membrane. All cells have a nucleus, except **red blood cells**.

⟡ *Cell – biological*

NUTRIENT CYCLES

⟡ *Carbon cycle, Ecosystem, Nitrogen cycle, Water – water cycle*

NUTRITION

This describes the process of taking in food and digesting it to provide **energy** for all the processes carried out by the **cells**, such as growth.

⟡ *Balanced diet, Digestion, Life processes, Photosynthesis*

OESTROGEN

A female **hormone** released by the **ovary** that causes the development of secondary sexual characteristics, development of the breasts, fat deposits around the hips, and growth of hair under the arms and around the pubic area. Oestrogen also increases the thickness of the uterus wall ready for the implantation of the **zygote**.

➤ **Menstrual cycle, Menstruation, Puberty, Reproduction**

OHM

The ohm is the **resistance** of a conductor in which the **current** is 1 A when a **potential difference** of 1 V is applied across it: e.g. 1 Ω of resistance is given by a resistor if a **voltage** of 1 V is required to push a current of 1 A through the resistor. So a higher resistance means more voltage is required. Resistance is measured in units called ohms, symbol Ω.

To calculate the resistance you need to know the voltage and current:

$$\text{resistance} = \frac{\text{voltage}}{\text{current}}$$

$$R = \frac{V}{I}$$

or

$$V = IR$$

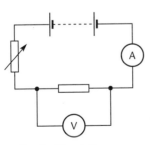

A circuit to investigate Ohm's Law

➤ **Ampere, Ohm's Law**

OHM'S LAW

The **current** through a metallic conductor is directly proportional to the **potential difference** across its ends, if the temperature and other conditions are constant.

You may have carried out a practical investigation to compare the relationship between the **voltage** and

the amount of **current** flowing in a circuit. The graph shows how the current flowing (*I*) is directly proportional to the voltage (*V*), at constant temperature.

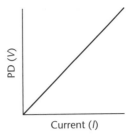

A graph showing the relationship between current and voltage, using a resistor in the circuit

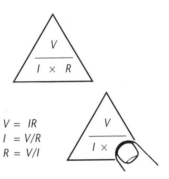

$$V = IR$$
$$I = V/R$$
$$R = V/I$$

A useful way of remembering Ohm's Law

Current and voltage

The current varies with voltage in different components; e.g. a **resistor** at constant temperature, a filament lamp and a **diode**. This relationship is shown by current–voltage graphs.

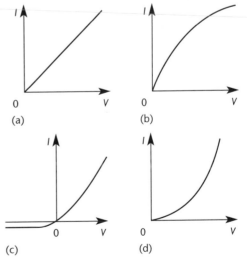

Current–voltage graphs: (a) resistor; (b) a filament lamp; (c) a diode; (d) a thermistor

● The **resistance** of a filament lamp increases as the temperature of the filament increases.

101

- The diode allows current to pass in one direction but current flow is almost zero in the opposite direction due to a very high resistance.

- In a light dependent resistor (LDR) the resistance decreases as light intensity increases, and in a thermistor the resistance decreases as temperature increases.

-+- **Ohm**

OIL DEPOSITS

-+- **Crude oil**

OPTICAL FIBRES

-+- **Total internal reflection**

ORGAN

An organ is a group of different kinds of tissue that carries out certain functions: e.g. the **heart** in mammals, and the leaf in plants.

-+- **Cell – biological, Organ systems, Tissues**

ORGAN SYSTEMS

In your body cells are grouped together to make tissues that in turn make organs that form organ systems. There are *seven* main organ systems in your body:

1. *The circulatory system*: carries **oxygen**, **glucose** and **amino acids** to every cell, and carries waste products such as **urea** and **carbon dioxide** away from the cells.

2. *The respiratory system*: takes in oxygen and removes carbon dioxide.

3. *The digestive system*: breaks down and absorbs the food taken into your body.

4. *The excretory system*: removes unwanted, harmful waste produced by your body, such as urea produced by the liver and removed by the **kidneys**.

5. *The skeletal system*: protects and supports your organs and muscles, and enables your muscles to move your body.

6. *The nervous system*: controls all the organs in your body and enables your body to respond to the information received by its sensory cells.

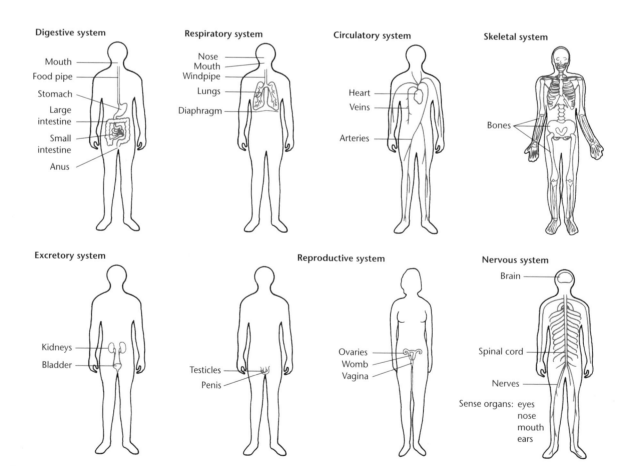

Digestive system
- Mouth
- Food pipe
- Stomach
- Large intestine
- Small intestine
- Anus

Respiratory system
- Nose
- Mouth
- Windpipe
- Lungs
- Diaphragm

Circulatory system
- Heart
- Veins
- Arteries

Skeletal system
- Bones

Excretory system
- Kidneys
- Bladder

Reproductive system
- Testicles
- Penis
- Ovaries
- Womb
- Vagina

Nervous system
- Brain
- Spinal cord
- Nerves
- Sense organs: eyes nose mouth ears

Organ systems

7. *The reproductive system*: enables you to make eggs or sperm so that you can pass on genetic information to create the next generation.

-+- **Life processes, Nervous system**

ORGANISM

The word organism means any living animal or plant, including **bacteria** and **viruses**.

-+- **Life processes**

OSMOREGULATION

Osmoregulation is the term used to describe the process of maintaining the correct fluid balance in our bodies. On average, there is about 58 per cent water in an adult person so it is essential that the amount of water remains constant.

● If too much water is drunk the body fluids become *dilute*

● If too much water is lost then the body fluids become too *concentrated*

Whichever of these situations arises, the body cells would cease to function properly. The organ that controls the amount of water leaving the body is the **kidney**, which works with the hypothalamus and anti-diuretic **hormone** (ADH) to achieve **homeostasis**.

CHECKPOINT

Complete the sentences using these words:

large   small   lot   little   concentrated   dilute

On a cold day, if a person has drunk a lot of water, the kidney allows a .... of fluid into the urine and so .... amounts of .... urine are produced.

On a hot day, if a person has not drunk much water, or lost water through sweating, the kidney allows very .... water into the urine and reabsorbs water into the blood and so .... amounts of .... urine are produced.

OSMOSIS

Osmosis is the diffusion of water **molecules** from a region of *higher* water concentration to a region of *lower* water concentration through a **partially permeable membrane**.

A concentrated sugar **solution** is placed in a bag made of Visking tubing (a material like cellophane). The bag and its contents are then placed in a beaker of water. After a short time the bag will be seen to be much bigger. Why?

The effect is due to the Visking tubing acting as a sort of **particle** sieve. Water particles are much smaller than sugar molecules. The tubing material contains tiny holes or pores, just big enough to let the *small* water particles pass into the bag, but not to let the *large* sugar particles out. As a result, the volume of the bag increases.

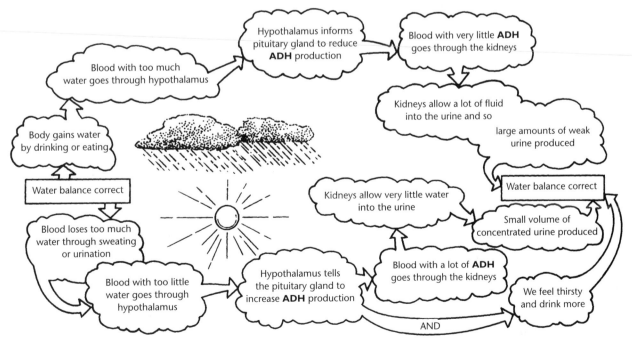

How fluid level is controlled in mammals

The movement of water from a dilute to a concentrated solution is called osmosis. Materials such as Visking tubing are called **partially permeable membranes**. If the process were allowed to continue, water would pass through the tubing walls until the concentration of the solutions inside and out were the same. Using a partially permeable membrane to separate the substances is called **dialysis**.

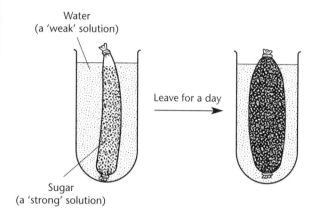

An experiment to show osmosis

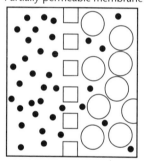

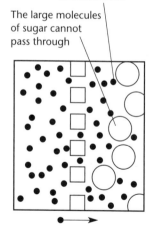

How osmosis works

-+- **Absorption in plants, Transport in plants**

OVARY

In animals the ovary is the female sex organ where the ova (eggs) are produced. **Oestrogen**, a female **hormone** is also released by the ovary.

-+- **Menstrual cycle, Puberty, Reproduction**

OVERHEAD CABLES

-+- **Generation of electricity, Transmission of electricity**

OVULATION

Ovulation is the release of an egg (ovum) from the **ovaries**. Every 28 days an ovum (egg) is released and passes down the egg tube where **fertilization** can occur.

-+- **Menstrual cycle, Puberty, Reproduction**

OVUM

The ovum (egg cell) is the female **gamete** released by the ovaries. It contains cytoplasm, yolky grains and a nucleus. It is covered by a thick membrane, and by a hard shell in birds and reptiles.

-+- **Ovulation, Sexual reproduction**

OXIDATION

Oxidation is the removal of **electrons** from a substance. This often occurs with the addition of **oxygen** (hence oxidation), although this is not always the case. When **carbon** is burned and **carbon dioxide** is produced, we say the carbon has been oxidized:

$$\text{carbon} + \text{oxygen} \rightarrow \text{carbon dioxide}$$
$$\text{C} + \text{O}_2 \rightarrow \text{CO}_2$$

Similarly, when iron reacts with chlorine, iron chloride is produced. Here, the iron has been oxidized:

$$\text{iron} + \text{chlorine} \rightarrow \text{iron chloride}$$
$$2\text{Fe} + 3\text{Cl}_2 \rightarrow 2\text{FeCl}_3$$

The iron has been oxidized because electrons have been removed from its atoms to form Fe^{3+} ions:

$$\text{Fe} - 3\text{e}^- \rightarrow \text{Fe}^{3+}$$

We need to understand oxidation when we talk about **corrosion** of **metals** and **combustion**, both of which are examples of oxidation.

Sometimes we refer to the oxidation state of a substance. This indicates how much it has been oxidized, i.e. how many electrons have been removed: e.g. in the case of iron, the +3 state is more highly oxidized than the +2 state:

Oxidation states of iron	
Atom/ion	Oxidation state
Fe	0
Fe^{2+}	+2
Fe^{3+}	+3

-+- **Blast furnace, Redox reactions, Reduction**

OXIDIZING AGENT

An oxidizing agent is a substance that is very good at 'pulling' *electrons* away from another substance or adding **oxygen** to a substance. Oxygen is a good oxidizing agent as are fluorine, chlorine and potassium manganate (VII).

-+- *Oxidation*

OXYGEN

Oxygen is a gas that makes up about one-fifth of the air around us. It is colourless and has no smell. Oxygen gas contains **molecules** of oxygen; its chemical formula is O_2.

Oxygen is a very important gas because it is needed to support living things (respiration) by reacting with food substances (sugars) to provide energy. The balance of oxygen in the air is maintained because when plants **photosynthesize** they produce oxygen as a by-product.

Oxygen is also the gas that allows things to burn; it reacts with the 'fuel' to produce an oxide and releases energy as heat. This is called **combustion**. Oxygen is very important in industry and is manufactured by separating it from the air. It is usually stored as liquid oxygen (by cooling it sufficiently to make it liquid). Rockets have to carry their own supply of oxygen in order to burn the fuel (hydrogen) that they also carry.

-+- **Aerobic respiration, Anaerobic respiration, Breathing, Energy, Ozone layer**

OXYGEN DEBT

-+- *Anaerobic respiration*

OXYHAEMOGOBLIN

-+- *Breathing*

OZONE LAYER

The ozone layer surrounds the **Earth** in the part of the upper **atmosphere** known as the stratosphere. The stratosphere is vital to life because it shields us from the most harmful types of **ultraviolet** (u.v.) radiation from the sun. If more u.v. radiation penetrates, then the number of cases of skin **cancer** will increase. There is also strong evidence that increased exposure to u.v. would harm crops, affecting the world's food supply.

Ozone is a form of **oxygen** that has three **atoms** in each **molecule** (O_3) compared with the usual form we breathe that has two atoms in each molecule (O_2).

In simple terms, ozone protects us by a series of **chemical reactions**. Some types of UV radiation will split the oxygen molecule (O_2) to form oxygen atoms. These are very reactive and can combine with oxygen molecules to form ozone (O_3):

u.v. radiation

$$O_2 \rightarrow O. + O.$$
$$O. + O_2 \rightarrow O_3$$

The ozone produced then absorbs other types of u.v. radiation, which converts them back to oxygen molecules and atoms:

$$O_3 \rightarrow O_2 + O.$$

Although these reactions protect us from the harmful u.v. radiation, their balance is being upset by the release of chemicals such as **chlorofluorocarbons** (CFCs) from **aerosols** etc., and oxides of nitrogen (from car exhausts), which also react with the ozone making fewer ozone molecules available at any time to absorb the u.v. radiation.

-+- **Air, Greenhouse effect, Pollution**

P

P-WAVES

P waves (pressure waves) are **longitudinal waves** that travel quickly and pass through liquids and solids. They travel more quickly through the **Earth's** core than the mantle.

✛ **Earthquakes**

PANCREAS

✛ **Digestion**

PARALLEL CIRCUIT

In a parallel circuit the components are connected to the same **electromotive force** (e.m.f.) so that the same **potential difference** (p.d.) is applied to each part.

The diagram shows two lamps connected in a parallel circuit. Each lamp glows brightly as it has the total **voltage** across it. In this circuit the lamps each take 0.2 A so the reading of 0.2 A on ammeter A_2 and A_3 is the same, but the total current, measured by A_1 and A_4, is 0.4 A.

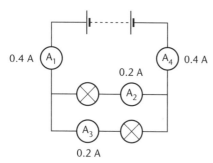

Current in a parallel circuit

● The advantage of a parallel circuit is that if one lamp is faulty the others stay alight. This is especially useful in wiring decorative lights, e.g. on a Christmas tree, or along a street. Most household power sockets are connected in parallel with the mains supply.

● Disadvantages of parallel circuits are that they can be complex to wire up correctly, and use up more wire, which can be expensive.

✛ **Circuit symbols, Electricity, Series circuit**

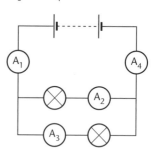

CHECKPOINT

The diagram below shows a circuit. If the reading on A_1 is 0.5 A and on A_2 is 0.25 A, what are the readings on A_3 and A_4?

PARTIALLY PERMEABLE MEMBRANES

A concentrated sugar **solution** is placed in a bag made of Visking tubing (a material like cellophane). The bag and its contents are then placed in a beaker of diluted sugar solution. After a short period of time the bag will be seen to be much bigger. What is the explanation?

The Visking tubing is acting as a sort of **particle** sieve. The tubing is made up of tiny holes or pores, just big enough to let the small water particles (which are moving) pass through, but *not* the large sugar particles.

Materials such as Visking tubing are called partially permeable membranes. If allowed to continue, water would pass through the tubing walls until the concentration of the solutions inside and out is the same. The movement of water from a weak to a strong solution is called **osmosis**. Using a partially permeable membrane to separate the substances is called **dialysis**.

Partially permeable membrane

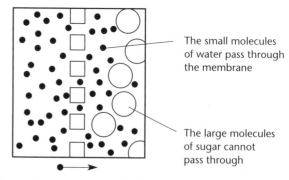

The small molecules of water pass through the membrane

The large molecules of sugar cannot pass through

Osmosis through a partially permeable membrane

✛ **Transport in plants**

PARTICLE

The word particle usually refers to the 'particles that make up all matter', i.e. **solid**, **liquid** or **gas**. These particles include **atoms**, **molecules** and **ions**. They are so small that they cannot be seen even through the most powerful microscope. The particles that make up all matter are also moving.

 **Brownian motion, Diffusion, Kinetic theory, Osmosis**

PEPSIN

 *Digestion*

PERIODIC TABLE

The periodic table shows the **elements** arranged in order of increasing **atomic number** and **mass**. The simplest and lightest **atoms** are at the top left of the table and the most complex and heaviest are at the bottom right of the table. The elements are arranged in a grid pattern of rows and columns. Each row is called a period and each column is called a group.

CHECKPOINT

The diagram shows an outline of the periodic table.

1. Which letter represents: (a) a noble gas; (b) a halogen; (c) a very reactive metal?
2. How are the elements arranged in the periodic table?
3. What property is shared by the elements in one vertical group?

Atoms vary in complexity depending on how many **protons**, **neutrons** and **electrons** they have. Protons and neutrons are found in the **nucleus**; electrons are found orbiting the nucleus in 'shells'. Each shell can hold a set amount of electrons:

- First shell – two electrons
- Second shell – eight electrons

Periods

A period is a horizontal row of elements, which go across the table. Each period corresponds to an electron shell:

- As you move across the *first* period you are filling the *first* electron shell:

atom:	H	He
atomic number:	1	2
electron configuration:	1	2

- As you move across the *second* period you are filling the *second* electron shell:

atom:	Li	Be	B	C	N	O	F	Ne
atomic number:	3	4	5	6	7	8	9	10
electron configuration:	2,1	2,2	2,3	2,4	2,5	2,6	2,7	2,8

- In the *third* period you are filling the *third* electron shell:

atom:	Na	Mg	Al	Si	P	S	Cl	Ar
atomic number:	11	12	13	14	15	16	17	18
electron configuration:	2,8,1	2,8,2	2,8,3	2,8,4	2,8,5	2,8,6	2,8,7	2,8,8

The periodic table

- As you go *across* the table the atoms are getting heavier (more protons and neutrons).

- As you go *down* the table the atoms are getting bigger (more electrons, which take up more space).

Trends across a period

A period is a horizontal row of elements. Each period corresponds to an electron shell. As you move across a period you are adding one **electron** to the outer shell of the atom each time:

- Elements change from **metals** to non-metals

- Number of electrons in outer shell increases from one to eight

- Number of outer electrons equals the group number

- **Valency** of elements increases from one to four in groups 1–4, then decreases from four to one in groups 4–7

- Melting points and boiling points of elements increase to a maximum for group 4 then decrease again to group 0

- The oxides of the elements change from basic to acidic

- The formulae of compounds of the elements show the change in valency or oxidation number

Trends down a group

A group is a vertical column of elements that go down the table. As you go down a group, the atoms have the same number of electrons in their outer shell: e.g. group 1:

The groups show general trends (gradual change of properties) from top to bottom of the group with increasing **atomic number**:

- The diameter of the atom increases so the atom become larger

- The number of electrons in the outer shell is equal to the group number, e.g. **alkali metals**, group 1, have one electron in their outer shell

- Elements with the same number of electrons in their outer shell behave in similar ways in chemical reactions

- The atoms lose their outer electrons more easily

- The **density** of the element increases

Trends across the third period

Metal/non-metal	Na	Mg	Al	Si	P	S	Cl	Ar
	m	m	m	n/m	n/m	n/m	n/m	n/m
Outer shell electrons	1	2	3	4	5	6	7	8
Valency	1	2	3	4	3	2	1	0
Oxidation no.	+1	+2	+3	+4	−3	−2	−1	0
Melting point °C	98	650	660	1,410	44	113	−100	−189
Boiling point °C	880	1,100	2,470	2,355	280	444	−35	−186
Oxide nature	Basic	Basic	Amphoteric	Acidic	Acidic	Acidic	Acidic	–
Formula of oxide	Na_2O	MgO	Al_2O_3	SiO_2	P_2O_3	SO_2	Cl_2O	–
Formula of chloride	$NaCl$	$MgCl_2$	$AlCl_3$	$SiCl_4$	PCl_3	S_2Cl_2	Cl_2	–

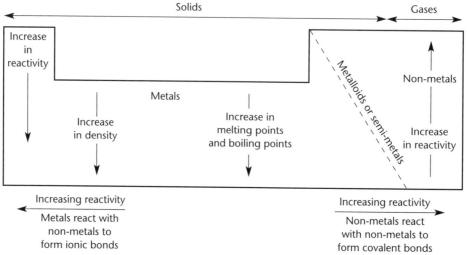

Atom	Electron configuration
H	1
Li	2,1
Na	2,8,1
K	2,8,8,1

Remember: It is how electrons are arranged in their shells that determines how atoms behave in chemical reactions.

-+- **Atomic structure, Chemical symbol, Ion**

PERISTALSIS

Wave-like movements of the intestines that propel the contents (i.e. the food) through the digestive system.

-+- **Balanced diet, Digestion, Fibre**

PESTICIDES

Gardeners and farmers often use chemical pesticides to control insects that are damaging crops and other plants. Herbicides are also used to kill unwanted plants that otherwise affect the yield of crops. Although these chemicals may be used only in very

small quantities, the concentration of chemical builds up each stage of the **food chain**, and accumulates in the top **carnivore**, e.g. a bird of prey such as an owl or hawk. Because the chemicals affect each organism in the food chain, the top carnivore will receive the highest concentration, and be affected the most. It may be killed or have very low rates of reproduction.

The advantage of using chemical pesticides is that they are very effective and fast working.

-+- **Biological control, Food production, Pollution**

PHOTOSYNTHESIS

Green plants use energy from sunlight to convert **carbon dioxide** and **water** into **carbohydrates** (e.g. glucose) and **oxygen**. This process is called photosynthesis. The light energy is absorbed by chlorophyll, the green pigment in plant leaves, which is contained in chloroplasts in some plant cells.

The equation for photosynthesis is:

carbon dioxide and water → carbohydrates and oxygen

$$\underbrace{6CO_2 + 6H_2O}_{\text{reactants}} \xrightarrow[\text{chlorophyll}]{\text{sunlight}} \underbrace{C_6H_{12}O_6 + 6O_2}_{\text{products}}$$

The glucose is converted into other sugars and stored as starch.

Oxygen is released as a waste product and used by animals and plants for **respiration**.

You may have carried out a series of investigations to show that light, carbon dioxide and water are necessary for photosynthesis.

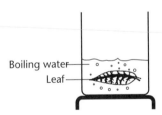

1. Leaf is boiled in water (about 2 min). (Purpose: To break down cell walls and to stop the action of enzymes within the leaf)

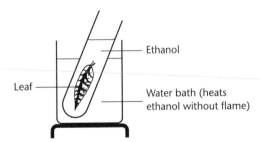

2. Leaf is warmed in ethanol (until leaf is colourless) CAUTION: ETHANOL IS FLAMMABLE; NO FLAMES SHOULD BE USED AT THIS STAGE.
(Purpose: To extract the chlorophyll, which would obstruct observations later. Chlorophyll dissolves in ethanol but not in water)

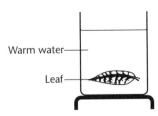

3. Leaf is dipped into the warm water (briefly). (Purpose: To soften the now brittle leaf)

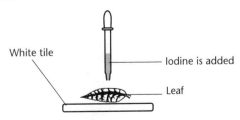

4. Leaf is placed on white tile and iodine added (Purpose: Iodine shows the presence (blue–black) or absence (orange–brown) of starch; colours are shown against the white tile)

(a) Testing a leaf for starch

> *Remember: To show that photosynthesis has occurred, a plant must be destarched by placing it in the dark for two days to use up any starch that has been stored. The plant can then be used in investigations and a starch test carried out on a leaf to see if starch has been formed as shown in figure (a).*

Investigations on photosynthesis

- To show that chlorophyll is necessary for photosynthesis, use a variegated leaf that has areas of green and white. Starch should be present in the green areas only, as shown in figure (b).

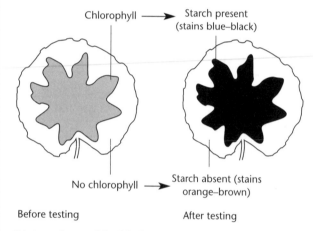

(b) A variegated leaf before and after testing for starch

- To show that light is necessary, a piece of foil is wrapped around part of the leaf to exclude the light. Starch should be present only in the areas exposed to light, as shown in figure (c).

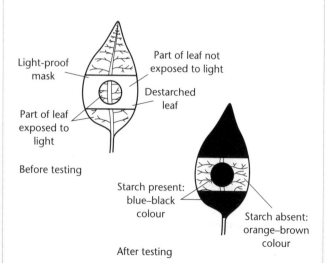

(c) A partially covered leaf before and after testing for starch

- To show that carbon dioxide is necessary, enclose part of the plant in a flask containing potassium hydroxide, which absorbs the carbon dioxide. Starch should be present only in the leaves where carbon dioxide was available, as shown in figure (d).

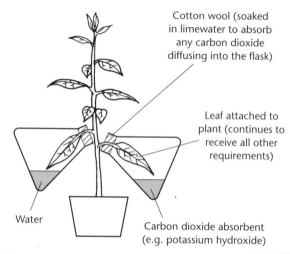

(d) Apparatus to show that carbon dioxide is needed for photosynthesis

- To show that oxygen is released during photosynthesis a plant can be trapped under a funnel, as shown in figure (e). The gas released can be tested with a glowing splint. The splint should relight showing the gas is oxygen. This experiment can also be used to study the rate of photosynthesis by measuring how many bubbles are produced per minute, given different intensities of light. The outcome is likely to be shown in figure (f).

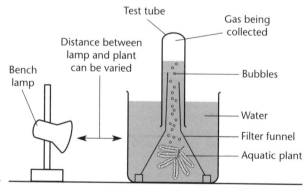

(e) Experiment to demonstrate the effect of light intensity on the rate of photosynthesis

Uses of the products of photosynthesis

Green plants convert the glucose formed during photosynthesis to other sugars, insoluble starch, oils and amino acids.

- Insoluble starch is stored in roots, stems and leaves. For example, the potato is a stem tuber

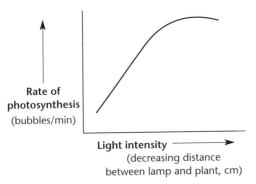

(f) Graph to show the effect of light intensity on the rate of photosynthesis

which stores starch, when these tubers are planted, the 'eyes' produce new shoots using the stored starch; maize grains store starch in the endosperm so that when germination takes place there is a plentiful supply of energy for the growth of the shoots and roots.

- Sucrose is stored in fruits, for example, apples, pears
- Oils (lipids) are stored in seeds as an energy supply for germination
- *Amino acids* are used for making new **proteins** for growth

---

CHECKPOINT

1. Complete the equation for photosynthesis:

   .... + water → .... + ...
   ....

2. List **three** factors that can limit the rate of photosynthesis.

3. Explain why plants need nitrates for healthy growth?

-❖- *Limiting factors*

pH SCALE

pH is a scale of *acidity/alkalinity*. The numbers on the scale range from 1 to 14:

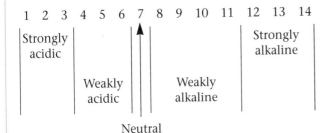

The acidity of a particular substance or solution can be measured using a suitable **indicator** that

changes colour at different pH values, or more accurately, with a pH meter. These are some examples of the pH of everyday materials: lemon juice has a pH of 2; pure water is pH 7; ammonia solution has a pH of 11.

pH is really a measure of the hydrogen ion (H^+) concentration in the solution. It is the H^+ ion that gives rise to acidity. High hydrogen ion concentrations, (i.e. strongly acidic), have *low* pH numbers.

-❖- *Acid, Alkali, Universal indicator*

PHLOEM

-❖- *Transport in plants*

PITUITARY GLAND

This is an endocrine gland that secretes a number of different *hormones*, to control the action of other endocrine glands. It is known as the 'master' gland of the body and is the most important endocrine gland.

-❖- *Adrenalin, Homeostasis, Osmoregulation*

PLANET

A planet is a body that orbits the **Sun**, e.g. the **Earth**, Mercury, Jupiter. Planets do not emit light but they reflect light from the Sun, and therefore appear as *'stars'* in the night sky.

-❖- *Solar system*

PLANT HORMONES

Auxins

The growth hormones in plants are auxins that stimulate or inhibit growth in plants. These hormones are released in the shoot tip and root tip and move through the plant by **diffusion**. They affect the zone of elongation just behind the shoot tip (plumule) and behind the root tip (radicle).

Plant shoots grow towards the stimulus of light and plant roots grow towards the stimulus of **gravity**. These responses are known as tropic responses; shoots are positively *phototropic* and roots are positively *geotropic*. These responses are brought about by the action of **hormones**.

- **Phototropism – response to light**: Auxins accumulate on the side of the shoot away from the light. The auxins stimulate the growth of the shoot so that the side away from the light, which has more auxins, grows more rapidly. This has the effect of bending the shoot towards the light so that more **photosynthesis** can take place. This is the positive phototropic response, as shown in the diagram.

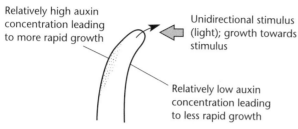

Positive phototropism in a shoot tip

The shoot tip produces substances that inhibit the growth of the side shoots so if the shoot tip is removed, as in the pruning of a hedge, the side shoots grow outwards and the hedge becomes bushier.

- **Geotropism – response to gravity**: If the root tip is emerging from the seed horizontally, auxin hormones accumulate on the lower side of the root. Auxins in the root have the effect of inhibiting growth so that the side on top grows more rapidly. This has the effect of bending the root downwards towards **water** and **mineral salts** – a positive geotropic response (towards **gravity**), shown in the diagram.

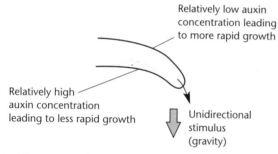

Positive geotropism in a root tip

If the shoot tip is emerging from the seed horizontally, the auxin has the opposite effect and stimulates growth of the lower side of the shoot so that it curves upwards towards the light. This is described as a negative geotropic response (away from gravity).

Commercial uses of growth hormones

Artificially synthesized hormones are used to control growth and reproduction in plants in many ways, e.g.:

- To stimulate the formation of fruit without the need for fertilization; e.g. growth substances can be applied to unpollinated flowers to produce 'seedless' fruits such as citrus fruits and grapes.

- In stimulating root growth in cuttings; e.g. horticulturists using rooting hormone powder to promote the growth of roots in cuttings.

- Hormone weed killers can be applied to lawns to disrupt the growth patterns of certain weeds.

CHECKPOINT

List **two** uses of commercially produced plant hormones.

✦ **Food production**

PLATE TECTONICS

It is thought that the **Earth's** crust consists of a number of large 'plates' and it is the interaction of these plates that is described as plate tectonics. The plates are thought to be moving at relative speeds of a few centimetres per year.

There are basically three ways the plates can move in relation to each other:

- The plates can *slide past* each other along a common boundary. The plane along which motion occurs is a vertical fracture or fault. **Earthquakes** can arise when there are sudden movements along these faults due to a build-up of energy, e.g. the San Andreas fault in Southern California.

- The plates can *slide towards* each other so that the thinner, denser ocean plates are pushed beneath the more buoyant continental plates, forcing the continental crusts upwards. Strong pressures build up giving rise to **earthquakes** and **volcanoes**, e.g. Chile, Japan and Alaska, as well as narrow zones around the Pacific Basin.

- The plates can *pull apart* from each other so that gaping cracks appear in the ocean crust. **Magma** continually rises to fill the gap and form new ocean crust. This is described as 'sea floor spreading'. **Earthquakes** can also occur but are usually too small to be of significance, e.g. in the mid-Atlantic ocean ridges.

Continental drift

It can be seen from the diagram that the edges of the continents have shapes that appear to fit closely together, even though they are now separated by oceans.

The theory that best explains this observation is that more than 300 million years ago the land masses formed a super continent called Pangaea. The Americas fitted closely against Africa and Europe, and the continents of Antarctica and Australia and subcontinents of India and Madagascar were closely grouped around the Southern tip of Africa. Two hundred million years ago the separation of the continents began as the Americas pulled away from the rest of Pangaea, leaving a great rift that became the Atlantic Ocean. Later, other fragments pulled away from Africa and from each other. The theory of plate tectonics helps to explain how the continents have moved apart in this way.

In the mantle, convection currents as a result of heat released by radioactivity may be a possible cause of movement of plates.

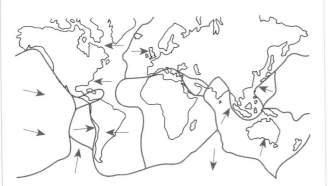

The large plates of rock that form the Earth's crust

CHECKPOINT

Use the theory of plate tectonics to explain how the continents could have moved apart to reach their present positions. You may use diagrams if you wish.

POLLUTION

Any harmful substances that enter the **environment** can be described as pollution, especially if they reach unusually high levels, e.g.

- *Air pollution*: Dust, smoke, soot, **sulphur dioxide**, carbon monoxide, lead oxide, nitrogen oxides. Mostly produced by burning **fossil fuels**, such as coal or petrol.

- *Water pollution*: Oil, detergent, sewage, **fertilizers**, industrial waste.

- *Soil pollution*: Dumping of rubbish, chemicals, cars, **radioactive** waste.

- *Noise pollution*: Aeroplanes, engines, industrial machinery, motorbikes, loud music.

-✦- **Acid rain, Biodegradable, Catalysts, Diffusion, Ecosystem, Environment, Nitrates, Nuclear power, Ozone layer**

POLYMER

-✦- **Addition polymerization**

POPULATIONS

A population is the number of organisms of the same **species** in a particular area: e.g. the number of snails in a garden, the number of oak trees in a woodland.

The new population starts with low numbers in the 'lag phase', and then shows a very rapid increase in number in the 'log' phase. When resources limit growth then a stabilization phase is reached and the population remains fairly constant, until there is a change in one of the **limiting factors**, such as availability of food, space or disease

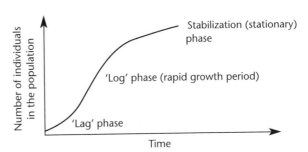

A typical growth curve for a population

-✦- **Competition, Food production, Predator – prey, Pyramid of numbers, Sampling populations**

POTENTIAL DIFFERENCE

-✦- **Electromotive force, Voltmeter**

POTENTIAL ENERGY

Potential energy is a form of **energy** that is stored; e.g. the energy stored in a wound-up spring, the energy stored in an object that is raised up.

-✦- **Gravitational potential energy**

POWER

Power is the rate of doing **work**, and is measured in **joules** per second (J/s) or **watts** (W). The formula is:

$$\text{power} = \frac{\text{amount of work done}}{\text{time taken to do the work}}$$

E.g. if a person does 50 J of work in 10 s then his/her rate of working is 50/10 = 5 J/s or 5 W.

CHECKPOINT

A student whose weighs 450 N, climbs a 5 m flight of stairs in 6 s. What is the student's power output?

Power, voltage and current

Power is the rate of energy transfer and can be represented by the formula:

power = potential difference × current
(watt, W)   (volt, V)   (ampere, A)

PREDATOR – PREY

A predator is an animal that obtains energy from other animals that it captures by hunting, e.g. a tiger, a fox. The graph shows how the **population** of the prey affects the population of the predator.

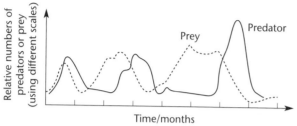

The population of the prey affects the numbers of the predator

Adaptation of predators and prey

Adaptation means an animal or plant having special features that enable it to survive in a particular environment.

For example, animals in desert and arctic regions need to adapt to extremes of climate in the following ways:

- Their body size and surface area.
- The thickness of hair (fur).
- Amount of body fat.
- Camouflage.

A good example of adaptation is the polar bear which is adapted to live in a very cold climate in the arctic. The bear:

- Is large and has a relatively small surface area to mass ratio.
- Has a thick layer of fur which traps air and gives insulation.
- Has large deposits of body fat for insulation and energy.
- Has white fur to camouflage it against the snow and ice.

In desert regions animals such as camels are adapted to withstand extremes of temperature and shortage of available water.

The camel has:

- A long, thin body shape which increases its surface area to mass ratio to allow heat to escape.
- The ability to drink large amounts of water when available and to store water in fat deposits in its hump.
- Large feet which spread out to prevent it sinking in the sand.

Predators such a lions and cheetahs are adapted for hunting prey by having powerful muscles to enable

them to chase their prey, eyes at the front of their head to give good distance vision, and good camouflage to help them blend in with their surroundings and not be visible to their prey. The prey such as zebra and springbok have eyes at the side of their head to give good all-round vision when they are feeding. They are also camouflaged and able to run very fast for long periods.

The prey is an animal that provides food for a predator that hunts and kills the prey, e.g. a rabbit being killed by a fox.

Plant adaptations

Plants adapt to survive arid conditions. One example is the thorn tree which has very small leaves to reduce water loss by transpiration. The thorns prevent herbivores from eating the leaves and the seed pods have a very thick coat to withstand long periods of drought.

⊹ *Adaptation, Biological control, Competition, Food chains and food webs, Herbivore, Natural selection*

PRIMARY CONSUMER

Herbivores are primary consumers. They obtain **energy** directly from green plants, e.g. a cow or rabbit feeding on grass is a primary consumer.

⊹ *Food chains and food webs*

PRODUCERS

⊹ *Ecosystem, Food chain and food webs*

PROTEIN

A protein is a naturally occurring polymer that is made of small **monome**r units called amino acids. There are about 20 different naturally occurring **amino acids**, each containing a **nitrogen atom**. Different combinations of these amino acids can be combined in a polymer to make up different proteins.

Plants manufacture proteins using sugars and starches (produced by **photosynthesis**), together with **nitrates** and **water** (absorbed through their roots) as raw materials. The nitrates provide the nitrogen atom. Proteins are used to build and repair cell walls.

Each acid contains – NH_2 group (amino)   e.g. H_2N ⬚ COOH

and – COOH group (acid)   or H_2N △ COOH

The different shapes represent different amino acids

A typical protein

Proteins are polymers, the monomer units are amino acids

Proteins in action

Humans need proteins to carry out metabolic functions, and our source of protein comes from eating plant or animal material. Some foods such as cheese, eggs, meat etc., are a rich source of protein. Because the protein **molecules** are very large and cannot pass through the gut wall, they are broken down by **enzymes** into amino acids. These are absorbed and may be reassembled later by the body into proteins.

> *Remember: Enzymes are also proteins.*

✥ **Balanced diet, Digestion**

PROTON

The proton is a sub-atomic particle found in the **nucleus** of an **atom**. It has a mass unit of 1u and carries one positive charge. The number of protons in an atom is given by the atom's **atomic number**. There are always the same number of **electrons** (each of which has a negative charge) as protons in an atom, so atoms are electrically neutral.

✥ **Atomic structure, Periodic table**

PUBERTY

Puberty (adolescence) is a time when a person's reproductive organs mature as summarized in the table.

Changes that occur at puberty	
Girls	Boys
Ovaries release eggs in monthly (menstrual) cycle	Testes produce sperm
Breasts (mammary glands) develop	Penis grows bigger
Hips broaden	Voice deepens
Under-arm and pubic hair grows	Under-arm, pubic and facial hair grows

> *Remember: These changes are brought about by hormones.*

✥ **Hormones, Menstruation, Ovary, Reproduction**

PULMONARY ARTERY AND VEIN

● The pulmonary artery carries *deoxygenated* blood from the right ventricle of the **heart** to the lungs.

● The pulmonary vein carries *oxygenated* blood from the lungs to the left atrium of the heart.

> *Remember: Arteries always carry blood **away** from the heart, even though the pulmonary artery is carrying **deoxygenated** blood.*

✥ **Aerobic respiration, Artery, Blood system, Breathing, Vein**

PYRAMID OF BIOMASS

The amount of energy stored in a **food chain** can be found by weighing all the living organisms at each level of the food chain to find the total **mass** or **biomass** of organisms. The biomass decreases along the food chain, because less **energy** is available at each stage.

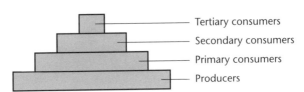
— Tertiary consumers
— Secondary consumers
— Primary consumers
— Producers

Pyramid of biomass

CHECKPOINT

Look at this food chain:

oak tree → caterpillars → small birds → hawk

Which of the following diagrams shows the pyramid of biomass for this food chain?

a   b

c   d

✥ **Food chains and food webs, Pyramid of numbers**

PYRAMID OF NUMBERS

At each stage of the food chain there are usually many more organisms lower down the **food chain**. If you were to count all the living organisms in a food chain there may be thousands of **producers**, supplying **energy** for hundreds of **herbivores** that in turn supply energy for a few **carnivores**.

At each stage of the food chain there is a *decrease* in the number of organisms as there is *less* energy available.

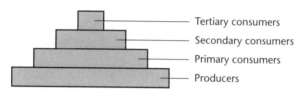

Pyramid of numbers

Sometimes a pyramid of numbers can look like this, where one organism, an oak tree, provides energy for *many* caterpillars, which provide energy for a *few* shrews, and in turn provide energy for just *one* owl.

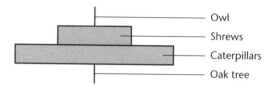

Pyramid of numbers based on one oak tree

-⊹- *Food chains and food webs, Pyramid of biomass*

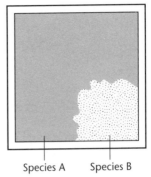

Quadrat

Species A   Species B

Using a quadrat to estimate percentage cover

Quadrat

A quadrat is an open, square frame, usually made of wood or wire, which can be used in fieldwork for marking out a measured area of ground to be studied. For example, $\frac{1}{4}m^2$ quadrat can be placed at random and the numbers of individuals of a particular **species** inside the quadrat can be counted. This process can be repeated a number of times to find an estimate of the **population** per metre square.

✦ *Ecosystem, Mark – release – recapture, Sampling populations*

RADAR

Radar stands for radio detection and ranging. High-frequency radio pulses are emitted and reflected by distant objects, and the reflections are displayed on a screen. Radar is widely used in air traffic control, shipping and weather forecasting.

❖ **Radio waves, Satellites**

RADIATION

Radiation is the transfer of energy by **infrared radiation**, which can pass through a vacuum and be reflected. **Energy** is transferred from hot objects that lose heat to their surroundings. Dark, matt surfaces radiate more heat than light shiny surfaces.

> Remember: The hotter the object the more heat it will radiate.

❖ **Conduction, Convection, Kinetic theory**

RADIOACTIVITY

Radioactivity is caused by the spontaneous breakdown of some nuclei in **atoms** that are unstable. Those **isotopes** that are unstable (called radioisotopes) emit **energy** in the form of heat and **radiation** to become more stable. In the process the atom decays into an atom of a different **element**. The *rate of decay* is measured by the term **half-life**, the time taken for half the atoms to disintegrate.

For example, carbon-14 is a radioisotope whose **nucleus** contains six **protons** and eight **neutrons** (the basic atom of carbon has only six neutrons and is not unstable). When the carbon-14 nucleus breaks down it emits energy and decays into the isotope nitrogen-14. Some radioisotopes, e.g. carbon-14, are naturally occurring; others such as plutonium-239 can be manufactured. Naturally occurring radioisotopes are usually found in the heavier elements, or are the isotopes of lighter elements that have more neutrons present in their nuclei.

Types of radioactivity

When a radioactive nucleus breaks down it can emit up to three types of radioactivity:

- **Alpha-particles**: Fast-moving helium nuclei, which can be represented as $^4_2 He^{2+}$
- **Beta-particles**: Fast-moving electrons, which can be represented as $^0_{-1} e^-$
- **Gamma-rays**: A form of electromagnetic radiation with very short wavelength.

Type of emission	Description	Penetrating power	Deflection
Alpha-particles	Fast-moving helium nuclei (two protons, two neutrons)	Absorbed by a few centimetres of air or stopped by a thin sheet of paper	Weakly deflected by a magenetic field
Beta-particles	Fast-moving electrons	Easily passes through air or paper; stopped by thin sheets of metal	Deflected by a magnetic field
Gamma-rays	Short wavelength electromagnetic radiation	Very penetrating; stopped by thick sheets of lead or thick concrete	Not deflected by a magnetic field

Alpha-radiation

Alpha-particles are fast moving helium nuclei of mass 4 and charge 2+ (groups of two **protons** and two **neutrons**):

- They are easily stopped by a sheet of paper and will not travel very far through the air.
- They are weakly deflected by a magnetic field.

Beta-radiation

Beta-particles are very fast-moving electrons and travel further through the air than alpha particles and are more difficult to stop. They are able to penetrate skin, but can be stopped by thin sheets of metal and are deflected by a magnetic field.

Gamma-radiation

Gamma-rays are a form of **electromagnetic radiation** emitted from the nucleus. They are the most penetrating of the three types of radiation, *alpha*, *beta* and *gamma* and are only stopped by several centimetres of lead. They have very short **wavelengths** and are not deflected by electric and **magnetic fields**.

Gamma-rays are used to irradiate food in order to prolong shelf-life of food (this does not make the food radioactive) but can affect the taste of some foods and so is not suitable for all.

Natural radiation

We are constantly exposed to radioactivity from natural sources referred to as **background radiation** arising from cosmic rays penetrating the atmosphere, from soil, rocks, etc.

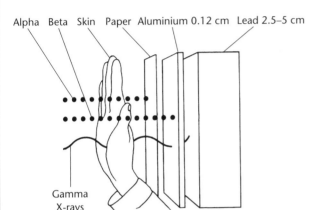

Alpha Beta Skin Paper Aluminium 0.12 cm Lead 2.5–5 cm

Gamma
X-rays

The three types of radioactivity

CHECKPOINT

Which type of radiation is stopped by a few sheets of paper:

(a) alpha-particles,
(b) beta-particles,
(c) gamma-rays
(d) X-rays?

Detecting radioactivity

Radioactivity was first discovered because of its ability to 'fog' photographic plates, in the same way that light affects photographic film. This is the way **X-ray** photographs are taken today. Radioactivity also ionizes gases through which it passes; this is the basis of modern detection methods, such as the **Geiger–Müller** tube. The tube is filled with gas, mainly argon. As radiation passes into the tube it ionizes some of the gas atoms, causing a tiny electric current that can be measured. Ion production is directly related to radiation levels.

Biological effects

The biological effects of radiation on living tissue depends several factors:

- The strength of the radiation
- The length of exposure
- How much of the tissue (how many cells) is exposed

There may be no serious effect if only a few cells are damaged, although a plant or animal may die if enough cells are killed. If the radiation dose is high enough **cancer** may develop in animals. There may also be genetic **mutations** causing future offspring to be different from their parents.

Uses

Radioisotopes can be used in a variety of ways in industry, in medicine, in **food production**, or in radiocarbon dating:

- By measuring the amount of radiation that passes through a material, a manufacturer can check the thickness of metal, the amount of toothpaste in a tube, soap powder in a packet, etc.

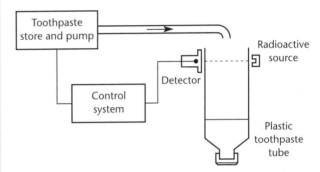

Toothpaste store and pump

Radioactive source

Detector

Control system

Plastic toothpaste tube

Using radioactivity to check the level of toothpaste in a tube

- All living things contain a large amount of **carbon**. Most of the carbon atoms are of the isotope carbon-12; a small proportion are of the radioactive isotope carbon-14. The proportion of carbon-12 to carbon-14 is the same for all living things, but when an organism dies, the amount of carbon-14 decreases (half-life 5730 years). By measuring the amount of radioactive carbon left one can date the item by reference to the **half-life** curve. This technique of carbon-14 dating was used to date the Turin Shroud.

- Small amounts of radioisotopes can be introduced into underground water systems. Geiger counters can then be used to detect the position of leaks.

- Food can be preserved by directing radiation (usually gamma-rays) onto fresh food. This process can:

  - Destroy **bacteria** and prevent the growth of moulds
  - Sterilize the contents of sealed packets
  - Reduce the sprouting of vegetables and prolong the ripening of fruits

  This irradiation does *not* make the food radioactive, but cannot be used for all food because it can change the taste.

● Controlling pests: large numbers of male insects are reared in the laboratory and sterilized by exposing them to a controlled dose of gamma-rays. They are then released into the wild where they mate. However, the females with which they mate do not produce any young, so the insect population is quickly reduced.

Radioactive decay

Radioactive decay is the spontaneous breakdown of an unstable nucleus, which can then emit either alpha, beta, or gamma radiation.

When radioactive atoms decay and emit particles they change into other atoms, e.g.:

● **Uranium**-238 loses an *alpha*-particle:

$$^{238}_{92}U \rightarrow \, ^{234}_{90}Th + \, ^{4}_{2}He^{2+}$$

● Carbon-14 loses a *beta*-particle:

$$^{14}_{6}C \rightarrow \, ^{14}_{7}N + \, ^{0}_{-1}e^{-}$$

Radioactive atoms can be created by bombarding non-radioactive atoms with other particles. These could be alpha-particles, beta-particles or more often fast-moving neutrons.

CHECKPOINT

1. How do carbon-12 and carbon-14 differ from each other?

2. When carbon-14 decays it emits a beta-particle. What is a beta-particle?

3. How does the nucleus of the carbon-14 atom change when it decays?

✦ *Nuclear fission, Nuclear fusion, Nuclear power*

RADIO WAVES

Radio waves are **electromagnetic** radiation and have the longest **wavelength** in the electromagnetic spectrum. They are used to transfer information such as sound and TV pictures over long distances.

Long, medium and short waves are used for local radio as they can be bent around obstacles such as hills. Very high **frequency** (v.h.f) and ultra-high frequency (u.h.f) waves have shorter wavelengths and need a clear path from the transmitter to the receiver.

✦ *Microwaves, Radar*

RATES OF REACTION

When a **chemical reaction** takes place the **particles** of the reactants collide (bump into each other). The more often the particles collide the more likely they are to react and so the faster the reaction.

The *speed* at which a reaction takes place can vary and depends on a number of factors:

● The *surface area* of any solid reactants

● The *concentration* of reactants (including pressure in the case of **gases**)

● The *temperature*

● The presence of a **catalyst**

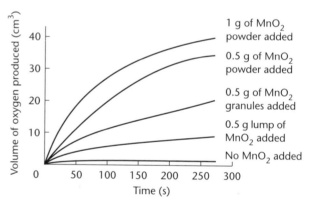

Adding manganese (IV) oxide to hydrogen peroxide affects the rate at which oxygen is produced

> *Remember: The rate of a reaction can be detected by the rate of formation of the product or the rate of disappearance of the reactant.*

	Typical wavelength values					
Waves	*Long*	*Medium*	*Short*	*v.h.f*	*u.h.f*	*Micro*
Wavelength, m	1500	300	30	3	0.3	0.3
Frequency, MHz	0.2	1	10	10^2	10^3	10^4
Use			← TV →			
	← Radio →					Radar

1. State **four** factors that affect the rate of a chemical reaction.

2. What must happen to the reactant particles so that a reaction takes place?

Increasing reaction rates

The speed of a reaction can be increased in a number of ways. Let us look at the reaction between calcium carbonate and hydrochloric acid to produce calcium chloride, water and carbon dioxide:

calcium + hydrochloric → calcium + water + carbon
carbonate   acid   chloride   dioxide

$$CaCO_3 + 2HCl \rightarrow CaCl_2 + H_2O + CO_2$$

- *Increasing the surface area of solid reactants*:
  A greater surface area provides more opportunities for particles to collide. Powdered calcium carbonate reacts much faster than lumps of calcium carbonate (marble chips) because its surface area is much greater and more calcium carbonate is in contact with the acid. Stirring the powder in the acid will further increase the speed of reaction for the same reason.

- *Increasing the concentration of the reactants*:
  This increases the number of particles present and so increases the chance of any collision. If the concentration of the hydrochloric acid is increased there is more chance of the particles interacting and the reaction will proceed at a faster rate.

- *Increasing the temperature of the reactants*:
  Increased temperature provides the particles with more kinetic energy so they will move faster, increase the number of collisions per second and hence increase the rate of the reaction.

-|- Catalysts, Kinetic theory

REACTIVITY SERIES

Metals react to form positive **ions**; some metals are *more* reactive than others, because *less* energy is required to remove electrons from their atoms, i.e. they form **ions** more easily. Metals can be placed in order of their reactivity, based on their ability to form ions; this order is their reactivity series and tends to be the same, no matter how, or with what, the metals are reacting.

The reactivity series helps to explain:

- Why some, but not all, metals corrode

- How we can prevent **corrosion**

- Why some metals and not others react with dilute acids

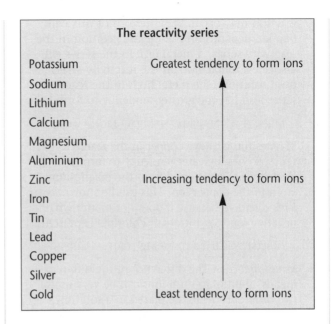

The reactivity series	
Potassium	Greatest tendency to form ions
Sodium	
Lithium	
Calcium	
Magnesium	
Aluminium	
Zinc	Increasing tendency to form ions
Iron	
Tin	
Lead	
Copper	
Silver	
Gold	Least tendency to form ions

- Why some metals can be extracted from their ores by **reduction** with carbon, yet others can only be extracted by **electrolysis**

- Why metals were discovered in the order that they were

-|- Blast furnace, Extraction of metals

REACTIONS OF METALS

- *Metals and oxygen*: When heated in air, metals form *oxides*, which are **bases**. The more reactive metals (those near the top of the **reactivity series**) will burn in air. (Gold is the only metal that is not oxidized by heating in air). For example, magnesium reacts with oxygen to form magnesium oxide.

$$2Mg(s) + O_2(g) \rightarrow 2MgO(s)$$

- *Metals and water*: The more reactive metals react with water to produce *hydrogen*.

Potassium, sodium, lithium and calcium react with cold water, producing hydroxides:

$$2Na(s) + 2H_2O(l) \rightarrow 2NaOH(aq) + H_2(g)$$

Magnesium, zinc and iron will react with steam producing oxides:

$$Zn(s) + H_2O(g) \rightarrow ZnO(s) + H_2(g)$$

- *Metals and acids*: All the metals in the reactivity series above copper will react with dilute acids.

The lower in the reactivity series the metal, the slower the reaction, e.g.:

$$Mg(s) + 2HCl(aq) \rightarrow MgCl_2(aq) + H_2(g)$$

Note: Dilute nitric acid does not react in this way.

- *Metals and metal salt solutions*: If a metal is placed in a **solution** of the salt of another metal a reaction may occur. Whether or not this will happen depends on the metal's position in the reactivity series. A metal *high* in the series will displace a metal *lower* in the reactivity series from solution. The metal high in the reactivity series also has the greater tendency to form ions:

$$Mg(s) + CuSO_4(aq) \rightarrow MgSO_4(aq) + Cu(s)$$

Magnesium is above copper in the reactivity series, so has a greater tendency to form ions; electrons are transferred from the magnesium atom to the copper ion. This can be shown as an *ionic equation*, because it does not matter what negative ion (e.g. nitrate or chloride) is present:

$$Mg(s) + Cu^{2+}(aq) \rightarrow Mg^{2+}(aq) + Cu(s)$$

- *Metals and cells*: The difference in the different metals' abilities to form ions can be very useful. If two different metals are placed in a solution containing ions and the metals are linked by a wire, then electrons will flow through the wire. This means that a **current** is flowing through the wire, and there is a voltage between the two metals. This arrangement is called a simple cell.

  The **voltage** that is produced between the two metals generally depends on their related positions in the reactivity series:

- If the metals are far apart in the series, e.g. magnesium, copper, a *large* voltage is produced

- If they are close together, e.g. iron/zinc, a *small* voltage is produced

  Refer back to the chart of the reactivity series.

- *Metals and corrosion*: **Corrosion** of a metal is a **chemical reaction**, and will only occur if the metal is in contact with a solution containing ions. As a metal corrodes it loses electrons to form positive ions:

$$\text{Metal atom} - \text{electron(s)} \rightarrow \text{metal ion}$$
$$M - e^- \rightarrow M^+$$

Metals corrode at different rates, depending on their position in the reactivity series; e.g. magnesium will corrode more quickly than copper.

Remember: The way in which a metal is extracted from its ore is related to its reactivity.

✢ *Alkali metals, Cell – electrical, Electrolysis – example, Extraction of metals*

RECEPTORS

Receptor organs contain sensitive cells that detect changes in stimuli, such as heat and light, and send impulses along a sensory nerve, e.g. the retina of the *eye* contains receptor cells that are sensitive to light and send impulses via the optic nerve to the **brain**.

✢ *Ear, Nervous system, Reflex arc*

RECESSIVE ALLELE

An allelle which is recessive has *no* effect on the appearance of an individual who has both the **dominant** and recessive alleles. A person who is **homozygous** for a characteristic has two recessive alleles and this will affect the appearance of the individual. For example, brown eye colour is dominant over blue eye colour.

- A person who is **heterozygous** has the allele from brown eyes and the allele for blue eyes. They appear to have brown eyes.

- A person who is **homozygous** has *both* recessive alleles for blue eyes and appears to have blue eyes.

✢ *Monohybrid inheritance*

RECTIFICATION

Electronic equipment such as radios often require **direct current** but are supplied by mains a.c. It is necessary to smooth out (rectify) the a.c. supply to give a steady d.c. current.

A **diode** placed in a circuit removes the negative half-cycle of the a.c. input to give a one-way **potential difference** across the equipment being used.

 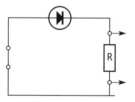

a.c. input | d.c. output across R

Half-wave rectification

✢ *Alternating current*

RECYCLING

Many manufactured items can now be recycled, e.g:

- **Glass** bottles are crushed and melted down to make new glass containers

- Old cars are crushed and useful **metal** is extracted to make other consumer goods

- Newspapers are pulped and reprocessed to make 'new' paper.

✢ *Biodegradable, Pollution*

RED BLOOD CELLS

Red blood *cells* contain cytoplasm surrounded by a cell membrane, but no nucleus. They are shaped like flattened discs and contain a pigment, **haemoglobin**, which makes the cell look red. Haemoglobin combines with oxygen to form *oxyhaemoglobin*, to transport oxygen to the cells of the body from the **capillaries** surrounding the lungs. There are about 25 billion red blood cells in your body; about 5 million for every 1 mm^3 of blood.

✛ **Blood system, Combustion – combustion in action, Smoking, White blood cells**

REDOX REACTIONS

A redox reaction is one in which both **oxidation** and **reduction** take place.

● Oxidation is the *addition* of oxygen or the *removal* of hydrogen. It is also the removal of **electrons**.

● Reduction is the *removal* of oxygen or the *addition* of hydrogen. It is also the addition of electrons.

Substances that are good at oxidizing substances are called **oxidizing agents**, e.g. oxygen and chlorine. Substances that are good at reducing other substances are called **reducing agents**, e.g. carbon and hydrogen.

As an example of a redox reaction, in the reaction between lead oxide and carbon, lead oxide is the oxidizing agent and carbon is the reducing agent:

Lead oxide + carbon → lead + carbon dioxide

$$2PbO + C \rightarrow 2Pb + CO_2$$

The lead oxide has been *reduced* to lead by the carbon, while the carbon has been *oxidized* to carbon dioxide.

In the reaction between iron and copper sulphate, the iron has been oxidized to Fe^{2+} **ions**, while at the same time the Cu^{2+} ions have been reduced to copper atoms (Cu). This reaction takes place because iron is higher in the reactivity series than copper:

iron + copper sulphate → iron sulphate + copper

$$Fe + CuSO_4 \rightarrow FeSO_4 + Cu$$

In the next example the iron has been oxidized to iron chloride. Three electrons have been removed from the iron atom. Chlorine has been reduced to the chloride ion, one electron has been added to each of the three chlorine atoms:

iron + chlorine → iron (III) chloride

$$2Fe + 3Cl_2 \rightarrow 2FeCl_3$$

Redox reactions in action

Oxidation cannot take place without reduction in a redox reaction because it involves the transfer of **electrons**.

The theory of **reduction** helps us to understand how metals are extracted from their ores. Carbon (as coke) is used as a reducing agent for some metals, e.g. iron and zinc.

The theory of oxidation helps us to understand the corrosion of metals. **Corrosion** involves the production of metal ions from their atoms, i.e. oxidation, e.g. iron rusts to form iron oxide in the presence of oxygen and water:

$$Fe - 3e^- \rightarrow Fe^{3+}$$

✛ **Electrolysis – examples, Extraction of metals**

REDUCING AGENT

A reducing agent is a substance that 'gives' **electrons**, adds hydrogen, or removes oxygen from another substance.

Carbon is a good reducing agent used in the extraction of metals from ores; hydrogen is also a good reducing agent. Metals near the top of the **reactivity series** (those with the greatest tendency to lose electrons and form ions) are also good reducing agents.

✛ **Blast furnace, Coke, Extraction of metals, Redox reactions**

REDUCTION

Reduction is the addition of **electrons** to a substance. This often occurs with the removal of oxygen or the addition of hydrogen. When **carbon** is heated with lead oxide it removes the oxygen from the lead oxide, which is *reduced* to lead:

lead oxide + carbon → lead + carbon dioxide

$$2PbO + C \rightarrow 2Pb + CO_2$$

The lead ions, Pb^{2+} in PbO, have been reduced to lead atoms Pb, i.e. electrons have been added.

✛ **Blast furnace, Oxidation, Redox reactions, Reducing agent**

REFLECTION

When a wave hits a barrier the direction of the wave changes and it is reflected away from the barrier:

● If a plane wave hits the barrier at *right angles* it 'bounces back' along its original path, at the same **wavelength**, **frequency** and **velocity**.

● If the wave hits the barrier at an *angle*, it is reflected at the same angle away from the barrier.

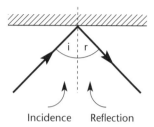

Incidence   Reflection

The angle of incidence equals the angle of reflection

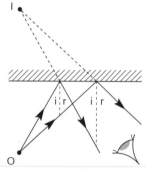

How an image is formed by a plane mirror. The image 'I' appears to be behind the mirror

> Remember: The angle of incidence equals the angle of reflection, and the wavelength, frequency and velocity stay the same.

Reflection of light

You see the world around you because light rays are reflected from different objects into your **eyes**. When you look at yourself in the mirror you see an image of yourself reflected in the mirror. Your image appears as far behind the mirror as you are in front

of the mirror. The image is described as a virtual or *imaginary* image. It is the same way up as you are, but the left and right sides are reversed.

One practical use of the reflection of light is the periscope.

CHECKPOINT

Complete these sentences using these words:

image   reflection   reversed   virtual

All waves reflect so that the angle of incidence equals the angle of .... When you see your reflection in a mirror, your .... is as far behind the mirror as you are in front of it. It is described as a .... image and is the right way up but the left and right sides are ....

✛ *Total internal reflection*

REFLEX ARC

The reflex arc is the functional unit of the **nervous system** and demonstrates how **homeostasis** may be achieved automatically. The reflex arc is the direct pathway from a **receptor** to an **effector**, via the central nervous system. Sensory and motor nerve cells (neurones) may connect directly, or through an intermediate neurone across a synapse. Synapses allow connections betwen many neurones so that impulses can be carried to different parts of the body.

Reflex responses provide a very fast, automatic response to a stimulus. The responses are instinctive and usually increase an animal's chance of survival. Examples are coughing, blinking and **eye** focusing, withdrawing a limb from a source of pain. The path taken by an impulse from a receptor in the knee-jerk reflex is shown in the diagram opposite.

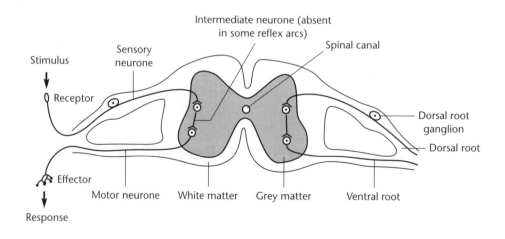

A reflex arc

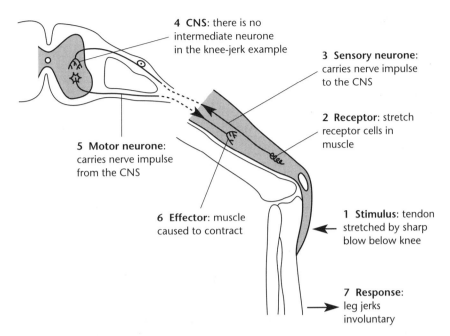

4 **CNS**: there is no intermediate neurone in the knee-jerk example

3 **Sensory neurone**: carries nerve impulse to the CNS

2 **Receptor**: stretch receptor cells in muscle

5 **Motor neurone**: carries nerve impulse from the CNS

1 **Stimulus**: tendon stretched by sharp blow below knee

6 **Effector**: muscle caused to contract

7 **Response**: leg jerks involuntary

The path taken by an impulse from a receptor in the knee-jerk reflex

---

CHECKPOINT

Complete the spaces to show the pathway taken by an impulse when a person touches a hot object and moves their hand away.

Receptor → .... → relay neurone → ....
→ effector

 Eye

REFRACTION

Refraction is the bending of light rays as they pass from one medium to another, e.g. waves travel at a certain speed in air, but when they pass into a different medium such as water, the speed slows down. The **velocity** of water waves decreases as they pass from deeper to shallower water i.e. their speed slows down.

Refraction of light

When light waves pass into glass or water at an angle, their speed slows down and they change direction. It is this change of angle which is *refraction*.

If a ray of light enters a glass block at 90°, then it leaves the block in the same direction. It is when the light ray enters at an *angle* that its direction changes, both on entering and leaving the glass. Light refracts or bends *towards* the normal (an imaginary line at 90° to the glass surface) as it enters the glass, which is more dense than the air. The light ray then refracts or bends *away* from the normal as it leaves the glass and passes into the air, a less dense medium.

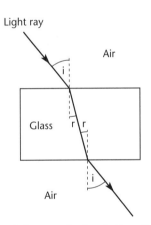

Light ray

Air

Glass

Air

The light ray is bent or 'refracted' as it enters and leaves the glass

---

CHECKPOINT

Describe and explain what happens when a light ray passes from air and enters a glass block at an angle.

 Eye, Reflection, Spectrum, Total internal reflection

RELATIVE ATOMIC MASS

The relative atomic mass of an element is based on the average mass of all the atoms in the element. Carbon-12 (an isotope of carbon) is given a relative atomic mass of 12.00; the masses of all other atoms are then compared with this standard mass. Atoms of magnesium are twice as heavy as carbon atoms, they have a relative atomic mass of 24.

Different **elements** have different proportions of **isotopes**. These are atoms which have different numbers of **neutrons** in their **nucleus** and may therefore have a different **mass** to another atom of the same element.

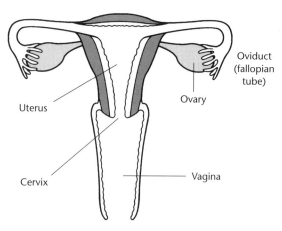

The human female reproductive system

-+- **Menstruation, Sex determination**

-+- **Atomic mass, Radioactivity**

RELAY

A relay is a simple switch, operated by an electromagnet, in which a *small* electric **current** controls a *larger* electric current by switching it on and off.

-+- **Electromagnetic relay**

REPRODUCTION

Human male and female reproductive organs fit together during sexual intercourse so that the sperm (male **gamete**) are placed well inside the female's body. Sperm are made in the testes and pass out of the male's body in a fluid (semen) through the penis during ejaculation. The sperm have only a short distance to swim to enter the uterus. They move across the uterus and travel along the Fallopian tubes towards the ovaries. If there is an egg in the fallopian tube, **fertilization** may take place. The fertilized egg (zygote) travels to the uterus and embeds itself in the lining (endometrium). If fertilization does not take place, the endometrium breaks down and is lost as part of the monthly **menstrual cycle**. Gestation in humans is about nine months; after birth human offspring require a great deal of parental care and attention.

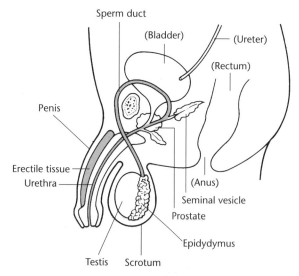

The human male reproductive system

CHECKPOINT

Which one of the following takes place when a sperm fuses with an egg:

(a) fertilization,
(b) intercourse,
(c) menstruation,
(d) ovulation?

RESISTANCE

Resistance is a force that opposes the flow of an **electric current** so that more energy is required to push the charged particles around the circuit. Resistance is measured in units called **ohms**, symbol Ω. A resistor has a resistance of 1 Ω if a voltage of 1 V is required to push a current of 1 A through it. The higher the resistance, the more **voltage** is required. The circuit itself can resist the flow of particles if the wires in the circuit are very *thin* and very *long*, as in the case of a filament in an electric light bulb. Due to this resistance, energy is given out as heat and light. Many household appliances, such as electric heaters, hair driers, toasters, ovens and electric fires use a high resistance wire in their elements so that heat is given out.

Four factors increase the resistance of a wire:

1. **Diameter**: *Thin* wires have *more* resistance than thicker wires.

2. **Length**: *Long* wires have more resistance than shorter wires.

3. **What it's made of**: *Iron* has *more* resistance than copper.

4. **Temperature**: *Hotter* wires have *more* resistance than cooler wires.

To calculate the resistance you need to know the voltage and current, and use the formula:

$$\text{resistance} = \frac{\text{voltage}}{\text{current}} \quad \text{or} \quad R = \frac{V}{I}$$

-+- **Ohm's law – current and voltage**

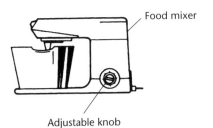

An everyday use of a variable resistor

1. State **four** factors that affect the resistance of a wire.

2. Name **two** household appliances that make use of the fact that a resistor is heated when a current flows through it.

3. The diagram shows a circuit. The reading on the ammeter is 2 A and the reading on the voltmeter is 5 V. What is the value of the resistor?

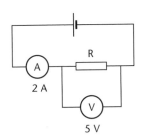

RESISTORS

Resistors are **conductors** that have a **resistance**. The value of a resistor is marked by colour bands on the outside that correspond to the value in **ohms**, Ω. These values can range from millions of ohms to a few ohms.

Resistors are devices that can be used to control the **current** flowing in a circuit, by offering **resistance** to the current.

● A *fixed* resistor is where there is a constant value of the resistor.

● A *variable* resistor (rheostat) is where the resistance can be changed, e.g. by sliding a contact along a length of wire to vary the resistance. For example, in a food mixer, the control knob can increase or decrease the speed of the mixer. The knob is acting as a variable resistor and letting different amounts of current through. When the knob is turned to a high setting, the resistance is *decreased* and *more* current flows to the motor so the speed increases.

-+- *Current – electrical, Ohm's Law*

RESPIRATION

Respiration is the release of **energy** from food, usually involving **oxygen**.

-+- *Aerobic respiration, Anaerobic respiration, Breathing*

REVERSIBLE REACTIONS

Some reactions involving particles are reversible, the reaction can proceed in both directions even at the same time. One example of a reversible reaction occurs in the Haber process, where **nitrogen** and hydrogen are combined to produce **ammonia**, but the ammonia simultaneously decomposes to produce nitrogen and hydrogen. The molecules of nitrogen and hydrogen make contact on the surface of a **catalyst** (iron) and react to produce ammonia.

$$\text{nitrogen} + \text{hydrogen} \rightleftharpoons \text{ammonia}$$
$$N_2 + 3H_2 \rightleftharpoons 2NH_3$$

The sign $\rightleftharpoons$, indicates that the reaction can go in both directions. By changing the conditions, we can determine in which direction the reaction proceeds and what proportion of ammonia is formed:

● High pressure favours the production of ammonia.

● High temperature increases the rate of reaction between nitrogen and hydrogen and the production of ammonia.

● High temperature also favours the decomposition of ammonia and the production of nitrogen and hydrogen.

A balance has to be made. Optimum conditions are usually about 400 °C and 200 atm.

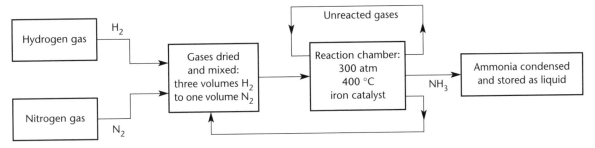

Stages in the production of ammonia

CHECKPOINT

1. What do you understand by a reversible reaction?

2. List **three** conditions that can affect the yield in a reversible reaction.

3. Write an equation for the production of ammonia.

-+- **Nitrates**

ROCK CYCLE

The rock cycle describes how rocks are continuously changing from one type into another over millions of years.

-+- **Earth, Erosion, Igneous rocks, Metamorphic rocks, Sedimentary rocks, Weathering**

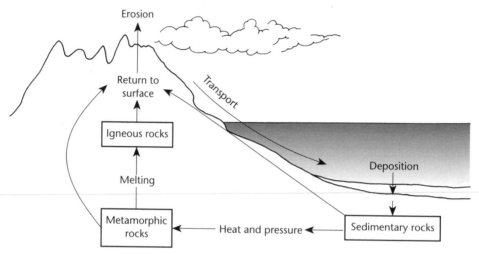

Over millions of years rocks change from one type to another

Colour of salts

Ion	Colour	Ion	Colour
Na$^+$	Colourless	Fe^{2+}	Green
K$^+$	Colourless	Fe^{3+}	Red
Cu^{2+}	Blue/green		

SALIVARY AMYLASE

✦ *Amylase*

SALTS

These are ionic substances formed in reactions between **acids** and **bases** or between acids and **metals**. When solutions of these salts are **evaporated**, crystals (**giant ionic structures**) are formed. Solutions of salts will conduct electricity, showing that they contain **ions**.

Naming salts

The name of the salt depends on the ions present. Each salt contains a positive ion (**cation**), which is obtained from the metal, (e.g. Na$^+$, sodium; Mg^{2+}, magnesium) and a negative ion (**anion**), which is obtained from the acid (e.g. SO$_4^{2-}$, **sulphate**; CO$_3^{2-}$, **carbonate**). The name comes from a combination of both ions, e.g. magnesium sulphate (Mg^{2+}SO$_4^{2-}$).

The charge on the metal ion depends on its group in the **periodic table**, although some metals (**transition metals**) can have ions with different charges. The charge on the ion is indicated by roman numerals in the name, e.g. iron (II) sulphate (FeSO$_4$) has the Fe^{2+} ion present; iron (III) sulphate (Fe(SO$_4$)$_3$) has the Fe^{3+} ion present.

Charges on metal ion

Patterns for salts

Colour of salts

The colour of salts is often due to the metal ion present:

Salts in action

Many salts are present in the sea and in the soil and provide plants with the elements they need, e.g.

- *Nitrogen*: **Nitrates** (NO$_3^-$) in the soil provide the **nitrogen** that is essential for the plant to manufacture **amino acids**.
- *Phosphorus*: Phosphates (PO$_4^{3-}$) are essential for every energy transfer within the cell.
- *Potassium*: (K$^+$) is needed for the activity of many **enzymes**.
- *Calcium*: (Ca^{2+}) raw material for cell walls.
- *Magnesium*: (Mg^{2+}) raw material for making chlorophyll.
- *Sulphur*: Sulphates (SO$_4^{2-}$) are the raw materials for making some amino acids.

Because these elements are needed by plants, their salts are manufactured as **fertilizers**. Examples are ammonium nitrate, ammonium phosphate and potassium chloride. Fertilizers containing these three salts are called N, P, K fertilizers because they provide nitrogen (N), phosphorus (P) and potassium (K).

Other salts can be used in a variety of ways. Calcium sulphate is used as wall plaster; silver chloride is used in photographic film emulsion; iron (II) sulphate is used in iron tablets to treat anaemia.

✦ *Chlorides, Minerals, Valency*

SAMPLING POPULATIONS

Sampling is a method of finding the size of a **population** that is too large to count: e.g. if you were asked to find the numbers of dandelions growing in a large field, it would take too long to count each plant so you could sample the population instead. One technique used to estimate population size is described below:

1. Measure the whole area of study.
2. Use a **quadrat** of known size, e.g. 0.25×0.25 m = $\frac{1}{4}$ m^2
3. Place the quadrat at random.
4. Count the numbers of a particular species of animal, or assess the proportion of the quadrat that is covered by a particular plant.
5. Record your result.

6. Repeat stages 3, 4, and 5 until data have been collected from ten quadrats.

7. Find the average numbers of the species, or average percentage cover of a plant per square metre.

8. Multiply by the total number of square metres to find the total population of the area.

➕ *Ecosystem, Habitat, Mark – release – recapture*

SAPROPHYTES

Saprophytes are organisms that feed on dead or decaying animals and plants. **Bacteria** and fungi are saprophytes that decompose organisms and return the nutrients to the soil.

➕ *Carbon cycle, Food chains and food webs, Nitrogen cycle*

SATELLITES

The **gravitational** pull of the **Earth** provides the pull required to make a satellite follow a circular path around the Earth. For a satellite to orbit just above the atmosphere it needs to orbit at about 8,000 m/s. The **Moon**, a natural satellite of Earth, orbits much further away from Earth at a speed of about 1,000 m/s.

Satellite pictures, like those on the TV weather news, are able to show the position and speed of the changing weather patterns: e.g. a satellite could show the development of a cold front, or the position of a depression as it moved across the Atlantic Ocean, and how temperature varies vertically through the **atmosphere**. The information from satellites is used together with other information from more conventional methods of collecting data such as using hydrogen-filled weather balloons that float in the atmosphere, and computer weather forecasts. Meteorologists are then able to pass information to national and local news stations as well as to aeroplanes and shipping.

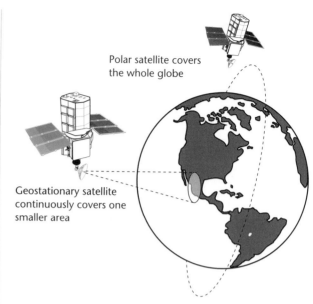

Polar satellite covers the whole globe

Geostationary satellite continuously covers one smaller area

Two types of satellite

The type of satellite used in weather forecasting is a *geostationary* satellite whose speed is the same as that of Earth and is held in orbit by the Earth's gravitational field. Some satellites are able to use both **infra-red** and visible light to collect data, which means that data can be collected during a 24-hour period as a frontal system develops.

➕ *Electromagnetic spectrum, Gravity, Solar cells*

SEASONS

The seasons are caused by the 23° tilt of the **Earth's** axis which means that different parts of the World get different amounts of sunlight:

● Winter occurs in the half of the Earth that is tilted *away* from the Sun;

● Summer occurs in the half of the Earth that is tilted *towards* the Sun.

When it is summer in the northern hemisphere it is winter in the southern hemisphere.

➕ *Solar system, Year*

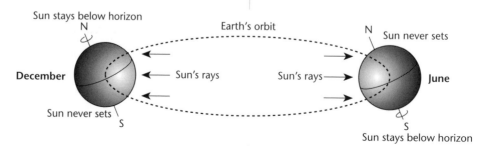

Sun stays below horizon
N

December

Sun's rays

Sun never sets
S

Earth's orbit

N
Sun never sets

Sun's rays

June

S
Sun stays below horizon

How the seasons are caused

SEDIMENTARY ROCKS

Sedimentary rocks are formed when other rocks in the **Earth's** crust are broken down or eroded in one or more ways:

- by the action of moving water
- by wind, ice and frost
- by changes of temperature
- by chemical action, such as acidic rain-water on **limestone**
- by the action of living organisms such as worms and plant roots

The result of **erosion** is to break down the rocks into smaller particles and eventually form soil. Different soils are formed from different types of rocks so soils will differ in their drainage properties, texture, pH and mineral composition. Rivers carry the fine particles such as gravels and sands, and deposit them on the sea bed, where they form successive layers over millions of years. As the layers become compressed, layers of sedimentary rocks or *strata* are formed, such as sandstone and **limestone**. You can sometimes see these strata at the coast where the layers may have been lifted up by movements of the Earth's crust.

-✦- **Fossils, Igneous rocks, Metamorphic rocks, Rock cycle**

SELECTIVE BREEDING

Selective breeding is how new varieties of animals and plants are produced by artificial selection. All the different varieties of dog have been produced by artificial selection of the wolf, a single wild **species**. Our domesticated cattle breeds, poultry, sheep and cereal crops have all been bred from wild species by generations of farmers, e.g.:

- A farmer may decide to cross-breed a sheep that produces high quality wool with a sheep that is very hardy and can tolerate harsh weather conditions
- Horticulturists cross-pollinate plants to produce new varieties that are resistant to disease and have increased yields.

Plant and animal breeding is now big business and so breeders are always on the look out for wild varieties that could be useful.

-✦- **Evolution, Food production, Genetic engineering, Hybrids, Monohybrid inheritance, Natural selection**

SELECTIVELY PERMEABLE MEMBRANE

-✦- **Partially permeable membrane**

SERIES CIRCUIT

All the components of a series circuit are connected one after the other. This means that the same amount of **current** flows through each part of the circuit and no current is used up by the circuit. An **ammeter** can be used to measure the amount of current flowing. The diagram shows a simple series circuit, using the conventional symbols for circuit diagrams.

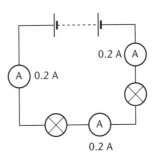

Current in a series circuit

-✦- **Circuit symbols, Current electricity, E.m.f., Parallel circuit,**

SEX DETERMINATION

In humans, the sex of an individual is determined by a small pair of chromosomes called the sex **chromosomes**:

- In a human female these chromosomes are homologous (identical) and are described as X chromosomes:
- In the male, one of the pair is smaller and is called the Y chromosome, with the larger being the X chromosome.

A female individual results from having two X chromosomes and a male from having an X and a Y chromosome. At **meiosis** all the female **gametes** carry an X chromosome whereas *half* of the male gametes carry an X chromosome and *half* carry a Y chromosome:

- If an X bearing sperm **fertilizes** the ovum then the zygote is XX and develops into a girl.
- If a Y bearing sperm **fertilizes** the ovum the zygote is XY and develops into a boy.

The expected ratio of female to male is therefore 1:1, as shown in the table.

Gametes	X
X	XX
Y	XY

> Remember: X egg with X sperm = female XX
> (gametes are all X)
> X egg with Y sperm = male XY (50 per cent of
> gametes are X, 50 per cent are Y)

⊹ *Monohybrid inheritance, Reproduction*

SEX LINKAGE

Certain conditions such as colour blindness and
haemophilia are linked to the X chromosome and
are more likely to affect a male than a female as only
a small part of the Y chromosome is homologous
with the X chromosome: e.g. the non-homologous
part of the X chromosome carries either the
dominant gene for normal vision or the **recessive
gene** for colour blindness. If a male inherits an X
chromosome bearing the recessive gene then he will
be colour blind.

The table shows the inheritance of colour
blindness.

Gametes	Xn
XN	XNXn
Y	XnY

N: normal colour vision
n: colour blindness

XNXn: normal daughter
XnY: colour-blind son

Inheritance of colour blindness

⊹ *Monohybrid inheritance, Variation*

SEXUAL REPRODUCTION

Sexual reproduction usually involves two parents. It
always involves the fusion of two **gametes** – one
male sex cell (sperm) and one female sex cell (egg).
The new cell produced, the **zygote**, divides many
times to form an **embryo** and eventually grows to
become the young organism. Two problems have to
be solved by organisms reproducing in this way:

● How to find a member of the opposite sex

● How to get the sperm and egg together

> Remember: Sexual reproduction is a source of
> genetic variation.

Different ways of overcoming these problems have
evolved:

● In humans, **fertilization** is *internal* so the egg and
sperm fuse inside the female's body.

● In frogs, fertilization is *external* with the sperm
being shed over the eggs that are laid in water.

Usually offspring that are produced by internal
fertilization are better protected as they develop
either in an egg with a tough shell, or inside the
mother, as in humans.

> Remember: The main advantage of **sexual
> reproduction** compared with **asexual
> reproduction** is that the offspring will vary from
> each other and from the parents – variety can
> mean the difference between success or
> extinction for the species in a constantly
> changing environment.

⊹ *Asexual reproduction, Natural selection,
Reproduction, Selective breeding, Species*

SKELETON

The function of your skeleton is to support your
body and give **muscles** a firm attachment so that
they can contract to move your bones.

Between your bones are *joints*; e.g.:

● At your shoulder is a ball and socket joint that
allows your arm to swivel around in any
direction.

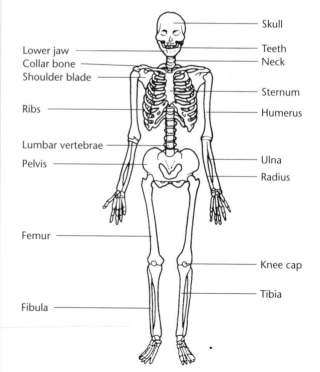

Skeleton

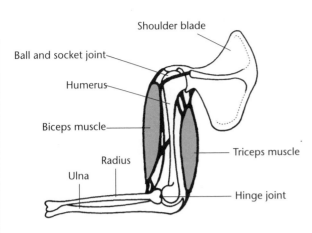

The bones and muscles of the upper arm showing the elbow and shoulder joints

● At your elbow is a hinge joint that allows your lower arm to move backwards and forwards.

✦ *Organ system, Reflex arc*

SMOKING

Cigarette smoking can affect the body in many ways:

● Chemicals in the tobacco smoke can cause **cancer** in the lungs, and as a result the lungs are destroyed.

● Carbon monoxide, a gas in cigarette smoke, mixes with **haemoglobin** in the **red blood cells** and makes the blood less efficient at carrying oxygen. As a result the blood vessels around the heart become weak and this may result in a heart attack.

● The tiny hairs in the lungs that remove dust and mucus from the lungs become paralysed, so sticky phlegm collects in the lungs, causing infection. Smokers try to move the phlegm by heavy coughing, which damages the lining of the lungs and reduces the number of air sacs in the lungs. There is less surface area for oxygen

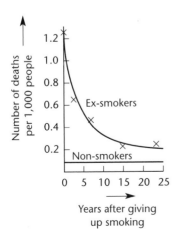

The risk of dying from lung cancer is reduced if you are a non-smoker

to diffuse into the blood stream so the smokers become out of breath and may suffer from bronchitis.

● Pregnant women who smoke can give birth to babies that are undersized and sometimes born prematurely.

CHECKPOINT

Describe **two** effects of cigarette smoking on the body.

✦ *Coronary artery disease, Drugs, Exercise*

SODIUM CHLORIDE

Sodium chloride is common **salt**, the salt we use on our food. The **chemical formula** for sodium chloride is NaCl. Sodium chloride contains sodium **ions** (Na^+) and chloride ions (Cl^-). It can be found in sea water, and is often extracted from sea water by allowing the water to **evaporate** in large, shallow ponds leaving white crystalline salts. The salts contain mostly sodium chloride but also other salts such as potassium chloride. In Britain, salt is found in large deposits in such places as Cheshire, where it is mined.

Sodium chloride is a compound of an **alkali metal** and a **halogen**. It is described as an alkali metal halide: an ionic compound that dissolves in water.

✦ *Alkali metals, Chemical equations, Compounds, Electrolysis, Ionic bonding*

SOLAR CELLS

These are photoelectric devices that absorb the **Sun's** energy and convert it into electricity. However, many thousands of solar cells are needed to produce useful amounts of electricity. One of their main uses is in **satellites** and spacecraft where conventional batteries would be difficult to replace!

✦ *Alternative energy, Solar energy*

SOLAR ENERGY

Solar energy is the energy from the **Sun**. A common use of solar energy Is to heat up water that is inside a solar panel. These panels are usually painted black so that they absorb as much heat as possible. The solar-heated water is then pumped to an ordinary hot water tank where the water can be heated electrically. It is obviously much cheaper to heat water that has already been warmed up than to heat water from cold. (See the diagram below.)

-+- *Alternative energy, Geothermal energy, Wave energy, Wind energy*

SOLAR SYSTEM

- The **Sun** is at the centre of our solar system.

- The sun is the source of light and other forms of **electromagnetic radiation**.

- Planets, asteroids and comets orbit around the Sun.

- The nine planets, including **Earth**, have elliptical orbits around the Sun owing to **gravitational** force of attraction that exists between the Sun and the planets (orbit time increases the furthur from the Sun).

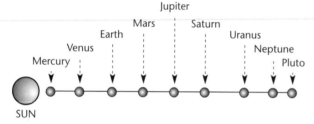

How the planets are arranged

- The planets are non-luminous, they reflect light from the Sun (**stars** emit their own light).

- Some planets have **satellites** that orbit around them.

There are two groups of planets:

- Those nearer the Sun (Mercury, Venus, Earth and Mars), have *small* diameters and high **density**.

- Those further away from the Sun (Jupiter, Saturn, Uranus, Neptune and Pluto) have *large* diameters (except Pluto) but *low* density.

> Remember: Planets that are furthur away from the Sun take longer to orbit the Sun and have lower mean temperatures than those nearer the Sun.

Please see the table opposite for the main members of the solar system.

> Remember: In the exam you may have to interpret data about the planets but you don't need to learn all this information.

-+- *Seasons, Stars, Year*

SOLID

All matter can be classified as either solid, **liquid**, or **gas**. These are called the three states of matter. In a solid the particles are close together and are vibrating in 'fixed' positions. Solids keep their shape and resist being changed in shape. Some solids occur naturally with straight sides and sharp corners; these are called crystals.

-+- *Brownian motion, Kinetic theory*

SOLUTE

A solute is a substance that will dissolve in a **solvent** to produce a **solution**. Solutes can be **solid**, **liquid** or **gas**:

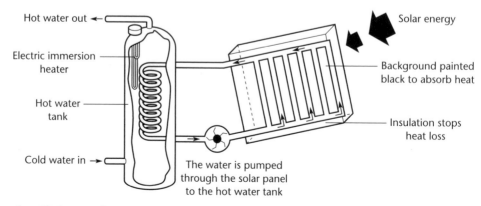

A hot water system that uses solar energy

The main members of the solar system										
Body	1 Diameter	2 Mass	3 Surface gravity	4 Density (g/cm³)	5 Period of spin			6 Angle of tilt between axis and orbit (°)	7 Average distance from Sun (Sun– Earth = 1)	8 Period of orbit (years)	9 No. of moons (* = plus rings)
	(Earth = 1)	(Earth = 1)	(Earth = 1)		Days	Hours	Minutes				
Sun	109.00	335 000.00	28.00	1.4	25	9		97			
Mercury	0.40	0.06	0.40	5.4	58	16		90	0.4	0.2	0
Venus	0.95	0.82	0.90	5.3	243	7		267	0.7	0.6	0
Earth	1.00	1.00	1.00	5.5		23	56	113	1.0	1.0	1
Moon	0.27	0.01	0.17	1.9	27	7		91	1.0	1.0	0
Mars	0.53	0.11	0.40	4.0		24	37	114	1.5	1.9	2
Jupiter	11.18	318.00	2.60	1.3		9	50	93	5.2	11.9	16*
Saturn	9.42	95.00	1.10	0.7		10	14	116	9.5	29.5	17*
Uranus	3.84	14.50	0.90	1.3		18		187	19.2	84.0	15*
Neptune	3.93	17.10	1.20	1.6		19		118	30.1	164.8	8*
Pluto	0.31	0.0022	0.20	2.0	6	9	17	?	39.4	249.0	1

Some examples of solutes		
Solution	Solute	Solvent
Lemonade	Carbon dioxide	Water
Wine	Alcohol	Water
Sea water	Salts	Water

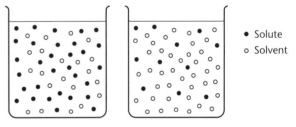

A concentrated solution   A dilute solution

• Solute
○ Solvent

Solutions

Solid solutes can be divided into two groups:

● Those that contain **ions** – these often dissolve in **water**

● Those that contain **molecules** – these are often insoluble in water but will dissolve in certain other solvents

SOLUTION

Solutions can be made by dissolving substances in other substances so that they are eventually mixed:

● The substance that is dissolved is called the **solute**.

● The substance that does the dissolving is called the **solvent**. A solvent is normally a liquid (it could be a gas). **Water** is a very good solvent. A solvent can be a solid, liquid or gas:

● A *concentrated* solution can be made by dissolving a *large* amount of solute in a *small* amount of solvent.

● A *dilute* solution can be made by dissolving a *little* solute in a *large* amount of solvent.

The concentration of solutions can be measured as grams of solute per cubic decimetre of solution (g/dm³) or as moles of solute per cubic decimetre of solution (mol/dm³). A *saturated* solution is one that contains the maximum amount of dissolved solute.

⎯✦⎯ *Acids, Molar solutions, Mole, Osmosis*

SOLVENT

A solvent is a substance – usually a liquid (sometimes a gas) that can dissolve another substance to produce a **solution**.

Water is a good solvent because it can dissolve many substances e.g. **salts**, sugar, or gases such as **oxygen** and **carbon dioxide**. Some substances, however, are insoluble in water, but may dissolve in other liquids, e.g. propane will dissolve nail varnish, xylene will dissolve sulphur. Solvents such as these are non-aqueous solvents and are important for dissolving oils and grease. Perchloroethene is a solvent used in 'dry cleaning' – dry because water is not involved. Correction fluid sometimes contains a solvent 1,1,1-trichloroethane, and carries a hazard warning symbol.

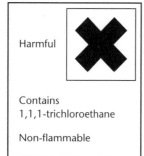

Harmful	✖

Contains
1,1,1-trichloroethane

Non-flammable

WARNING DO NOT
DRINK OR INHALE

A hazard warning on a correction fluid bottle

Solvent abuse

Many glues and other household products contain a chemical solvent that prevents them going solid. Sometimes people breathe in the fumes given off by these solvents. This practice is known as solvent abuse or more commonly 'glue sniffing'. People who abuse solvents in this way, often have a cough, sore throat, sores around the mouth, and are irritable and moody. The solvent fumes affect the **brain** and can produce a temporary sensation of pleasure. Prolonged solvent abuse can lead to a delirium and unconsciousness. People can die from falling down stairs or into water or choking on their own vomit.

-✦- *Alcohol, Drugs*

SOUND WAVES

Sound waves are the only waves that are **longitudinal waves**. These waves are like the waves produced by a long spring.

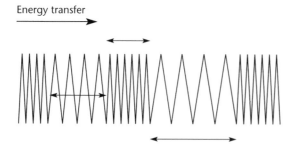

Energy transfer

The energy is being transferred along the spring, but the particles are oscillating from left to right

-✦- *Amplitude, Ear, Frequency, Loudspeaker, Microphone, Speed, Ultrasonic waves, Wavelength*

SPECIES

This word describes organisms that are related closely enough to breed successfully. The offspring can reproduce themselves when they mature. It is possible for horses and donkeys to produce offspring

called mules, but these are sterile and cannot breed. Of all the groups that we use to classify living things, the species (breeding group) is the smallest.

-✦- *Population, Selective breeding, Sexual reproduction*

SPECTRUM

White light is made up of seven different colours each of which has a different **wavelength**. When a ray of white light enters a prism each of the different wavelengths are **refracted** (bent) by different amounts because they travel through the prism at different speeds. This effect produces a spectrum of all the different colours that make up white light.

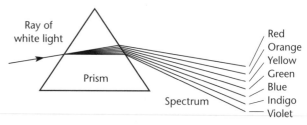

Ray of white light

Prism

Spectrum

Red
Orange
Yellow
Green
Blue
Indigo
Violet

White light is split into a spectrum of colours as it passes through the prism

-✦- *Universe*

SPEED

Speed is the distance travelled in a unit of time, such as metres per second (m/s), or kilometres per hour (km/h).

In the laboratory you may have made measurements of speed using a ticker-timer. This instrument is a type of clock that produces 50 ticks every second, equal to five ticks every 0.1 s. These ticks appear as dots on a strip of ticker-tape paper, which shows how far the tape has been moved between each dot. The time interval between each dot is 0.02 s.

● When the dots are *close together* the tape has been moved slowly.

● When the dots are *far apart* the tape has been moved quickly.

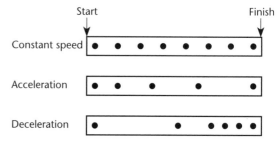

Start   Finish

Constant speed

Acceleration

Deceleration

Each piece of ticker tape shows a different type of movement

The ticker tape is usually attached to a moving trolley to study how the trolley moved. The tape shown below was produced by the trolley moving down the runway. The trolley started slowly and then accelerated.

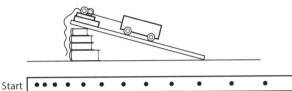

Start

The ticker tape shows how the trolley accelerated

CHECKPOINT

1. What is the average speed of a vehicle which travels 30 k in 15 min:
   (a) 2 km/h; (b) 45 km/h; (c) 120 km/h;
   (d) 250 km/h?

2. The graph shows how the speed of an object varies with time.

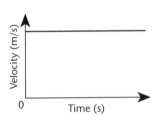

The object is:
(a) falling freely,
(b) moving with constant speed,
(c) moving with constant acceleration,
(d) moving with constant deceleration.

SPEED, FREQUENCY AND WAVELENGTH

$$\begin{array}{ccc} \text{Speed} & & \text{frequency} \times \text{wavelength} \\ \text{(metres per second)} & = & \text{(hertz)} \quad \text{(metres)} \end{array}$$

$$v = F \times \lambda$$

For example, if a wave is travelling with a **frequency** of 30 Hz and has a **wavelength** of 3 m, its velocity is 90 m/s.

The waves in the **electromagnetic spectrum** all travel at the same **velocity** of 300,000,000 metres per second or 3×10^8 m/s. **Sound waves**, however, travel much more slowly at approximately 330 m/s. For example, if a sound wave has a wavelength of 0.6 m, and travels at 330 m/s its frequency is 330/0.6 = 550 Hz.

-•- **Vehicle – stopping distance**

CHECKPOINT

1. What is the formula linking speed, frequency and wavelength?

2. What is the frequency of a sound wave, travelling at 330 m/s, which has a wavelength of 0.25 m?

SPERM

-•- **Gamete**

STARCH

Starch is a natural polymer that is made by green plants. It consists of long chains of glucose molecules (the monomer) joined together. Starch is a **carbohydrate** and as a food is a useful source of energy. The starch molecule is too large to pass through the gut wall into the **blood system**, so is broken down into smaller units in the digestive system.

-•- **Digestion, Hydrolysis**

STARS

Evolution of a star

● Stars **evolve** over millions of years and have a finite **life span**.

● The **Sun** is one of many millions of **stars** which make up the Milky Way **galaxy**; the universe is a system of an enormous number of galaxies held together by gravitational forces.

● *Distances* in the universe are measured in **light years**: the distance travelled by **light** on one Earth year.

● *Stars*: very large clouds of hydrogen, helium and dust which collapse under gravity; **hydrogen** gas is converted to **helium** in process of **nuclear fusion**; thermal energy is released when small hydrogen nuclei are joined together to form helium nuclei; surface temperature 6,000 °C.

CHECKPOINT

The flow chart below shows a possible life cycle of a middle-aged star, such as the Sun.

clouds of gas and dust → star contracts → main sequence star → star expands → red giant → X → dark body

What is X: (a) black hole; (b) galaxy; (c) nebula; (d) white dwarf?

-•- **Solar system**

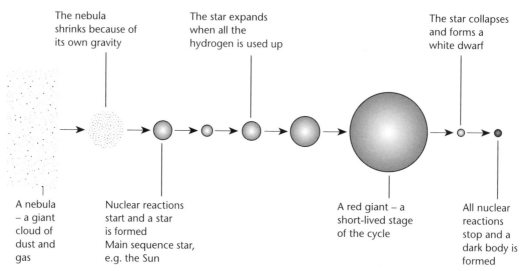

The nebula shrinks because of its own gravity

The star expands when all the hydrogen is used up

The star collapses and forms a white dwarf

A nebula – a giant cloud of dust and gas

Nuclear reactions start and a star is formed
Main sequence star, e.g. the Sun

A red giant – a short-lived stage of the cycle

All nuclear reactions stop and a dark body is formed

The life cycle of a star

STATE SYMBOLS

Chemical equations tell us which substances react and what products are formed. They can also tell us the *state* of the reactants or products, if for example they are in a gaseous form or if they are dissolved in ***water***. This is important because some reactants will only react if they are in a particular state. We can show the state of reactants and products by adding symbols of state:

- (g) means ***gas***
- (l) means ***liquid***
- (s) means ***solid***
- (aq) means dissolved in water

Examples of the use of these symbols are:

$$2Na(s) + Cl_2(g) \rightarrow 2NaCl(s)$$
$$Mg(s) + 2HCl(aq) \rightarrow MgCl_2(aq) + H_2(g)$$

HCl (aq) indicates that dilute hydrochloric acid is being used.

-⫶- *Chemical reactions, Ionic equations*

STATES OF MATTER

-⫶- *Gas, Kinetic theory, Liquid, Solid*

SUGARS

Sugars are ***carbohydrates***: sugar molecules consist of carbon, hydrogen and oxygen atoms. Simple sugars are manufactured by plants during the process of ***photosynthesis***.

Two common sugars are:

- **Glucose**: Chemical formula $C_6H_{12}O_6$ – the simple sugar produced by plants during ***photosynthesis***.

- **Sucrose**: Chemical formula $C_{12}H_{22}O_{11}$ – the sugar we use to sweeten tea, found in large amounts in plants such as sugar cane; sucrose is like a double glucose molecule.

-⫶- *Digestion*

SULPHATES

Sulphates are ***salts*** that contain the sulphate ***ion*** (SO_4^{2-}). Examples are copper sulphate, magnesium sulphate, calcium sulphate. Most sulphates are ***soluble*** in water, except those of calcium, barium and lead. Calcium sulphate is found as the rock gypsum and is used for making plaster.

-⫶- *Chemical formulae, Valency*

SULPHUR DIXOIDE

Sulphur dioxide (SO_2) is a poisonous, choking ***gas***. Sulphur dioxide is formed when sulphur is burned in air:

$$\text{sulphur} + \text{oxygen} \rightarrow \text{sulphur dioxide}$$
$$S(s) + O_2(g) \rightarrow SO_2(g)$$

Since sulphur is present as an impurity in ***fossil fuels*** such as coal and oil, that are burned to ***generate electricity***, sulphur dioxide can be released into the ***atmosphere*** as a pollutant.

When ***metals*** are extracted from metal sulphide ores, the ore is first roasted to produce a metal oxide, and sulphur dioxide is a waste product:

lead sulphide + oxygen → lead oxide + sulphur dioxide

Sulphur dioxide is a major contributor to ***acid rain*** because it reacts with oxygen and ***ozone*** in the atmosphere to produce ***sulphuric acid***.

-⫶- *Pollution*

SUN

The Sun is one of billions of **stars** that make up a **galaxy** known as the Milky Way. There are billions of galaxies like the Milky Way in the **universe**. The Sun is made of hydrogen and helium gas; the temperature is about 6000 °C at its surface. At the centre of the Sun the temperature is much higher and this is where **nuclear fusion** is taking place as the hydrogen is being converted to helium. The Sun is about half way through its life cycle of 9,600 million years and is about a million times larger than **Earth**.

-+- **Solar system, Stars**

S-WAVES

-+- **Earth, Earthquakes, Transverse waves**

SYNAPSE

-+- **Reflex arc**

TESTIS

The male sex organ that produces sperm, or male sex cells (**gametes**). The testes are usually held in the *scrotum*, a bag of skin that hangs outside the body where the temperature is slightly lower than that inside the body. The sperm develop better at a lower temperature. Inside the testis is a 50 cm long, narrow tube where the sperm are produced by **meiosis**.

✦ *Fertilization, Reproduction*

THREE-PIN PLUG

- The *live* wire is coloured brown, and is connected to the live pin.

- The *neutral* wire is coloured blue, and is connected to the neutral pin

- The *earth* wire is coloured green and yellow, and is connected to the earth pin at the top of the plug.

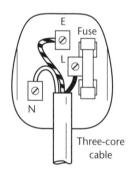

The correct connections for a three-pin plug

CHECKPOINT

Complete the table to show what pin each colour wire should be connected to:

Colour	Pin
Blue	....
Brown	....
Green and yellow	....

✦ *Earth wire, Fuse*

TIDAL ENERGY

Tidal energy involves using the massive changes in the level of the sea that occur twice a day as a result of the gravitational effect of the **Sun** and **Moon** on the **Earth**. This causes regular tidal movements of the oceans that are used to push water into reservoirs, from where the water is used to drive turbines and produce electricity. There is a very large power station on the coast of Brittany in France that uses tidal energy.

✦ *Alternative energy, Generation of electricity, Tides, Wave energy*

TIDES

The **Moon** exerts a **gravitational** pull on the water that is on the surface of the **Earth**. The effect of this, on the side *nearest* the Moon, is to pull the water towards the Moon and produce a high tide. A high tide also happens on the side of the Earth *furthest away* from the Moon. Due to the rotation of the Earth these high tides happen every 12 h.
  Although the **Sun** is much further away from the Earth, it too has a gravitational pull on the Earth:

- When the Sun and Moon are *in line*, about twice a month, their combined gravitational pull causes a very high tide or 'spring' tide. These tides have very *large* tidal ranges, this means they have 'very high' high tides and 'very low' low tides.

- When the Sun and Moon are at *right angles* with each other, about twice a month, the gravitational effect is cancelled out and weak tides, called 'neap' tides, with *small* tidal ranges are produced. These tides have 'low' high tides and 'high' low tides.

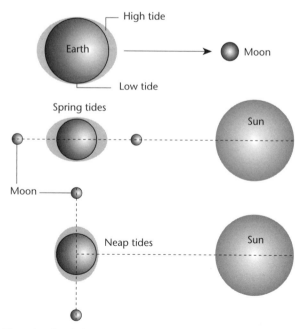

How 'spring' tides and 'neap' tides are caused

✦ *Tidal energy, Year*

TISSUE

A tissue is a collection of **cells** that work together, e.g. **muscle** tissue in animals, and **xylem** tissue in plants.

-+- **Cell – biological, Organ, Organ system**

TOTAL INTERNAL REFLECTION

Anything light can travel through is called a medium, e.g. **air**, **water** and **glass**. When light travels from a denser to a less dense medium, e.g. from glass to air, there is a strong **refracted** ray, and a weak ray that is **reflected** back into the glass. When the angle of incidence reaches a certain critical angle of incidence, then total internal reflection occurs. All the light rays are reflected back inside the glass block.

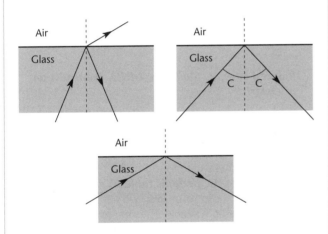

Two practical uses of total internal reflection are:

- Optical fibres
- Periscopes

Fibre optics

An optical fibre consists of two types of glass (the *core glass fibre* and the cladding glass fibre). When light passes through the optical fibre it is continually being totally internally reflected, 'bouncing' along the fibre; it does not matter if the fibre is coiled or knotted, the light will still get through. The two types of glass must be very pure, ensuring that this is so is the most difficult part of the manufacturing process.

Optical fibres are now being used instead of copper cable to carry telephone messages. The messages are carried as pulses of light. Optical fibres are better than copper cables in that they can carry many more messages for the same thickness of cable.

Optical fibres allow for the rapid transmission of data using digital signals. These signals are sent as pulses of light. Information, such as the Internet and other types of communication between computers, can be transmitted at high speed.

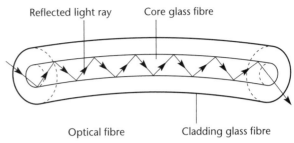

Fibre optic

-+- **Lasers**

Periscope

One practical use of the reflection of light is the periscope.

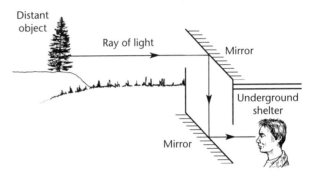

An observer in an underground shelter uses a periscope to see above the ground

---

CHECKPOINT

1. Describe what happens when total internal reflection occurs in glass.

2. State **two** uses of total internal reflection.

-+- **Reflection, Refraction**

TRANSFORMERS

There are three important facts to remember about transformers:

- Transformers change **voltage**
- Transformers only work on **alternating current**
- Transformers contain an iron core and two coils of wire, a primary coil and a secondary coil

A *step-up* transformer:

- Gives out a *higher* voltage than the input voltage
- Has more turns on the secondary coil than the primary coil

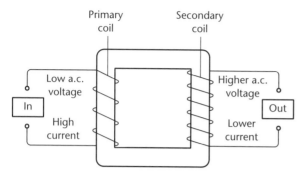

A step-up transformer gives out a higher voltage than the input voltage

A *step-down* transformer:

- Gives out a *lower* voltage than the input voltage

- Has more turns on the primary coil than the secondary coil

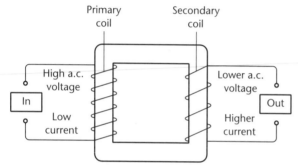

A step-down transformer gives out a lower voltage than the input voltage

When the primary coil is connected to an alternating current, it acts like an **electromagnet** that is switched on and off very quickly, causing a current to flow backwards and forwards. This sets up a changing **magnetic field** in the iron core that **induces** an alternating current in the secondary coil.

You can calculate the voltage induced in the secondary coil using the following formula:

$$\frac{\text{voltage across secondary coil}}{\text{voltage across primary coil}} = \frac{\text{number of turns in secondary coil}}{\text{number of turns in primary coil}}$$

$$\frac{V_2}{V_1} = \frac{N_2}{N_1}$$

For example, if a step-down transformer has 100 turns on the primary coil and ten turns on the secondary coil, you can calculate the output voltage, given that the input voltage is 240 V:

$$V_2 = \frac{10}{100} \times 240 = 24 \text{ V}$$

The output voltage is 24 V.

> *Remember: One of the main uses of transformers is in the National Grid system where **step-up** transformers **increase** the voltage and **lower** the current so that less electricity is wasted as heat. **Step-down** transformers are used in many household appliances such as televisions, computers, radios and washing machines in order to reduce the mains voltage to a lower voltage.*

CHECKPOINT

A step-down transformer has 300 turns on the primary coil and an input voltage of 240 V. The secondary coil has an output voltage of 40 V. How many turns must there be on the secondary coil:

(a) 40;   (b) 50;   (c) 100;   (d) 300?

✦ *Induced current, Mains electricity, Transmission of electricity*

TRANSITION METALS

The transition metals are found in a block between group 2 and 3 of the **periodic table**. When these metals react they can form **ions** with different charges (they have variable **valency**); the charge on their ions is usually 1+, 2+ or 3+: e.g. copper can form ions of Cu^+ or Cu^{2+}; iron can form ions of Fe^{2+} or Fe^{3+}.

The size of the charge on the ion in a compound is shown by roman numerals: e.g. in copper (II) oxide, the ion present is Cu^{2+}; in copper (I) oxide, the ion present is Cu^+.

The compounds of transition metals are also often coloured.

Some transition metal compounds			
Compound	*Colour*	*Formula*	*Metal ion*
Copper (II) sulphate	Blue	$CuSO_4$	Cu^{2+}
Iron (II) sulphate	Green	$FeSO_4$	Fe^{2+}
Iron (III) oxide	Red	Fe_2O_3	Fe^{3+}
Copper (I) oxide	Red	Cu_2O	Cu^+
Copper (II) oxide	Black	CuO	Cu^{2+}

They share the following properties:

- High melting points

- High density

- Used as catalysts

- Form brightly coloured compounds due to the colour of the metal ion: e.g. iron, manganese, copper and zinc

Uses of transition metals:

- **Iron**: When mixed with carbon and other elements, iron is used to make steel alloys such as stainless steel

- **Copper:** Used for electrical wiring, water pipes, and mixed with other metals to make brass and bronze

- **Zinc:** Used as a coating for galvanized steel, and mixed with other metals to make brass

---

CHECKPOINT

1. List **three** properties shared by the transition metals.

2. State **two** examples of transition metals and give *one* use of each example.

✦ *Electroplating, Metals as elements, Salts*

TRANSMISSION OF ELECTRICITY

Electricity from a power station is transmitted across the country by the National Grid system. The commonest method is by overhead power cables, carried on pylons. Sometimes, underground transmission lines are used. Each method has its advantages and disadvantages:

- **Overhead cables**: These are cheaper to install, and easier to repair, but unsightly, dangerous to people (especially those using kites), and to people moving boats with high masts or when carrying fishing rods.

- **Underground cables**: These are more expensive to install, and more difficult to repair, but can be hidden underground and present no danger to people.

Electricity is transmitted from power stations at voltages of 400,000 V. The reason for using such high **voltages** is that there is a very low current and

energy loss is very small. If electricity was transmitted at a lower voltage there would be a greater current and more energy would be lost as heat.

CHECKPOINT

In the National Grid system, what is carried by the overhead cables:

(a) alternating current at low voltage,
(b) alternating current at high voltage,
(c) direct current at low voltage,
(d) direct current at high voltage?

✦ *Generation of electricity, Mains electricity, Transformers*

TRANSPIRATION

Transpiration is the loss of water vapour by **evaporation** from the leaves of plants. Water vapour moves out of the leaf through the stomata (tiny holes), which are usually found on the underside of the leaf. The stomata can close to prevent excessive water loss by the plant.

The following factors increase the rate of transpiration:

- Light intensity

- Increase in temperature

- Increase in air movement

- Decrease in humidity

A potometer can be used to investigate the rate of water loss from a plant. The rate of movement of the air bubble indicates the rate of transpiration (see overleaf for diagram).

CHECKPOINT

List **three** factors that would decrease the rate of water loss from plant leaves.

✦ *Transport in plants, Water cycle*

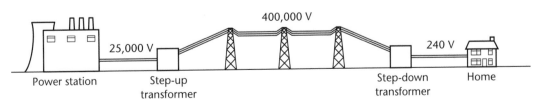

How electricity gets from the power station to your home

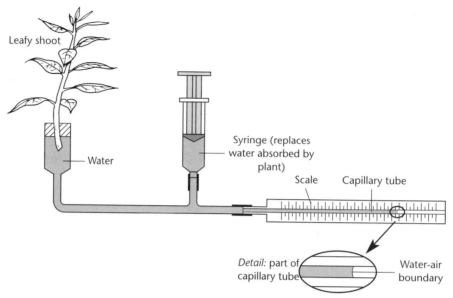

Leafy shoot

Water

Syringe (replaces
water absorbed by
plant)

Scale   Capillary tube

Detail: part of
capillary tube

Water-air
boundary

The potometer

TRANSPORT IN PLANTS

The vascular tissues in plant stems, leaves and roots transport materials around the plant. There are two types of tissue: xylem and phloem.

- The xylem tubes are dead cells that carry **water** and **mineral salts** from the roots to the leaves. This can be observed by cutting a stem and placing it in a red dye. After a few hours the red dye appears in the xylem tissue of the stem.

- The phloem tubes carry food such as dissolved **sugars** from one part of the plant to another.

➕ *Osmosis, Partially permeable membrane, Transpiration*

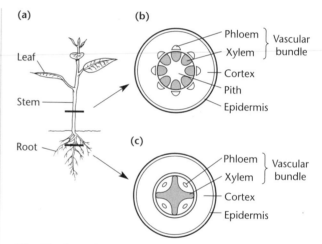

(a)

Leaf

Stem

Root

(b)

Phloem ⎫ Vascular
Xylem ⎬ bundle
Cortex
Pith
Epidermis

(c)

Phloem ⎫ Vascular
Xylem ⎬ bundle
Cortex
Epidermis

Distribution of vascular tissues in a dicotyledonous plant (vertical and transverse sections): (a) complete plant; (b) stem section; (c) root section

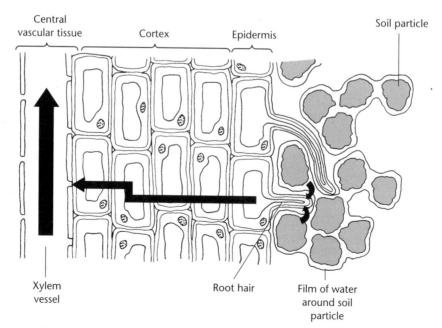

Central
vascular tissue

Cortex

Epidermis

Soil particle

Xylem
vessel

Root hair

Film of water
around soil
particle

Absorption of water and minerals in the root (arrows show direction of water movement)

CHECKPOINT

1. Describe the process by which water enters the root hair cells from the soil.

2. What is transported in each of the following tissues:
   (a) xylem,
   (b) phloem?

TRANSVERSE WAVE

Transverse waves are like the waves produced in a piece of rope when it moves up and down. **Energy** is transferred along the wave, although the **particles** only move up and down, at right angles to the direction of the wave.

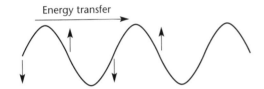

Energy transfer

Energy is being transferred along this tranverse wave, but the particles only move up and down

Examples of transverse waves are:

- Electromagnetic waves

- Waves in water

- S-waves (shake waves) produced when earthquakes occur

CHECKPOINT

When a person makes a rope move up and down to represent wave motion, what is being transferred along the rope?

⬩ *Earthquakes, Longitudinal wave*

TROPHIC LEVEL

⬩ *Ecosystem – energy transfer through the ecosystem, Food chains and food webs*

ULTRASONIC WAVES

Sound waves with frequencies higher than 20,000 Hz can be reproduced by electronic systems. One of the uses of these ultrasonic waves is in hospitals for pre-natal scanning of a foetus. High frequency waves are emitted and passed through the abdomen of the pregnant woman. An image of the foetus is produced on a screen so that the radiographer can check that the foetus is developing normally.

> ### CHECKPOINT
>
> Why is it preferable to use ultrasonic waves and not X-rays to examine a foetus developing in a woman?

ULTRAVIOLET RAYS

Ultraviolet rays are a form of **electromagnetic radiation**. Their wavelengths are shorter than those of visible light. Ultraviolet rays cannot be detected by the human **eye** but it is thought that some insects such as bees may be able to detect the rays. Ultraviolet rays cause burning of the skin when exposed to sunshine and causes the skin to produce the pigment melanin, which gives light-skinned people a suntan. Prolonged exposure to ultraviolet rays may cause harmful skin **cancers**, especially in fair-skinned people.

One use of ultraviolet rays is in the security marking of electrical equipment and other valuable objects. The marking only shows up under ultraviolet light so that stolen goods can be identified and returned to their owners.

UNIVERSAL INDICATOR

Indicators can be used to detect the difference between **acids** and **alkalis**. The most commonly used indicator is universal indicator because it not only tells us if something is **acid** or **alkaline** but also if the acid (or alkali) is strong or weak. It can be used as a liquid (usually green) or soaked onto a type of blotting paper and used as a paper. The paper has to be wet in order to work because acids only behave as acids in solution. The colour of the indicator matches a number that indicates the acidity of the solution:

- If a solution turns the universal indicator light green, then it is neutral and has a pH of 7.

- If a solution turns the universal indicator yellow, then it is a weak acid and has a pH of 6.

The *strength* of an acid or alkali is measured on the **pH scale**. This has a range of 1 to 14 and is a measure of the hydrogen ion concentration (acidity).

> *Remember: Low numbers indicate high acidity (and high H⁺ ion concentration)*

Following an acid/alkali reaction

Indicators can also be used to follow the course of a **neutralization** reaction between an acid and an alkali.

- If universal indicator is added to a strong alkaline solution the indicator will turn violet.

- If a solution of acid is added a small amount at a time then the indicator will change colour through blue to green at which point the solution is neutral (the acid has reacted with all the alkali present).

- If acid is continued to be added the indicator will eventually turn red indicating the solution is now strongly acidic.

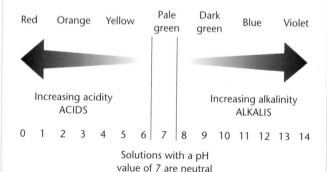

Universal indicator and the pH scale

⊹ *Litmus*

UNIVERSE

The 'big bang' theory of the origin of the Universe suggests that an explosion may have occurred about 15 thousand million years ago to create the Universe. At one time **galaxies** may have been much closer to each other and may have been one big mass. It would seem that galaxies are now moving away from each other, possibly as a result of a massive explosion or 'big bang'. Evidence for this is suggested by the fact that the light from other galaxies has shifted to the red end of the **spectrum**. The further away galaxies are, the bigger this 'red shift'.

CHECKPOINT

Explain how light from stars in distant galaxies can be used to support the theory that the universe is expanding.

-+- *Solar system, Stars*

URANIUM

Uranium is a metallic ***element*** – chemical symbol U. The main source of uranium is pitchblende, in which it is found as an oxide. Uranium has three ***isotopes*** – U-238, U-235 and U-234.

U-235 is of great importance because it is used as a nuclear fuel. When bombarded with ***neutrons*** it breaks into smaller pieces, releasing vast amounts of energy:

$$^{235}_{92}U + n \rightarrow {}^{144}_{56}Ba + {}^{90}_{36}Kr + 2n + energy$$

All the isotopes of uranium are radioactive, U-238 decays to produce U-234, but is not used as a nuclear fuel.

-+- *Nuclear power, Radioactivity*

UREA

Urea is a waste product produced by the breakdown of excess ***amino acids*** in the liver, and removed from the body by the ***kidneys***. It passes out of the body in ***urine***. Adults excrete about 30 g a day. Urea is a white, crystalline solid that is manufactured industrially for preparing urea-formaldehyde plastics, barbiturates (drugs) and as a ***fertilizer***.

> Remember: Urea is made in the **liver** and excreted by the **kidneys**.

-+- *Excretion*

URINE

Urine consists mainly of water, with some dissolved salts and ***urea***. It is excreted from the ***kidneys***. Urine is carried by the ureter to the bladder, and then to outside the body by the urethra. A doctor will sometimes test your urine to see if there are any substances present that may indicate that there is something wrong with you: e.g. if there is sugar present in the urine it may indicate that a person is ***diabetic*** and in need of medical treatment.

> Remember: The **ureter** carries urine from the kidney to the bladder. The **urethra** carries urine from the bladder to outside the body.

-+- *Excretion, Osmoregulation*

UTERUS

The uterus (womb) is part of the female reproductive system. It is a thick-walled muscular organ where the ***zygote*** (fertilized egg) is implanted after ***fertilization***. During the development of the zygote into an ***embryo*** and ***foetus*** it is protected and nourished while it is in the uterus.

-+- *Menstruation, Reproduction*

VACCINE

A vaccine usually contains weakened or dead *micro-organisms* that are injected into the body to help overcome an infectious disease.

✦ *Antibody, White blood cells*

VALENCY

A *chemical formula* for a *compound* shows the ratio of *atoms* present in that compound and whether they are joined by *ionic* or *covalent* bonds. Each atom has a 'combining power' which is called the *valency*. The valency of an atom depends on the number of *electrons* in its outer shell and hence its position in the *periodic table*: e.g. atoms in *group 1* have a valency of one; atoms in group 2 have a valency of two.

In general, as one moves across the *periodic table* the valency gradually increases to a maximum of four, then gradually decreases to zero, although there are some important exceptions.

Valencies for some elements								
	Na	Mg	Al	Si	P	S	Cl	Ar
Outer shell electrons	1	2	3	4	5	6	7	8
Group number	1	2	3	4	5	6	7	0
Valency	1	2	3	4	3	2	1	0

● When atoms react to form *ions*, one atom has to *lose* electrons whereas the other atom has to *gain* electrons. Those atoms (non-metals) like sulphur, that have six electrons in their outer shell, can be considered to have two spaces (to complete the full set of eight). It is easier to fill two spaces than it is to remove six electrons.

● When atoms join to form *molecules* the number of electrons leaving one atom must equal that being gained by the other. It may help to imagine the atoms with hooks representing their valencies:

● **Example 1:** Sodium will react with chlorine to form a compound, sodium chloride:

Na has a valency of one

Cl has a valency of one:

When these atoms combine *all* hooks must be attached:

 so the formula is NaCl.

● **Example 2:** Magnesium will react with chlorine to form magnesium chloride:

Mg has a valency of two: (Mg)

Cl has a valency of one: (Cl)

When they join, *all* hooks must be attached, so we need an extra Cl to take care of the otherwise spare hook:

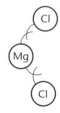

So the formula is $MgCl_2$. The subscript 2 refers to two atoms of what is immediately in front, in other words two chlorine Cl atoms.

● **Example 3:** The formula of aluminium oxide:

Al has a valency of three (Al)

O has a valency of two (O)

When they join, *all* hooks must be attached:

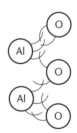

So the formula is Al_2O_3.

Sometimes we can regard a collection of atoms, referred to as a *radical*, as having a valency e.g.:

Compound		Valency
Sulphate	SO_4^{2-}	2
Nitrate	NO_3^-	1
Carbonate	CO_3^{2-}	2
Hydroxide	OH^-	1

● **Example 4:** The formula of copper nitrate:

Cu has a valency of two

NO_3^- has a valency of one

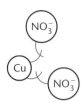

So the formula $Cu(NO_3)_2$

The use of brackets with the subscript two outside means two of whatever is inside the brackets.

> Remember: You will not be expected to remember all the valencies for these atoms or radicals, but it is worth remembering how they are related to the **position** in the periodic table.

CHECKPOINT

Which of the following formulae correctly shows the reaction between sodium and chlorine?

(a) $Na + Cl_2 \rightarrow NaCl_2$
(b) $Na + Cl \rightarrow NaCl$
(c) $2Na + Cl_2 \rightarrow 2NaCl$
(d) $2Na + Cl_2 \rightarrow 2NaCl_2$

-+- **Salts**

VARIATION

Organisms vary in their appearance even within the same family. These variations are the result of the new genes (called **mutations**) and new mixtures of **genes** (produced during **sexual reproduction**).

There are two types of variation between individuals of the same **species**:

● **Discontinuous variation**: This is a *marked* change from one characteristic to another and enables us to separate individuals into distinct groups. One example is blood grouping. We all

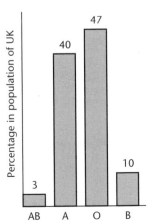

Discontinuous variation in human blood groups

belong to one of the four main groups: A, B, AB and O (there are no in-between groups). The information in the genes accounts for most of this type of variation and the environment affects it very little.

● **Continuous variation**: This refers to characteristics that *gradually* change within a population. We cannot separate individuals into distinct groups. Your height and weight are good examples of this sort of characteristic. Many genes may influence height and weight, but the environment can be important also. In any large population you would get a whole range of heights and weights.

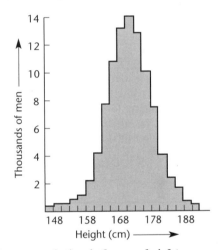

Continuous variation in human height

CHECKPOINT

Which of the following is an example of discontinuous variation:

(a) blood group,
(b) hair colour,
(c) height,
(d) weight?

> Remember: Variation, such as differences in height, can be caused by the interaction of genetic factors with environmental factors, such as the availability of food for animals or the amount of light for plants.

-+- **Natural selection, Selective breeding, Sex linkage**

VASOCONSTRICTION

This is the narrowing or constriction of **blood** vessels, especially those just below the surface of the skin. This results in heat being *retained* in the body. Vasoconstriction can cause a person to look very pale in the face.

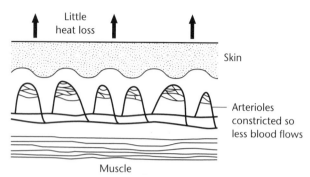

Vasoconstriction

✦ *Artery, Blood system, Body temperature, Homeostasis, Vasodilation, Vein*

VASODILATION

This is the dilation or widening of blood vessels, especially those just below the surface of the skin. This results in heat being *lost* from the blood and the person cools down. Vasodilation can cause a person to look flushed and red in the face.

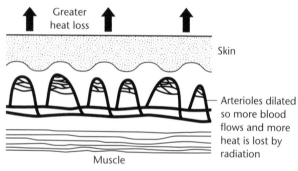

Vasodilation

> *Remember: Vasoconstriction: Heat is kept in. Vasodilation: Heat is lost.*

✦ *Artery, Blood system, Body temperature, Homeostasis, Vasoconstriction, Vein*

VEHICLE-STOPPING DISTANCE

Friction between surfaces is needed to slow down and stop a moving vehicle. When a car brakes to stop, **kinetic energy** is transferred to the brakes and to the road. The amount of energy transferred is equal to the braking force times the distance taken to stop.

Factors affecting vehicle-stopping distance

$$\frac{\text{stopping}}{\text{distance}} = \left(\frac{\text{thinking}}{\text{distance}} + \frac{\text{braking}}{\text{distance}}\right)$$

- *Speed of the vehicle*: If cars A and B have the same **mass** but car A is travelling at *twice* the **mass** of car B, car A needs *four times* the stopping distance of B.

- *Mass of the vehicle*: If cars A and B are travelling at the same speed but car A has *twice* the mass of car B, car A needs *twice* the stopping distance of B.

- *Friction between the wheels and the road*: Wet or icy roads have less friction than dry roads.

- *Friction between the tyres and brakes*: Smooth tyres and worn brakes have less friction than tyres with a good depth of 'tread' on them.

- *Reaction time of the driver*: The 'thinking time' before braking can be affected by concentration, alcohol intake, drugs and tiredness.

> *Remember: Travelling twice as fast needs four times the stopping distance.*

CHECKPOINT

List **four** factors that affect how long it takes for a vehicle to stop.

✦ *Force – balanced and unbalanced, Friction*

VEIN

Veins are large thin-walled **blood** vessels that carry blood towards the **heart**. With the exception of the **pulmonary vein**, the veins carry deoxygenated blood from the rest of the body. The veins have valves that allow the blood to flow in one direction only.

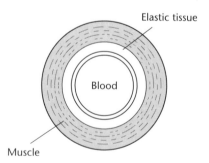

Veins have much thinner walls than arteries

✦ *Artery, Blood system*

VELOCITY

Velocity is the distance travelled in a certain direction in unit time.

> *Remember: Velocity is a vector quantity because it has direction, whereas speed is a scalar quantity.*

$$velocity = \frac{distance\ moved\ in\ a\ stated\ direction}{time\ taken}$$

The units of velocity are metres per second m/s or kilometres per hour km/h.

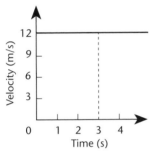

A graph showing constant velocity

CHECKPOINT

State the difference between *speed* and *velocity*.

-⊹- **Acceleration, Free-fall**

VENTILATION OF LUNGS

-⊹- **Breathing**

VIRUS

-⊹- **Micro-organisms**

VISKING TUBING

-⊹- **Osmosis, Partially permeable membrane**

VITAMINS

Vitamins are required in small amounts in a **balanced diet**.

Vitamins are often necessary for **enzymes** to work properly, and a lack of vitamins in the diet causes health problems and can lead to deficiency diseases:

Vitamin	Benefits	Source
A	Resistance to infection; vision in dim light; health of mucus membranes	Butter, milk, carrots, liver
B	Health of nervous system; release of energy	Liver, yeast, wheat
C	Health of blood vessels and skin	Citrus fruit, potatoes, green vegetables
D	Good bone development	Fish liver oil, butter, milk, action of sunlight in skin

- A lack of vitamin A causes poor 'night' vision, and can result in blindness in many less developed countries
- A lack of vitamin B causes beri-beri (a type of paralysis)
- A lack of vitamin C causes scurvy
- A lack of vitamin D causes rickets (poor bone formation resulting in 'bandy' legs)

-⊹- **Minerals**

VOLCANO

A volcano is a large cone-shaped mountain that is formed when steam, lava, rocks and gases are pushed out from inside the **Earth** by the pressure of gases and steam. The **magma** that flows out on the surface at a temperature of 1,000 °C is a mixture of lava and volcanic gases. Some eruptions produce large amounts of volcanic dust particles that enter the atmosphere and cause cloud formation. It is thought that the volcanic ash in the **atmosphere** may also cause cooling of the Earth as the particles prevent radiation from the **Sun** reaching the Earth.

Some of the effects of volcanoes are the destruction of towns and villages, and the removal of agricultural land and forests. A major volcanic eruption took place in 1976 in China where over one million people were killed. On the beneficial side:

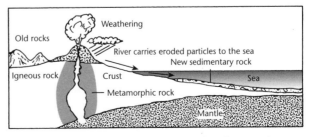

How new rocks are formed from volcanic eruptions

volcanic ash forms a very fertile soil; and molten rock underground heats underground water forming steam that can be used to generate *electricity*.

-+- *Alternative energy, Earthquake, Fault, Plate tectonics, Rock cycle*

VOLT

A volt, symbol V, is the SI unit of electric potential, *potential difference* or *electromotive force*. One volt is defined as the potential difference between two points in an electric circuit if 1 J of work is done, transferring 1 C of charge between the points.

-+- *Coulomb, Joule*

VOLTAGE

The voltage is the *potential difference* between two points of a circuit measured in volts.

-+- *Cathode ray oscilloscope, Cell – electrical, Electromotive force, Reactivity series, Resistance, Voltmeter*

VOLTMETER

A voltmeter is used to measure *voltage* (p.d.) in an electrical circuit. The voltmeter is placed in *parallel* with the component where the *energy* is being transferred: e.g. when charge flows through a lamp, a voltmeter is placed across the lamp and measures the change of electrical energy to heat and light. The voltage is the same across all the components connected in parallel. The units are volts (V).

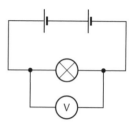

The voltmeter is in parallel with the lamp

-+- *Cathode ray oscilloscope, Electromotive force*

WATER

Water is a liquid – chemical formula H_2O. It freezes at 0 °C and boils at 100 °C. Water has its maximum density at 4 °C while still liquid, rather than in its solid form as ice. This is why ice floats on water. Water can dissolve many different substances; it is called 'the universal solvent'.

Water as a solvent

Liquids containing **ions** will often dissolve other *ionic* substances, while liquids that are molecular (contain **covalent bonds**) will often dissolve other *covalent* substances.

Water is an oddity, because it consists of water molecules in which the atoms are *covalently* bonded, yet it dissolves *ionic* substances. This is because the water molecule is *polar* (it has a slight negative charge at one end and a slight positive charge at the other). This is because the oxygen atom attracts the electron pairs of the bonds formed with the hydrogen atoms more strongly. Water can therefore dissolve *ionic* substances. Water will also dissolve *molecular* compounds that are polar, e.g. sugar and ethanol.

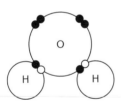

The polar water molecule

Water cycle

Water in the ocean is continuously being **evaporated** by the heat of the **Sun**, and this vapour condenses to form **clouds**. When the clouds are blown over hills and mountains, they release the condensation as rain. Some of the water drains through the ground and back to the sea by rivers, and some of it is absorbed through the roots of plants, and is evaporated from the leaves in the process of **transpiration**. Rain also dissolves some of the poisonous gases in the air, such as **sulphur dioxide**, and forms dilute sulphuric acid, which falls as **acid rain**.

WATT

The watt is a unit of **power**. A power of one watt is produced when 1 J of **work** is done in 1 s. The symbol for the watt is W.

> *Remember: watts = volts × amps.*

CHECKPOINT

What power is used by a lamp, on a 240 V household supply, that has a current of 0.25 A flowing through it?

✦ **Joule, Work**

WAVELENGTH

The wavelength is the distance between one point of a wave and the next point at the same place: e.g. the distance between the crest of one wave and the next. The symbol for wavelength is λ. Wavelength is equal to the **speed** of the wave, V, divided by its **frequency**, f.

$$\text{wavelength } (\lambda) = \frac{\text{speed } (V)}{\text{frequency } (f)}$$

✦ **Amplitude, Frequency, Speed**

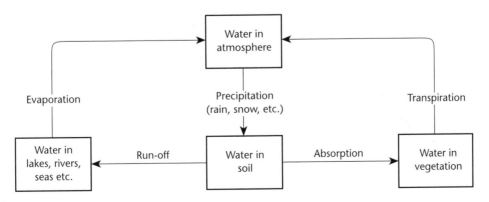

The water cyle

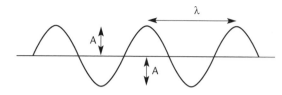

Wavelength (A = amplitude)

CHECKPOINT

The diagram shows a simple wave form.

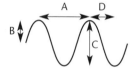

Which letter, A, B, C or D, shows the wavelength?

WAVE ENERGY

Waves are produced as the wind blows across the surface of the sea or any open stretch of water. A wave power machine converts the up and down movement (*gravitational energy*) of the waves into electricity. There is a very great potential for *generating electricity* by this means but there are many technological problems to be overcome. One advantage of wave energy, however, is that it will never run out.

-+- *Alternative energy, Geothermal energy, Solar energy, Tidal energy, Wind energy*

WEATHERING

Weathering is the action of wind, rain, **water**, ice, frost and chemicals on the surface of a rock. These substances cause the rock to be eroded and the surface of the rock breaks up into smaller particles. These particles are often carried by wind and rivers and deposited in other places.

-+- *Erosion, Rock cycle, Sedimentary rocks*

WEIGHT

Weight is a result of the gravitational pull of **Earth** on a mass. Weight is measured in **newtons**, symbol N. The weight of the object varies according to where it is measured: e.g. an object would weigh less on the **Moon**, although its mass would stay the same. The **mass** of the Moon is smaller than that of **Earth**, so the gravitational pull of the Moon is about one-sixth that of Earth.

Remember: An object of mass of 10 kg would weigh 16 N on the Moon, whereas on Earth it would weigh about 100 N.

-+- *Air pressure, Free-fall, Gravitational potential energy*

WHITE BLOOD CELLS

There are about 20 million white blood cells in your body, that's about 7,000 for every 1 mm³ of blood. The function of white blood cells is to protect the body against disease, either by producing **antibodies** that kill **bacteria**, or by engulfing and destroying bacteria.

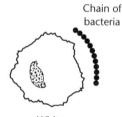

Chain of bacteria

White blood cell

White blood cells engulf and destroy bacteria in your body

-+- *Blood, Red blood cells*

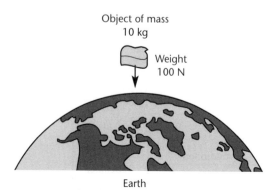

Object of mass 10 kg
Weight 100 N

Earth

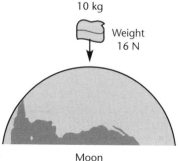

Object of mass 10 kg
Weight 16 N

Moon

Object of mass 10 kg
Weight zero

Space

On the moon the mass of the object stays the same but the weight changes

---

What is the function of white blood cells:

(a) to help clot the blood,
(b) to transport carbon dioxide from the cells,
(c) to transport oxygen to the cells,
(d) to destroy bacteria in the body?

WIND ENERGY

Wind turbines (windmills) convert **kinetic energy** into **electricity**. Wind turbines are often used on isolated islands where it is difficult to transmit electricity from the mainland. A common wind turbine used in this way may have a very large blade about 20 m long, and be capable of **generating** enough electricity for about 2,000 houses.

-┼- *Alternative energy, Geothermal energy, Solar energy, Transmission of electricity, Wave energy*

WORK

Work is done when a **force** moves an object. Work is measured by multiplying the force used by the distance moved, $W = F \times D$. The unit of work is a **joule** (J).

For example, if a person pushes a box with a force of 200 N over a distance of 10 m they have done $200 \times 10 = 2000$ J of work.

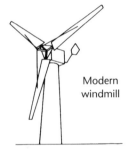

Work = force × distance moved

-┼- *Power, Watt*

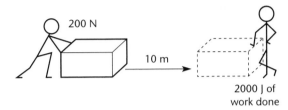
An aerogenerator that has long blades can generate 1 MW of electricity

Traditional windmill

Modern windmill

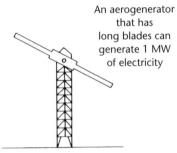

Using wind energy to generate electricity

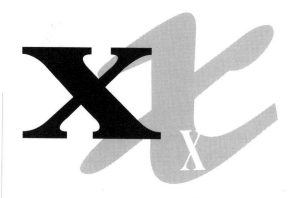

X-RAYS

X-rays are **electromagnetic** waves that have a very short **wavelength**, between 10^{-9} and 10^{-11} of a metre. X-rays are able to pass through many materials and are therefore used to 'see' through dense objects.
  For example:

- At many airports suitcases are passed through X-rays to search for any metal objects that may be dangerous.

- In hospitals, X-rays are used to identify where bones may be broken.

- You may have had an X-ray photograph taken of your teeth at the dentist. The X-rays pass through the object and fall onto a photographic plate. The amount that passes through an object depends on the object's density, so the photographic plate shows images of features such as bone, etc., but not muscle.

- X-rays are also used by scientists to help find out the internal structure of materials such as crystals, and used in industry to show hidden flaws in sheet metal.

-⊹- *Mutations*

XYLEM

-⊹- *Transport in plants*

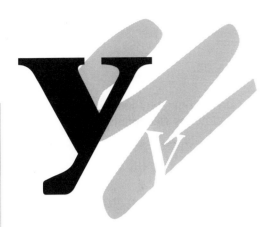

YEAR

A year is the time taken for the **Earth** to orbit the **Sun**, about 365 days. In practice, the orbit takes 365.25 days, so every four years an extra day is added on to the year to compensate for the additional day. The year with the extra day is called a *leap* year and the extra day is 29th February.

CHECKPOINT

Which one of the following is correct? A year is the length of time:

(a) between summer and winter,
(b) between two full moons,
(c) for the Earth to orbit the Sun,
(d) for the Earth to rotate on its axis?

The diagram is not to scale

➕ *Eclipse of the Moon, Eclipse of the Sun, Seasons, Solar system, Tides*

YEAST

Yeast is a single-celled fungus that produces **enzymes**. The enzymes can be used to break down starch and sugar into **alcohol** and **carbon dioxide** in the process known as **fermentation**.

During fermentation, yeast cells reproduce by budding; small portions of a parent yeast cell can separate to form 'daughter' cells. The cells bud to form long chains.

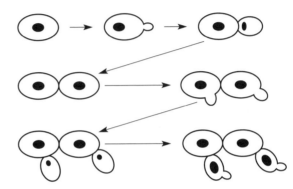

Reproduction in yeast cells by budding

➕ *Alcohol, Asexual reproduction*

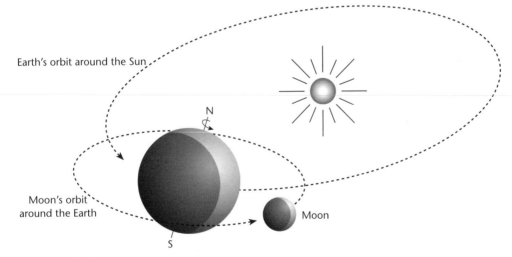

How the Earth orbits the Sun

ZINC

Zinc is a **metallic element**, symbol Zn. It is fairly high in the **reactivity series** so is quite reactive. Zinc is used in *galvanizing* where it is coated onto iron in order to protect the iron from **corrosion**. It is also welded in blocks onto ships hulls as a form of sacrificial protection. Zinc is obtained from its ore (zinc blende; zinc sulphide) by smelting in the **blast furnace** or sometimes by **electrolysis**.

+ *Transition metals*

ZYGOTE

A zygote is formed when a female sex cell is **fertilized** by a male sex cell: e.g. in humans, an egg (ovum) joins with a sperm. The zygote will develop by dividing rapidly and form an **embryo**.

+ *Cloning, Gametes, Hormones – fertility treatment, Meiosis, Mitosis, Ovary, Reproduction, Sexual reproduction, Testis*

APPENDIX 1

COURSEWORK AND ASSIGNMENTS

Coursework is worth 25 per cent of your total assessment mark for Key Stage 4 Science. Coursework assess those skills grouped under the heading Experimental and Investigative Science in Appendix 2. These assessments are usually based on practical work carried out during your science lessons.

An **assignment** can be any type of written task that a teacher asks you to do. Although the use of the word 'assignment' varies between schools, teachers and subjects, it usually means an extended piece of work that is done over a period of several days, or even a week or more. The emphasis in an assignment is on you to take responsibility for your own learning and use any available resources to produce an independent piece of work. The assignment you hand in to your teacher may include research you have done using your *Homework Handbook* and other sources of information.

Assignment-based learning can take place outside the laboratory, and even outside school. You may find your assignment leads you to link with other subjects in school such as technology, mathematics, geography. You may find yourself linking with a local industry, or investigating an environmental issue in the community. You will need to plan your time effectively and possibly negotiate with your teacher about how you should arrange out of school visits.

> *Remember: You may have to develop new skills when dealing with people in the outside world!*

For example, when you are studying energy resources, you may be asked to do an assignment to investigate how insulation affects heat loss. An assignment of this type may start in the laboratory with measuring heat loss from a container of hot water and extend to investigating the effectiveness and costs of different types of insulation used in the home.

For some assignments you may be asked to submit a plan of a possible investigation. You will need to use your scientific knowledge and any relevant information in this *Homework Handbook* and other reference books to help you plan a procedure, identify key factors to control and make a prediction about what might happen. You will need to select appropriate equipment to use to give accurate, reliable results.

Assessment

> *Remember: Your name, date, class or set should be written on your assignment.*

When submitting coursework assignments you should have:

- A clear heading or title, which is underlined.

- An introduction that describes the investigation and states what you are trying to find out; known as your hypothesis.

- A list of any equipment or apparatus you may have used.

- A series of statements, arranged in sequence, describing how you used the apparatus to obtain accurate, reliable results.

- A description of any safety precautions you have taken, such as wearing safety goggles.

- An organized record of what you saw, observed and measured; some of these results may be presented as a table or graph.

- A summary that explains how your results support or undermine your original hypothesis, identifying any patterns or trends shown by your data; this is often described as a conclusion.

- A description of any problems you had, such as how you obtained accurate results, and how you overcame them.

- A mention of possible sources of error.

- A suggestion for further investigation to provide more accurate results or extend your investigation.

- A list of any sources of information, such as references to books, that you have used.

> *Remember: Every diagram, table or graph should have a heading and labels.*

APPENDIX 2

KEY STAGE 4 PROGRAMME OF STUDY

The requirements of the programmes of study apply across experimental and investigative science, life processes and living things, materials and their properties and physical processes.

EXPERIMENTAL AND INVESTIGATIVE SCIENCE (SC1)

Contexts derived from Life Processes and Living Things, Materials and their Properties and Physical Processes should be used to teach pupils about experimental and investigative methods. On some occasions, the whole process of investigating an idea should be carried out by pupils themselves.

1. Planning experimental procedures

Pupils should be taught:

a To use scientific knowledge and understanding drawing on secondary sources where appropriate, to turn ideas suggested to them, and their own ideas, into a form that can be investigated.

b To carry out preliminary work where this helps to clarify what they have to do.

c To make predictions where it is appropriate to do so.

d To consider the key factors in contexts involving a number of factors.

e To plan how to vary, or control key variables.

f To consider the number and range of observations or measurements to be made.

g To recognize contexts, e.g. fieldwork, where variables cannot readily be controlled and to make judgements about the amount of evidence needed in these contexts.

h To select apparatus equipment and techniques, taking account of safety requirements.

2. Obtaining evidence

Pupils should be taught:

a To use a range of apparatus and equipment safely and with skill.

b To make observations and measurements to a degree of precision appropriate to the context.

c To make sufficient relevant observations and measurements for reliable evidence.

d To consider uncertainties in measurements and observations.

e To repeat measurements and observations when appropriate.

f To record evidence clearly and appropriately as they carry out the work.

3. Analysing evidence and drawing conclusions

Pupils should be taught:

a To present qualitative and quantitative data clearly.

b To present data as graphs, using lines of best fit where appropriate.

c To identify trends or patterns in results.

d To use graphs to identify relationships between variables.

e To present numerical results to an appropriate degree of accuracy.

f To check that conclusions drawn are consistent with the evidence.

g To explain how results support or undermine the original prediction when one has been made.

h To try to explain conclusions in the light of their knowledge and understanding of science.

4. Evaluating evidence

Pupils should be taught:

a To consider whether the evidence collected is sufficient to enable firm conclusions to be drawn.

b To consider reasons for anomalous results and to reject such results where appropriate.

c To consider the reliability of results in terms of the uncertainty of measurements and observations.

d To propose improvements to the methods that have been used.

e To propose further investigation to test their conclusions.

LIFE PROCESSES AND LIVING THINGS (SC2)

Work on the ways in which animals and plants function as organisms should be related to cell structure and the underlying chemical reactions. Relationships between inheritance, variation and evolution should be considered. Work on energy transfer within an ecosystem should be related to pupils' knowledge and understanding of energy transfer in other systems.

I. Life processes and cell activity

Pupils should be taught:

a The life processes common to plants and animals.

b That organ systems are adapted for their roles in life processes.

c That plant and animal cells have some similarities in structure.

d How substances enter and leave cells through the cell membrane by diffusion, osmosis and active transport.

e That the nucleus contains chromosomes that carry the genes.

f How cells divide by mitosis so that growth takes place, and by meiosis to produce gametes.

2. Humans as organisms

Pupils should be taught:

Nutrition

a The structure of the human digestive system.

b The processes involved in digestion, including the roles of enzymes, stomach acid and bile.

Circulation

c The structure of the human circulatory system, including the composition and functions of blood.

Breathing

d The structure of the thorax.

e How breathing, including ventilation of the lungs, takes place.

Respiration

f That respiration may be either aerobic or anaerobic, depending on the availability of oxygen.

g That an 'oxygen debt' may occur in muscles during vigorous exercise.

Nervous system

h The pathway taken by impulses in response to a variety of stimuli, including touch, taste, smell, light, sound and balance.

i How the reflex arc, which involves a nerve impulse carried via neurones and across synapses, makes possible rapid response to a stimulus.

j The structure of the eye and how it functions in response to light.

Hormones

k The way in which hormonal control occurs. including the effects of insulin and sex hormones.

l Some medical uses of hormones, including the control and promotion of fertility and the treatment of diabetes.

Homeostasis

m The importance of maintaining a constant internal environment.

n How waste products of body functions are removed by the lungs and kidneys.

o How the kidneys regulate the water content of the body.

p How humans maintain a constant body temperature.

Health

q The defence mechanisms of the body, including the role of the skin, blood and mucous membranes of the respiratory tract.

r The effects of solvents, alcohol, tobacco and other drugs on body functions.

3. Green plants as organisms

Pupils should be taught:

Nutrition

a The reactants in, and products of, photosynthesis.

b That the rate of photosynthesis may be limited by light intensity, carbon dioxide concentration or temperature.

c How the products of photosynthesis are utilized by the plant;

d The importance to healthy plant growth of the uptake and utilization of mineral salts.

Hormones

e The hormonal control of plant growth and development, including commercial applications.

Transport and water relations

f   How plants take up water and transpire.

g   The importance of water in the support of plant tissues.

h   That substances required for growth and reproduction are transported within plants.

4. Variation, inheritance and evolution

Pupils should be taught:

Variation

a   How variation may arise from both genetic and environmental causes.

b   That sexual reproduction is a source of genetic variation, while asexual reproduction produces clones.

c   That mutation is a source of genetic variation and has a number of causes.

Inheritance

d   How gender is determined in humans.

e   The mechanism of monohybrid inheritance where there are dominant and recessive alleles.

f   That some diseases can be inherited.

g   That the gene is a section of DNA.

h   The basic principles of cloning, selective breeding and genetic engineering.

Evolution

i   The fossil record as evidence for evolution.

j   How variation and selection may lead to evolution or to extinction.

5. Living things in their environment

Pupils should be taught:

Adaptation and competition

a   How the distribution and relative abundance of organisms in a habitat can be explained in terms of adaptation, competition and predation.

b   How the impact of human activity on the environment is related to population size, economic factors and industrial requirements.

Energy and nutrient transfer

c   How food chains may be described quantitatively using pyramids of numbers and pyramids of biomass.

d   How energy is transferred through an ecosystem.

e   The role of microbes and other organisms in the decomposition of organic materials and in the cycling of carbon and nitrogen.

f   How food production can be managed to improve the efficiency of energy transfer.

MATERIALS AND THEIR PROPERTIES (SC3)

Work on the properties of materials should be related to pupils' knowledge of structure and bonding. Work on chemical reactions should emphasize patterns and predictions made from these patterns, including how knowledge about chemical reactions is applied when new substances are manufactured.

I. Classifying materials

Pupils should be taught:

Atomic structure

a   That solids, liquids and gases are all composed of particles.

b   That atoms consist of nuclei and electrons.

c   The charges and relative masses of protons, neutrons and electrons.

d   About mass number, atomic number and isotopes.

e   About a model of the way electrons are arranged in atoms.

f   That the reactions of elements depend upon the arrangement of electrons in their atoms.

Bonding

g   That new substances are formed when atoms combine.

h   That chemical bonding can be explained in terms of the transfer or sharing of electrons.

i   How ions are formed when atoms gain or lose electrons.

j   That ionic lattices are held together by the attraction between oppositely charged ions.

k   That covalent bonds are formed when atoms share electrons;

l   That substances with covalent bonds may form simple molecular structures or giant structures.

m   The physical properties of some substances with giant structures and some with simple molecular structures.

2. Changing materials

Pupils should be taught:

Useful products from oil

a How oil deposits are formed.

b That crude oil is a mixture of substances, most of which are hydrocarbons, which can be separated by fractional distillation.

c The use as fuels of some of the products from crude oil distillation.

d The products of burning hydrocarbons.

e That there are different groups of hydrocarbons.

f That alkanes are saturated hydrocarbons, and alkenes are unsaturated hydrocarbons containing one double covalent bond between carbon atoms.

g That hydrocarbon molecules can be cracked to form smaller molecules, including alkenes.

h That addition polymers can be made from alkenes formed during cracking.

i Some uses of addition polymers.

Useful products from metal ores and rocks

j That metal ores are found in the Earth.

k That the way in which a particular metal is extracted from its ores is related to its reactivity.

l An example of how a reactive metal can be extracted by electrolysis.

m An example of how a less reactive metal can be extracted by reduction with carbon or carbon monoxide.

n An example of how a metal can be purified by electrolysis.

o That a variety of useful substances can be made from rocks and minerals.

Useful products from air

p How nitrogen can be converted to ammonia in industry.

q How nitrogenous fertilizers are manufactured, and their effects on plant growth and the environment.

Representing reactions

r To represent chemical reactions by word equations.

s To represent reactions, including electrolytic reactions, by balanced equations using chemical symbols.

Quantitative chemistry

t To use chemical equations to predict reacting quantities.

u To determine the formulae of simple compounds from reacting masses.

Changes to the atmosphere

v How the atmosphere and oceans evolved to their present composition.

w How the carbon cycle helps to maintain atmospheric coin position.

Geological changes

x How igneous rocks are formed by the cooling of magma, sedimentary rocks by the deposition and consolidation of sediments, and metamorphic rocks by the action of heat and pressure on existing rocks.

y How the sequence of, and evidence for, these processes is obtained from the rock record.

z How plate tectonic processes are involved in the formation, deformation and recycling of rocks.

3. Patterns of behaviour

Pupils should be taught:

The Periodic Table

a That the periodic table shows all elements, arranged in order of ascending atomic number.

b The connection between the arrangement of outer electrons and the position of an element in the periodic table.

c That elements in the same group of the periodic table have similar properties.

d That there is a gradual change in the properties of the elements from the top to the bottom of a group.

e The properties and uses of the noble gases.

f The properties and reactions of the alkali metals.

g The properties, reactions and uses of simple compounds of the alkali metals.

h The properties, reactions and uses of the halogens.

i The properties, reactions and uses of simple compounds of the halogens.

j Similarities between transition metals and characteristic properties of their compounds.

k Some uses of transition metals.

Rates of reactions

l That there is great variation in the rates at which different reactions take place.

m How the rates of reactions can be altered by varying temperature or concentration, or by changing the surface area of a solid reactant, or by adding a catalyst.

n   That reactions can occur when particles collide.

o   That the rates of many reactions can be increased by increasing the frequency or energy of collisions between particles.

Reactions involving enzymes

p   How the rates of enzyme-catalysed reactions vary with temperature.

q   The use of enzymes in the baking, brewing and dairy industries.

Reversible reactions

r   That some reactions are reversible.

s   How the yield of products from reversible reactions depends on the conditions.

t   That some manufacturing processes are based on reversible reactions.

Energy transfer in reactions

u   That changes of temperature often accompany reactions.

v   That reactions can be exothermic or endothermic.

w   That making and breaking chemical bonds in chemical reactions involves energy transfers.

PHYSICAL PROCESSES (SC4)

The links between electricity and magnetism, between forces and motion and between light, sound and other waves, and the relationship of energy to these areas, should be made clear. Work on the solar system and the wider Universe should relate to pupils' knowledge of physical processes.

1. Electricity and magnetism

Pupils should be taught:

Energy and potential difference in circuits

a   How to measure current in series and parallel circuits.

b   That energy is transferred from batteries and other sources to other components in electrical circuits.

c   That resistors are heated when charge flows through them.

d   The qualitative effect of changing resistance on the current in a circuit.

e   How to make simple measurements of voltage.

f   The quantitative relationship between resistance, voltage and current.

g   How current varies with voltage in a range of devices, including resistors, filament bulbs, diodes, light-dependent resistors (LDRs) and thermistors.

h   That voltage is the energy transferred per unit charge.

i   The quantitative relationship between power, voltage and current.

Mains electricity

j   The difference between direct current (d.c.) and alternating current (a.c.).

k   The functions of the live, neutral and earth wires in the domestic mains supply, and the use of insulation, earthing, fuses and circuit breakers to protect users of electrical equipment.

l   That electrical heating is used in a variety of ways in domestic contexts.

m   How measurements of energy transferred are used to calculate the costs of using common domestic appliances.

Electric charge

n   About common electrostatic phenomena, in terms of the movement of electrons.

o   The dangers and uses of electrostatic charges generated in everyday situations.

p   The quantitative relationship between steady current, charge and time.

q   About electric current as the flow of free electrons in metals or of ions during electrolysis.

Electromagnetic force

r   That like magnetic poles repel and unlike magnetic poles attract.

s   That a force is exerted on a current-carrying wire in a magnetic field and the application of this effect in simple electric motors.

Electromagnetic induction

t   That a voltage is induced when a conductor cuts magnetic field lines and when the magnetic field through a coil changes.

u   How simple a.c. generators and transformers work.

v   The quantitative relationship between the voltages across the coils in a transformer and the numbers of turns in them.

w   How electricity is generated and transmitted.

2. Forces and motion

Pupils should be taught:

Force and acceleration

a   How distance, time and speed can be determined and represented graphically.

b About factors affecting vehicle-stopping distances.

c The difference between speed and velocity.

d About acceleration as change in velocity per unit time.

e That balanced forces do not alter the velocity of a moving object.

f The quantitative relationship between force, mass and acceleration.

g That when two bodies interact, the forces they exert on each other are equal and opposite.

Force and non-uniform motion

h The forces acting on falling objects.

i Why falling objects may reach a terminal velocity.

Force and pressure on solids, liquids and gases

j How extension varies with applied force for a range of materials.

k How liquids behave under pressure, including simple everyday applications of hydraulics.

l How the volume of a fixed mass of gas at constant temperature is related to pressure.

3. Waves

Pupils should be taught:

Characteristics of waves

a That light and sound can be reflected, refracted and diffracted.

b The conditions for total internal reflection and its use in optical fibres.

c About longitudinal and transverse waves in ropes, springs and water.

d That waves can be reflected, refracted and diffracted.

e The meaning of frequency, wavelength and amplitude of a wave.

f The quantitative relationship between the speed, frequency and wavelength of a wave.

g That waves transfer energy without transferring matter.

The electromagnetic spectrum

h That the electromagnetic spectrum includes radio waves, microwaves, infra-red, visible light, ultraviolet waves, X-rays and gamma-rays.

i Some uses and dangers of microwaves, infra-red and ultraviolet waves in domestic situations.

j Some uses of radio waves, microwaves, infra-red and visible light in communications.

k Some uses of X-rays and gamma-rays in medicine.

Sound and ultrasound

l About sound and ultrasound waves, and some medical and other uses of ultrasound.

Seismic waves

m That longitudinal and transverse waves are transmitted through the Earth, producing wave records that provide evidence for the Earth's layered structure.

4. The Earth and beyond

Pupils should be taught:

The solar system and the wider Universe

a The relative positions of the Earth, Moon, Sun, planets and other bodies in the Universe.

b That gravitational forces determine the movements of planets, moons, comets and satellites.

c How stars evolve over a long time-scale.

d About some ideas used to explain the evolution of the Universe into its present state.

5. Energy resources and energy transfer

Pupils should be taught:

Energy transfer

a That differences in temperature can lead to transfer of energy.

b How energy is transferred by the movement of particles in conduction, convection and evaporation.

c How energy is transferred by radiation.

d That insulation can reduce transfer of energy from hotter to colder objects, and how insulation is used in domestic contexts.

e The meaning of energy efficiency and the need for economical use of energy resources.

Work, power and energy

f The quantitative relationship between force and work.

g To calculate power in terms of the rate of working or of transferring energy.

h The quantitative links between kinetic energy, potential energy and work.

6. Radioactivity

Pupils should be taught:

a That radioactivity arises from the breakdown of an unstable nucleus.

b That there is background radioactivity.

c That there are three main types of radioactive emission, with different penetrating powers.

d The nature of alpha and beta particles and of gamma radiation.

e The meaning of the term 'half-life'.

f The beneficial and harmful effects of radiation on matter and living organisms.

g Some uses of radioactivity, including the radioactive dating of rocks.

(Reproduced with courtesy of HMSO, Crown copyright.)

CHECKPOINT ANSWERS

Absorption   You should have used the words in this order: villi, glucose, amino acids.

Acceleration
1. d, U–V.

2. $\text{Acceleration} = \dfrac{\text{change in velocity}}{\text{time taken for change}}$

   change in velocity = $10 - 20 = -10$ m/s

   $\text{acceleration} = \dfrac{-10}{20} = -0.5$ m/s^2

   The negative sign means the bus is decelerating.

Acid   You should have used the words in this order: Hydrogen, salt, carbon dioxide.

Addition polymers
1. An addition polymer is a long chain of monomers. Alkenes formed during cracking are used to make addition polymers.

2. One example is poly(ethene) made from ethene, an alkene.

3. Plastic food wrapping, insulation for wiring.

Aerobic respiration   food + oxygen → carbon dioxide + water + energy

Alkali metals
1. An ion with a positive charge, +1.

2. As you go down the group, the number of shells increases and the outer electron is further away from the positive nucleus and more easily lost; e.g. potassium is much more reactive than lithium.

3. Hydrogen.

Anaerobic respiration   Oxygen, debt, anaerobically, lactic acid.

Atmosphere
1. Respiration, combustion.

2. Green plants take in carbon dioxide and use it in the process of photosynthesis.

Atomic number   Protons.

Atomic structure   You should have used the words in this order: electrons, protons, neutrons, electrons, proton, neutron, electron.

Atomic structure – patterns for atoms
1. First shell – max two electrons
   Second shell – max eight electrons

2. See diagram below

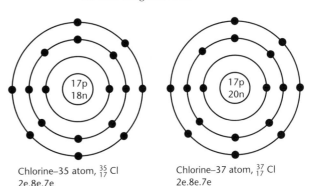

Chlorine–35 atom, $^{35}_{17}$Cl   Chlorine–37 atom, $^{37}_{17}$Cl
2e.8e.7e   2e.8e.7e

Background radiation   Natural: Radioactive rocks and minerals. Man-made: nuclear waste/TV sets.

Blood   (d) To transport oxygen to the cells

Blood system   away

Body temperature

Vasodilation	Vasoconstriction
more blood reaches capillaries	*less* blood reaches capillaries
more heat reaches skin surface	*less* heat reaches skin surface
more heat is lost to surroundings	*less* heat is lost to surroundings

Breathing   When you breathe in, the ribs move *up and out*. The diaphragm *flattens* and air *rushes in*.

Carbon cycle   X is photosynthesis, Y is respiration.

Chemical equations   (Mg) + (H)(Cl) → (Mg) + (H)(H)
                                    (H)(Cl)   (Cl)
                                                  (Cl)

Conduction   Aluminium, copper, iron.

Convection   You should have used the words in this order: energy, particles, gases, high, lower.

Covalent bonding   You should have used the words in this order: electrons, outer, double, two, molecule.

Crude oil	You should have used the words in this order: hydrocarbons, fractional distillation, fuels, cracking.		They only work within a narrow range of temperature and pH.

Current and charge
The charge in coulombs = 2 × 20 = 40 C
The joules = 40 × 12 = 480 J

Digestion
You should have used the words in this order: large, soluble, enzymes, amylase, stomach, proteins.

Direct current
Direct current flows one-way whereas in alternating current, the direction of flow changes 50 times per second.

Eclipse of the Sun
(d) The Moon is between the Earth and the Sun

Electric motors
1. A force will be exerted on the wire and the wire will move upwards. (The direction of force is at right angles to the current direction and field direction.)

2. Electric motors, moving coil loudspeaker.

Electrolysis
1 Complete the table:

	Positive	Negative
Electrode	Anode	Cathode
Ion	Cation	Anion

2. (a) Cation (b) The positive ions gain electrons and become atoms.

3. (a) Chlorine gas (b) hydrogen gas.

4. Using a d.c. electric current and two electrodes to break down or split up a substance.

Electro-magnetic spectrum
(a) gamma radiation. This has a shorter wavelength than X-rays. The position of visible light and microwaves should give you a clue.

Endothermic
The energy required to break the N–H bonds in ammonia is greater than the energy released when H–H and N–N bonds are formed.

Energy efficiency
efficiency = $\dfrac{\text{power output}}{\text{power input}}$ = $\dfrac{60}{100}$ = 0.6 or 60 per cent.

Enzymes
1. They are specific to a particular substrate.

2. Enzymes in yeast are used in brewing to make beer and in the baking industry to make bread. Enzymes are also used in biological washing powders and in the manufacture of some new types of food such as mycoprotein.

Evolution
Able to run faster than other rabbits.
Able to resist disease better than other rabbits.
Better camouflage against its surroundings than other rabbits.

Excretion
(b) To remove harmful waste produced by the body

Exothermic
The energy required to break the H–H and Cl–Cl bonds is less than the energy given out when the H–Cl bonds are formed.

Extraction of metals
1. Iron

2. It is above carbon in the reactivity series and is too reactive to give up its oxygen to carbon

3. By electrolysis

4. Copper

Eye
(a) Iris,
(b) lens,
(c) retina,
(d) optic nerve

Food chains and food webs
1. (d) Rabbits

2. (a) It is reflected
(b) excretion and respiration

Food production
Any two of: fertilizers add nutrients to the soil; pesticides control disease in plants; selective breeding and genetic engineering to produce high-yielding, disease resistant crops.

Force – balanced and unbalanced
You should have used the words in this order: balanced, speed, unbalanced, accelerate.

Force and acceleration
$a = f/m$ $a = 15/3$ = 5 m/s^2

Force and extension
(d) 50 mm

Free-fall
1. Falling objects have two forces acting on them: the weight of the object acting downwards and the drag force exerted upwards on the object. When an object falls through air, the drag force is air resistance.

2. Objects accelerate as they fall until the drag force is equal and opposite to the weight. When this happens the object falls at constant velocity described as terminal velocity.

3. The sky diver can change his or her terminal velocity by altering his/her shape and increasing or decreasing his/her air resistance.

Fuse Current = watts ÷ volts, 50 ÷ 250 = 0.2 A, so a 3 A fuse should be used.

Gas laws The correct order of words is: temperature, pressure, increase, more often

Gene Cell → nucleus → chromosome → gene → DNA

Generators 1. Kinetic energy → electrical energy

2. When the coil is turned in a magnetic field between two magnets, a voltage is induced that causes a current to flow.

Giant structures 1. Any metal, such as copper

2. Any two of: high boiling points, high melting points, conduction of electricity

Half-life (c) One-quarter. In 20 years, one-half would be left, in another 20 years, one-quarter of the original is left

Halogens 1. An ion with a negative charge, –1.

2. As you go down the group, the larger the atom. The number of electron shells increases. The outer electron shell is further away from the pulling power of the positive nucleus, e.g. iodine is much less reactive than fluorine.

3. Metal halides are formed, e.g. sodium chloride.

Homeostasis Any two of: control of body temperature, regulation of water content, control of blood sugar

Hydraulics The correct order of words is: the same, different, largest, smaller, the same

Hydrocarbons fuel + oxygen → carbon dioxide + water
$$CH_4 + 2O_2 \rightarrow CO_2 + 2H_2O$$

Hydrocarbons – alkanes and alkenes Saturated hydrocarbons have single covalent bonds between the two carbon atoms whereas unsaturated hydrocarbons have double covalent bonds between the two carbon atoms.

Induced current 1. How fast the magnet or coil is moved; how many turns there are on the coil; the strength of the magnetic field

2. Generator (alternator), transformers

Insulation Insulation works by reducing the transfer of energy from a warm building to colder outside air by trapping a layer of air, which is a poor conductor of heat.

Insulin The correct order of words is: insulin, glycogen, liver, glycogen, glucose.

Ionic bonding The correct order of words is: electrons, ions, ion, loses, atom, gains

Ionic bonding – properties of ionic compounds 1. Each ion is surrounded by many ions of the opposite charge resulting in strong forces of attraction.

2. They have high boiling points and high melting points.

Isotopes Isotopes have the same number of protons and different numbers of neutrons in their nuclei.

Kinetic theory (b) More widely spaced.

Longitudinal waves (d) Sound waves – all the other waves are transverse waves

Magnets and magnetic fields (d) Both poles are N poles so they repel each other

Mains electricity 2 kW × 2 h = 4 units
4 units × 10 p = 40 p

Metals Gold is not combined with any other element in the Earth's crust. Iron is combined with oxygen as iron ore. Iron requires very high temperatures to extract the iron from its ore, and a suitable reducing agent had to be found that would remove the oxygen from the iron ore.

Mole (b) The mass of 1 mol of water is 18 g [(2 × 1) + 16 = 18]. There are two moles of water so they contain 2 mol of oxygen = 2 × 16 = 32.

Mole – determining the formula of a simple compound	Moles of lead $4.14/207 = 0.02$ mol of lead atoms Moles of bromine $3.20/80 = 0.04$ mol of bromine atoms 0.02 mol of lead atoms reacts with 0.04 mol of bromine atoms so 1 mol of lead atoms reacts with 2 mol of bromine atoms. The formula of lead(ll) bromide is $PbBr_2$.

Mole – predicting reacting quantities

Write the equation for the reaction:

calcium carbonate $\rightarrow$ calcium oxide $+$ carbon dioxide

$$CaCO_3(s) \rightarrow CaO(s) + CO_2(g)$$

First, convert masses to moles. The mass of 1 mol of calcium carbonate is $[40 + 12 + (3 \times 16)] = 100$. The number of moles used is $10/100 = 0.1$ mol. From the equation, 1 mol of calcium carbonate produced 1 mol of calcium oxide, 0.1 mol of calcium carbonate produces 0.1 mol of calcium oxide.

Monohybrid inheritance (a) All red-flowered plants

Mutations Any three of: radiation (X-rays, gamma-rays, u.v. rays) chemicals, meiosis

Nitrates The correct order of words is: Oxygen, catalyst, nitric acid, ammonia, ammonium nitrate

Nitrogen cycle
1. To break down dead animals and plants and form ammonium compounds that are converted into nitrates for use by the plants.
2. Fungi and bacteria.

Noble gases
1. They all have eight electrons in the outer shell.
2. They are very unreactive (inert).
3. Helium, used in airships; neon, used in fluorescent lighting and advertising signs.

Ohms Law – current and voltage The resistance of the device increases as the voltage increases.

Osmo-regulation The correct order of words is: lot, large, dilute, little, small, concentrated

Parallel circuits A_3 is 0.25 A; A_4 is 0.5 A

Periodic table
1. (a) E; (b) D; (c) B

2. The elements are arranged in increasing atomic number. The lightest and simplest are at the top left of the table and the most complex and heaviest are at the bottom right of the table.

3. They have the same number of electrons in their outer shell.

Photosynthesis
1. carbon dioxide + water $\rightarrow$
   reactants
   carbohydrates + oxygen
   products
2. Light intensity, carbon dioxide concentration, temperature
3. To make amino acids, proteins and DNA

Plant hormones Any two of: to stimulate root growth when taking cuttings; to stimulate fruit formation in unpollinated flowers; as weedkillers to destroy unwanted plants

Plate tectonics The Earth's crust is formed from a number of continental plates that are moving a few centimetres each year. This has resulted in North and South America moving away from Africa and Europe. Some of the plates are sliding past each other while some are sliding towards each other, pushing some of the plates beneath others. These movements are responsible for earthquakes and volcanoes that occur along fault lines.

Power
$$\text{power} = \frac{\text{amount of work done}}{\text{time taken to do the work}}$$
$$= \frac{450 \times 5}{6} = \frac{2250}{6} = 375 \text{ W}$$

Pyramid of biomass (c) The pyramid of mass means the amount of biomass not the number of organisms.

Radioactivity (a) Alpha-particles.

Radioactivity – radioactive decay
1. Carbon-12 has six neutrons but carbon-14 has eight neutrons.
2. A beta-particle is an electron.
3. A neutron splits into a proton and electron. The neutron number decreases by one and the proton number increases by one.

Rates of reaction
1. Temperature, concentration, surface area, use of a catalyst
2. The particles must bump into each other (collide)

Reflection	You should have used the words in this order: reflection, image, virtual, reversed
Reflex arc	Receptor → sensory, neurone → relay neurone → motor neurone → effector
Refraction	When the light ray enters the glass block at an angle it changes speed and direction because the glass block is denser than air. The light ray bends towards the normal as it enters the glass.
Reproduction	(a) fertilization
Resistance	1. Diameter, length, material, temperature 2. Examples include: electric fire, oven, toaster, hair drier 3 The resistor has a value of 2.5 Ω
Reversible reactions	1. The reaction can go in both directions 2. High pressure, high temperature (about 400 °C) and the presence of a catalyst 3. N_2 $3H_2$ $2NH_3$ nitrogen + hydrogen $\rightleftharpoons$ ammonia
Smoking	See bullet points in the text.
Speed	1. (c) 120 km/h. The distance travelled is for 15 min so multiply by four to find the distance travelled in 1h. 2. (b) Moving with constant speed.
Speed, frequency and wavelength	1. speed = frequency × wavelength $v = f \times \lambda$ 2. frequency = speed ÷ wavelength $= 330 \div 0.25 = 1{,}320$ Hz
Stars	(d) White dwarf

Three-pin plug

Colour	Pin
Blue	Neutral
Brown	Live
Green and yellow	Earth

Total internal reflection	1. When light travels from a denser to a less dense material, such as from glass to air, light is refracted. Total internal reflection occurs when the angle of reflection is increased so that the emergent ray cannot escape and is reflected back into the glass. 2. Optical fibres, periscopes
Transformers	(b) 50 turns. The ratio of input voltage to output voltage is 6 : 1, so the number of turns is 300 ÷ 6 = 50
Transition metals	1. High melting points, high density, form brightly coloured compounds 2. Iron, used to make steel alloys when mixed with carbon and other elements. Copper, used in electrical wiring and water pipes.
Transmission of electricity	(b) Alternating current at high voltage
Transpiration	Any three of: High humidity, no air movement, low light intensity, low temperatures
Transport in plants	1. Water molecules move from an area of high concentration of water molecules to a low concentration of water molecules through a partially permeable membrane. This process is known as osmosis. 2. (a) Water and mineral salts (b) dissolved sugars.
Transverse waves	Energy is being transferred
Ultrasonic waves	Ultrasonic waves do not damage living cells so they are used to examine soft tissue, such as a foetus. X-rays are suitable for examining hard tissue, such as bone.
Universe	The red shift of light from stars in distant galaxies shows that galaxies are moving apart. More distant galaxies are moving apart faster than nearer galaxies. These facts support the big bang theory that suggests an explosion occurred about 15 thousand million years ago and the Universe is still expanding.
Valency	(c) 2Na + Cl_2 → 2NaCl (There must be four atoms on each side to balance.)
Variation	(a) Blood group
Vehicle stopping distance	Speed and mass of vehicle, friction between brakes and tyres, tyres and the road, reaction time of driver
Velocity	Speed is a scalar quantity: the total distance travelled divided by time taken; velocity is a vector quantity, the total displacement in a particular direction, divided by time taken.

Watt	The power is $240 \times 0.25 = 60$ W. This means that the lamp is transferring 60 J of energy into heat and light every second.
Wavelength	'A' shows the wavelength, the distance of one crest to the next.

White blood cells	(d) To destroy bacteria in the body
Year	(c) For the Earth to orbit the Sun